Progress in Mathematics

1 EXTENSION

C000083515

Progress in Mathematics

Pupils' Book 1G   Pupils' Book 1C
Pupils' Book 2G   Pupils' Book 2C
Pupils' Book 3G   Pupils' Book 3C
Pupils' Book 4G   Pupils' Book 4C
Pupils' Book 5G   Pupils' Book 5C

Pupils' Book 1E

The remainder of the 'extension' books are in preparation.

For each pupils' book, there are:
Mental Tests and Phase Tests
Copy Masters
Answers

Progress
in
Mathematics

1   EXTENSION

Les Murray BA
Formerly Senior Teacher and Head of Mathematics, Garstang County High School

Stanley Thornes (Publishers) Ltd

First published in 1988 by Stanley Thornes (Publishers) Ltd, Old Station Drive, Leckhampton, Cheltenham GL53 0DN, UK

British Library Cataloguing in Publication Data

Murray, Les
    Progress in mathematics.
    1E
    1. Mathematics—Questions & answers—
    For schools
    I. Title
    510'.76

    ISBN 0-85950-729-7

Typeset by Tech-Set, Gateshead, Tyne & Wear.
Printed and bound in Great Britain at A. Wheaton & Co. Ltd., Exeter.

Preface

This book is the first of the higher level series. It is not intended that it should be worked through from cover to cover.

Although the order of contents is a suitable one to follow, the discretion of the teacher will determine the order of work and whether or not one chapter should be completed before another is attempted. The starting point for a pupil or class will not necessarily be at the beginning of a chapter. Numerous carefully graded questions have been provided to allow plenty of freedom — again the teacher must be selective. Few worked examples are given, thus allowing for alternative methods of introducing topics.

The material has been carefully planned to allow for the use of a calculator, but total dependence on calculator-use is not encouraged.

Photocopy masters are available for exercises where pupils may benefit by their provision, such exercises have been labelled **M** . The use of masters helps to eliminate laborious, time-wasting tasks, such as the copying out of tables; more time can be spent doing mathematics.

The completion of this book has been dependent on the valued help and advice given to me by many people, in particular Mr Clive Horsford of Lancaster Royal Grammar School, who painstakingly worked through the text and provided the answers; Mr J. Britton, Head of Mathematics at Copthall School, London, for his welcome advice and most useful comments and Mrs Alice Dickson of Garstang High School. My thanks also go to Casio Electronics and Texas Instruments for the loan of a selection of calculators, thus enabling me to consider the different characteristics of calculators in my writing; to Carol A.R. Andrews at the Department of Egyptian Antiquities at the British Museum, for the invaluable information provided; to Mr M.J. Stewart of the Royal Lancaster Hospital; to Mr Martin Beadle of the Meteorological Centre and Field Station, University of Lancaster; to Geoff Giles, deviser of Dime Projects Materials and to Derek Horseman, Mathematics Adviser, Lancashire County Council for some of the ideas used; to Ian Brodie for providing scientific data and to Lona Bond, Sharan Jeet Shan and Wilbert Garvin for providing lists of names.

Les Murray
1988

To PJB

Acknowledgements

The author and publishers are grateful to the following:

Hodder & Stoughton Ltd, for the excerpt from *Campanus Euclid* on p. 219, as reproduced from *The Story of Mathematics*.

Ronald Sheridan's Photo-Library for the photograph of the Cheops Pyramid at Giza, on p. 236.

Contents

1 Number and Approximations

Exercise 1

A Write, using figures:
1. three hundred and seven
2. fifty-six
3. thirty-eight thousand and twelve
4. seven million, sixty-one thousand, two hundred and eighty
5. six hundred thousand and twenty-nine
6. eighty thousand and forty
7. nine hundred and two thousand, seven hundred
8. three million, one hundred thousand and fifty-nine

B Write, using words:
1. 47
2. 796
3. 5082
4. 12 094
5. 683 015
6. 300 428
7. 9 235 640
8. 29 470 206

A Short History of Number

Thousands of years ago, primitive people had no need to use big numbers. Numbers for items such as the size of a family or how many fish were caught were all that were needed. Even today, tribes exist who do not have number names for numbers other than one or two. Everything more than two is called 'lots', 'much', 'many', 'heaps' or something similar.

1

Our number system comes from the Hindus, with Arab influence. How the symbols have changed over the years is shown below.

Date	Origin	Numerals										
		1	2	3	4	5	6	7	8	9	0	10
About 200 BC	Hindu	−	=		ᛨ		ᛉ	ʔ		ᛘ		∝
Second century AD	Hindu	−	=	≡	ᛨ	ᚱ	ᛈ	ʔ	५	ᚱ		∝
About AD 800	Hindu	？	২	ৣ	४	५	૯	७	८	९	०	
About AD 900	Arabic	١	٢	٣	٤	٥	٦	٧	٨	٩	•	
AD 976	Spanish	١	٢	٣	४	५	৮	٧	٨	٩	٠	
About AD 1400	Italian	١	٢	٣	٤	٥	٦	٧	٨	٩	٠	
AD 1480	Caxton (printer)	١	٢	٣	٤	٥	٦	٧	٨	٩	٠	

In the Hindu–Arabic system, large numbers can easily be written. Although numbers over a million were used, the word 'million' does not appear to have existed before the thirteenth century. Even as late as the sixteenth century it tended to be referred to as 'a thousand thousand'.

For many years, very large numbers were used without any thought of giving them special names. Consequently, the word 'billion' appeared and it had two different meanings. Historically, it first appeared as 1 000 000 000 000 (a million million); it was used in a manuscript in 1484 as meaning a million million (a one followed by 12 zeros). Unfortunately, the word 'billion' also appeared in some countries as meaning 1 000 000 000 (a thousand million); this version of a billion has been the accepted usage in the USA, the USSR and France.

Although a billion has been a million million throughout Britain for hundreds of years, government departments now take a billion to be a thousand million. Comparing the two systems, we have:

Name	As used throughout Britain for hundreds of years	As used in the USA
A billion	A million million (a one followed by 12 zeros)	A thousand million (a one followed by 9 zeros)
A trillion	A million million million (a one followed by 18 zeros)	A million million (a one followed by 12 zeros)
A quadrillion	A million million million million (a one followed by 24 zeros)	A thousand million million (a one followed by 15 zeros)

It is probably safer to avoid using the above words and to refer to a thousand million or a million million and so on.

A one followed by 100 zeros is called a *googol* and a one followed by a googol of zeros is called a *googolplex*. Try to imagine how big this number is.)

Exercise 2   Large Numbers

Here are some facts:

Light travels 299 792 km/s.

Light travels 9 460 700 000 000 km in a year.
(This distance is called a *light year*.)

The Moon has a diameter of 3476 km.

The Earth has a diameter of 12 757 km at the equator.

The distance from the centre of the Earth to the centre of the Moon is 384 400 km.

The distance from the Earth to the Sun is 149 600 000 km.

The mass of the Earth is 5 976 000 000 000 000 000 000 000 kg.

Uranus is 2 871 000 000 km from the Sun.

The distance from the Earth to the nearest star is about 43 000 000 000 000 km.

The Earth has an area of about 509 800 000 km^2.

The Pacific Ocean has an area of 165 242 000 km^2.

The Mediterranean Sea has an area of about 2 504 000 km^2.

Great Britain has an area of 229 850 km^2.

Annapurna 1 is about 8075 m high.

Cotopaxi is 5897 m high.

The River Nile is 6695 km in length.

Tugela Falls has a drop of 948 m.

The Eiffel Tower is 300 m high.

Sears Tower, in Chicago, has a height of 443 m.

Ben Nevis is 1343 m high.

The Arctic Ocean has an area of 13 986 000 km^2.

Kent has an area of 372 998 hectares.

Venus has a diameter of 12 231 km.

Saturn has a diameter of 120 858 km.

Mercury is 58 000 000 km from the Sun.

The Caribbean Sea has an area of 2 753 170 km^2.

Popocatépetl is 5452 m high.

The Amazon is 6518 km long.

The Indian Ocean has an area of 73 556 000 km^2.

Lake Michigan has an area of 58 016 km^2.

The Earth has a circumference of 40 078 km at the equator.

The Earth has a circumference of 40 008 km at the Poles.

New Guinea has an area of 899 895 km^2.

Gasherbrum 1 has a height of 8068 m.

Mars has a diameter of 6759 km.

Angel Falls has a drop of 979 m.

The North Sea has an area of 575 304 km^2.

The Golden Gate Bridge span is 1280 m.

The Empire State Building is 412 m high.

Saturn is 1 427 000 000 km from the Sun.

Lake Huron has an area of 59 596 km^2.

Lancashire has an area of 300 465 hectares.

The Atlantic Ocean has an area of 82 362 000 km^2.

Cuba has an area of 113 960 km^2

Vesuvius has a height of 1277 m.

The Verrazo Narrows Bridge span is 1298 m.

Hampshire has an area of 386 488 hectares.

A Answer the following using the given list of facts.

For each answer, write the number in words:

1. What is the height of the highest building?

2. What is the height of the highest mountain?

3. What is the height of the highest volcano?

4. Which waterfall has the highest fall?

5. Which planet has the greatest diameter?

5

6. Which planet is furthest from the sun?

7. Which river has the greatest length?

8. Which county has the largest area?

9. Which island has the greatest area?

10. What is the area of the largest lake?

11. Which sea (not ocean) has the greatest area?

12. How far does light travel in one year?

B List the names of the areas of water in order of size writing the largest first, then write the areas using numbers.

Note   < means 'is less than'.
          > means 'is greater than'.

Exercise 3

Copy the following, but fill in the correct sign < or > :

1. 106 ? 119

2. 693 ? 750

3. 2306 ? 2214

4. 5040 ? 5004

5. 8273 ? 7832

6. 9206 ? 9026

7. 12 309 ? 12 390

8. 56 007 ? 50 760

9. 74 132 ? 74 312

10. 400 502 ? 402 005

11. 79 863 ? 102 401

12. 3 061 216 ? 2 998 497

Exercise 4

1. Using each of the digits 3, 6 and 8 once only in each number, write in order of size (smallest first) as many different three-digit numbers as you can.

2. Write in order of size, largest first, all the three-digit even numbers that can be formed using the digits 2, 5, 8 and 9. A digit may only be used once in each number.

3. Using any of the digits 2, 4, 5, 6, 9 once only in each number, write:
   (a) the largest three-digit odd number that can be made,
   (b) the smallest four-digit odd number that can be made,
   (c) the smallest four-digit even number that can be made.

Exercise 5

If you fold a strip of paper in half, folding from left to right you obtain *one* crease.

If you fold the strip in half twice, you obtain *three* creases.

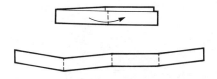

Investigate what happens when you make more folds. Make a table showing the number of folds and the number of creases.

No. of folds	No. of creases
1	1
2	3
3	
4	
etc.	

Approximations

Exercise 6

1. (a) Is 37 closer to 30 or to 40? So 37 should be rounded to ?.

(b) Is 82 closer to 80 or to 90? So 82 should be rounded to ?.

(c) Is 76 closer to 70 or to 80? So 76 should be rounded to ?.

(d) Is 45 closer to 40 or to 50?
It is half-way, so we shall round it *up* to 50.

We shall agree to round anything that is half-way, *upwards*.

2. (a) Is 680 closer to 600 or 700? So 680 should be rounded to ?.

(b) Is 326 closer to 300 or 400? So 326 should be rounded to ?.

(c) 750 should be rounded to ?.

3. (a) Is 3900 closer to 3000 or 4000? So 3900 should be rounded to ?.

(b) 2600 should be rounded to ?.

(c) 6300 should be rounded to ?.

(d) 4500 should be rounded to ?.

Exercise 7 **M**

1. Copy the names of the following mountains, then give their heights rounded to the nearest hundred metres:

Mountain	Height (m)
Everest	8848
Ararat	5165
Kilimanjaro	5963
Matterhorn	4505
Chimborazo	6272
Egmont	2526
Illampu	6550
Fujiyama	3778

2. Copy the names of the following rivers, then give their lengths rounded to the nearest 10 km:

River	Length (km)
Volga	3598
Danube	2832
Rhine	1359
Elbe	1152
Seine	771
Murray	2562
Amazon	6235
Missouri	4342
Mississippi	3764
Nile	6638

Exercise 8

1. Round these numbers to the nearest ten:
   (a) 47   (b) 52   (c) 89   (d) 65   (e) 35

2. Round these numbers to the nearest hundred:
   (a) 380   (b) 126   (c) 573   (d) 250   (e) 750

3. Round these numbers to the nearest thousand:
   (a) 6400   (b) 4250   (c) 7891   (d) 5500   (e) 3500

4. Round to the nearest ten:
   (a) 76   (c) 5172   (e) 2461   (g) 105   (i) 398
   (b) 246   (d) 6086   (f) 7137   (h) 275   (j) 96

5. (a) Round 28 638 to the nearest thousand.
   (b) Round 28 638 to the nearest hundred.
   (c) Round 28 638 to the nearest ten.
   (d) Round 28 638 to the nearest ten thousand.

Exercise 9 **M**

Note   All answers to the following questions must be whole numbers.

1. If 680 is the value of a number after it has been rounded to the nearest 10, what is the largest whole number it could have been before rounding?

2. 2730 is correct to the nearest 10. What is the smallest number it could have been before rounding?

3. The River Yangtze is 5470 km long correct to the nearest 10 km. What is its largest possible length before rounding? What is its smallest possible length?

4. Great Britain has an area of 229 800 km^2 correct to the nearest 100 km^2. What is its largest possible area before rounding? What is its smallest possible area?

5. The Red Sea has an area of 437 700 km^2 correct to the nearest 100 km^2. What is its largest possible area before rounding? What is its smallest possible area?

10

6. Copy and complete the following table of the world's longest bridge spans if the lengths have been rounded to the nearest 10 m:

Name of bridge	Length rounded to nearest 10 m	Smallest possible length (m)	Largest possible length (m)
Tacoma Narrows	850		
Severn	990		
Firth of Forth	1010		
George Washington	1070		
Mackinac	1160		
Golden Gate	1280		
Verrazo Narrows	1300		

Exercise 10

Write these numbers correct to one significant figure:

1. 38	**11.** 320	**21.** 1435	**31.** 5999
2. 42	**12.** 416	**22.** 3976	**32.** 4500
3. 56	**13.** 387	**23.** 2064	**33.** 987
4. 49	**14.** 261	**24.** 5800	**34.** 68 700
5. 25	**15.** 850	**25.** 6249	**35.** 14 260
6. 55	**16.** 251	**26.** 3268	**36.** 19 385
7. 380	**17.** 509	**27.** 8703	**37.** 9806
8. 410	**18.** 762	**28.** 6500	**38.** 27 495
9. 760	**19.** 98	**29.** 5441	**39.** 49 009
10. 870	**20.** 349	**30.** 5499	**40.** 99 450

2 Addition and Subtraction

Answer these:

1. 47
  + 34

2. 281
  + 326

3. 584
   72
  + 216

4. 5963
  + 2037

5. 6142
  3065
   37
  + 419

6. $39 + 28$
7. $452 + 79$
8. $394 + 266$
9. $728 + 476$
10. $2327 + 1234$
11. $4082 + 3129$
12. $39\,168 + 42\,782$
13. $41\,654 + 399$

14. $387 + 4928$
15. $48 + 3765 + 296$
16. $5102 + 3 + 86 + 788$
17. $607 + 40 + 5084 + 9$
18. $7814 + 392 + 3306$
19. $6147 + 23\,847 + 598$
20. $10\,603 + 9976 + 61 + 8435$

Exercise 2

Answer these:

1. 723
  − 416

2. 614
  − 365

3. 7208
  − 4069

4. 6007
  − 4139

5. 70 002
  − 3 793

6. $694 - 243$
7. $783 - 348$
8. $8346 - 2528$
9. $6573 - 3275$
10. $2967 - 747$
11. $570 - 236$
12. $2805 - 563$
13. $6027 - 5634$

14. $5103 - 4561$
15. $6080 - 2739$
16. $5430 - 2657$
17. $7006 - 2884$
18. $6002 - 4307$
19. $50\,010 - 20\,638$
20. $8008 - 3949$

Exercise 3

Copy these questions and fill in the missing digits:

1.
```
    3   5   2
+   2  [?] [?]
———————————————
   [?]  9   7
```

8.
```
    5   5  [?]
+  [?]  7   1
———————————————
   [?]  0   3  [?]
```

2.
```
    6  [?]  7
+   1   4  [?]
———————————————
   [?]  8   2
```

9.
```
    3   8   4
+  [?] [?] [?]
———————————————
    8   3   1
```

3.
```
    5  [?] [?]
+  [?]  7   6
———————————————
    1   2   5   4
```

10.
```
   [?] [?] [?]
+   5   7   3
———————————————
   [?]  0   7   1
```

4.
```
   [?]  7   5
-   3  [?]  2
———————————————
    4   2  [?]
```

11.
```
    5   1   6
-  [?] [?] [?]
———————————————
    3   4   7
```

5.
```
   [?]  5  [?]
-   5  [?]  7
———————————————
    3   1   7
```

12.
```
    7   0   2
-  [?] [?] [?]
———————————————
    2   0   9
```

6.
```
    3  [?]  6
-  [?]  4  [?]
———————————————
    1   8   8
```

13.
```
   [?] [?] [?]
-   2   8   5
———————————————
    6   1   9
```

7.
```
   [?]  5   3
-   4  [?]  6
———————————————
    3   2  [?]
```

14.
```
   [?] [?] [?]
-   4   1   6
———————————————
    2   8   8
```

13

15.

$$
\begin{array}{r}
6\ \ 0\ \ 0\ \ 4 \\
-\ \boxed{?}\ \boxed{?}\ \boxed{?}\ \boxed{?} \\
\hline
2\ \ 8\ \ 1\ \ 7
\end{array}
$$

17.

$$
\begin{array}{r}
\boxed{?}\ \ 3\ \ \boxed{?}\ \ 7 \\
-\ \ \ \ \ \boxed{?}\ \ 3\ \ \boxed{?} \\
\hline
1\ \ 4\ \ 6\ \cdot\ 8
\end{array}
$$

16.

$$
\begin{array}{r}
8\ \ \boxed{?}\ \ 6\ \ \boxed{?} \\
-\ \ \ \ \ 3\ \ \boxed{?}\ \ 7 \\
\hline
\boxed{?}\ \ 9\ \ 0\ \ 4
\end{array}
$$

18.

$$
\begin{array}{r}
1\ \ 0\ \ 2\ \ \boxed{?} \\
-\ \ \ \ \ \boxed{?}\ \ 4\ \ 1 \\
\hline
\boxed{?}\ \ 6
\end{array}
$$

Magic Squares

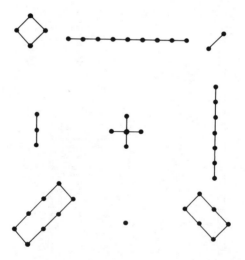

Chinese legend About 4000 years ago, Emperor Yu stood on the banks of the Yellow River and saw a divine tortoise come out of the river. It had two mysterious signs on its back. One was the *magic square* above. (In an arithmetical magic square, the sum of the numbers in each row, column and diagonal is the same.)

Albrecht Dürer's engraving called 'Melencolia' has a magic square on it (Germany 1471–1528). It shows the sullen mood of the thinker unable to make decisions.

It is a 4×4 magic square.

The date of the engraving is 1514 and can be seen in the magic square.

16	3	2	13
5	10	11	8
9	6	7	12
4	**15**	**14**	1

Exercise 4 M

Copy and complete the following magic squares:

1.

1	5	9
		4

4.

		16
	18	
20	10	

2.

4		8
	10	
12		

5.

		18
9		21
		6

3.

11	6	13
7		

6.

		11
10	5	6

7.

16			13
5	11		
	7	6	
4		15	1

11.

		4	
12		14	9
		13	2
5	10	7	

8.

15			6
		16	9
14	11	2	7
		13	

12.

18	13		4
9		16	
	19		
7		14	17

9.

	8		
10	15		13
	11	12	
	20	19	6

13.

	22	9		3
	14		8	20
19		13	25	7
	18	5	12	
23			4	

10.

8			10
		6	3
	7	9	
11	14		5

14.

22	24	6		15
	13	20	27	
25		9		
		23		12
3	10	17		26

Here is a 'totally magic' magic square!

1	12	7	14
8	13	2	11
10	3	16	5
15	6	9	4

1. Total the numbers in any block of four. Write what you notice.

2. Copy the magic square.

3. Cut off any number of columns then place them at the other side of the square. It is still magic!

4. Carry out step 3 with rows.

5. Test other magic squares in the same way.

Swiss mathematician Leonhard Euler (1707–83) discovered this magic square:

1	48	31	50	33	16	63	18
30	51	46	3	62	19	14	35
47	2	49	32	15	34	17	64
52	29	4	45	20	61	36	13
5	44	25	56	9	40	21	60
28	53	8	41	24	57	12	37
43	6	55	26	39	10	59	22
54	27	42	7	58	23	38	11

Magic constant = 260   Stop half-way, the total = 130

A chess knight can move from square 1 to square 64 in numerical order by following the normal knight's moves.

Copy and complete these magic squares:

1.

	11	9
8		

5.

16		4
	13	

9.

14		13	
	12		15
4	11		
17	6	10	

2.

10		
		16
18		

6.

19		
	13	
	21	

10.

	8	7	
10			13
	11	12	
	20	19	6

3.

19	12	
	16	

7.

	17	
14		8

11.

		9	31
	11	19	5
27		21	
1	23		

4.

17	3	
9		

8.

23		7
	11	

12.

6	13		
8	15	14	
11			18
	10		12

3 by 3 magic squares have 9 *cells*. In the magic square shown, the numbers in each row, column and diagonal total 27, so the *magic constant* (sometimes called *magic number* or *magic sum*) is 27.

13	2	12
8	9	10
6	16	5

Exercise 7

Throughout this exercise, write what you discover and, where possible, give reasons.

A **1.** Look at the given 3×3 (3 by 3) magic square:

8	7	12
13	9	5
6	11	10

   (a) What is its magic constant?

   (b) Multiply the number in the centre cell by 3. Write the value obtained.

   (c) Write what you notice about the answers to parts (a) and (b).

2. Repeat question 1 for other 3×3 magic squares. Try to find out if the result is always true.

B By investigating different 5×5 magic squares, try to find a similar result to that in part A. (Note that it is no use multiplying the number in each centre cell by 3.)

17	24	1	8	15
23	5	7	14	16
4	6	13	20	22
10	12	19	21	3
11	18	25	2	9

Exercise 8

The four shaded cells in each of the following diagrams are said to be *balanced about the centre square:*

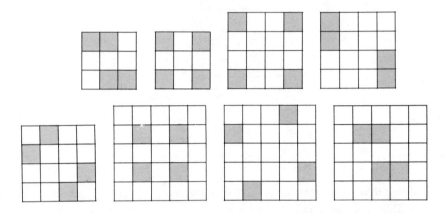

Note   There are many more possible groups of four cells that are balanced about the centre square.

A 1. Find the magic constant of any 4 × 4 magic square.

4	9	5	16
14	7	11	2
15	6	10	3
1	12	8	13

2. Add the four numbers in any group of four cells that are balanced about the centre square and write what you notice.

3. Repeat question 2 for other groups of four cells that are balanced about the centre square.

4. Add the four numbers in any block of four cells and write what you notice. Some possible blocks of four cells are shown in the following diagrams:

20

B For 3×3 magic squares, find the sum of the numbers in the different groups of four cells that are balanced about the centre square. Write what you notice.

C Repeat part B for 5×5 magic squares.

Exercise 9

The two cells in each of the following squares are balanced about the centre square:

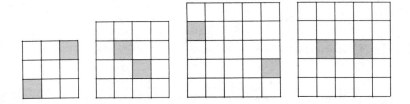

1. Write what you can discover about the sums of each pair of numbers that are balanced about the centre square in 3×3 magic squares.

2. Repeat question 1 for 4×4 magic squares.

3. Repeat question 1 for 5×5 magic squares.

Exercise 10

1. Add *any* number to the value in each cell of *any* magic square to form a new square. Will the new square always be a magic square?

2. A 3×3 square has *order* 3, a 4×4 square has order 4 and so on.
   (*a*) Write out two different magic squares that have the same order.
   (*b*) Add the numbers in corresponding cells to form a new square. An example is shown on the next page.

21

22	14	1	21
5	17	26	10
28	8	7	15
3	19	24	12

+

22	3	5	16
6	15	13	12
11	10	8	17
7	18	20	1

=

17			
		39	
18			

$14 + 3 = 17$

$26 + 13 = 39$

$8 + 10 = 18$

(c) Will the new square always be a magic square?

3. For *any* magic square, find the sum of the highest and lowest cell values. Divide the result by 2, then multiply that answer by the order of the magic square. Compare the final answer with the value of the magic constant for that magic square. Write what you notice.

Magic Triangles

Exercise 11 ══════════════════════════════ **M**

Copy and complete these triangles so that the numbers along each side give the same total. In questions 1 to 4 use the digits 1, 2, 3, 4, 5 and 6 once only in each answer.

1.

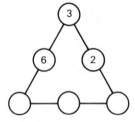

3.

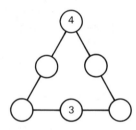

2.

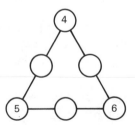

4.

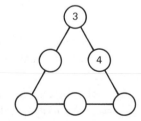

22

In questions 5 to 10, use the digits 1, 2, 3, 4, 5, 6, 7, 8 and 9 once only in each answer:

5.

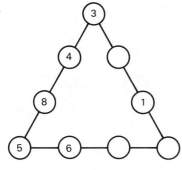

8.

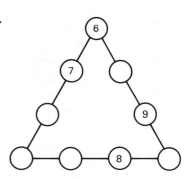

6.

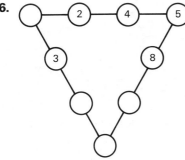

9.

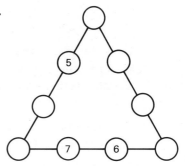

7.

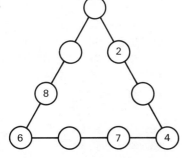

10.

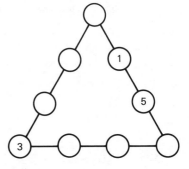

23

1. The numbers along each side
of the magic triangle shown,
total 11. By filling in the
numbers 1, 2, 3, 4, 5 and 6,
one in each of the six circles
of a triangle of the same size
as the one shown:

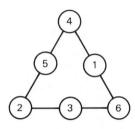

   (a) Find the magic triangle that has the largest possible total.
   What is that total?
   (b) Find the magic triangle that has the smallest possible total.
   What is that total?

2. By using a triangle having
nine circles, four along each
side, and filling in the
numbers 1, 2, 3, 4, 5, 6, 7, 8
and 9, one in each circle:

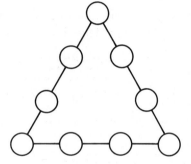

   (a) Find the magic triangle
   that has the largest
   possible total. What is
   that total?

   (b) Find the magic triangle that has the smallest possible total.
   What is that total?

Answer these as quickly as you can. Carry out the working in your
head and write the answers only.

1. $6 + 19 + 4$
2. $34 + 79 + 66$
3. $99 + 87$
4. $199 - 176$
5. $697 - 349$
6. $73 + 89 + 27$
7. $547 - 299$
8. $913 - 797$
9. $799 + 548$
10. $203 - 96$
11. $65 + 37 + 35 + 63$
12. $482 + 964 + 518$
13. $498 - 399$
14. $5087 - 2996$
15. $644 + 197 + 256$
16. $899 + 499 + 799$

Exercise 14

1. The total age of Ann, aged 18 years, Brenda, aged 16 years, and their brother Charles is 47 years. What will their total age be in fourteen years' time?

2. Find the sum of the digits of the number 86 497.

3. Find the sum of the digits of the answer obtained when 4396 is subtracted from 8907.

4. (*a*) From 5007, take 2818.   (*b*) Take 986 from 1521.

5. Add 4928 to the sum of 893 and 2765.

6. There were 786 pupils in a school. If 427 were boys, how many were girls?

7. I need 32 cm more string to give me a length that is 19 cm longer than 58 cm. How long is the string I have got?

8. Bronwen and Dominic, together, have the same number of stamps as Jane and Hamish. How many stamps has Dominic got if Bronwen has 2617, Jane has 3487 and Hamish has 2936.

9. The sum of two numbers is 143. If one of the numbers is 29 more than the other, find both numbers.

10. Surriya and Aled together had 62 pencils. If Aled had 16 more than Surriya, how many did each have?

11. Doreen and Michael each had 31 sweets. If Doreen gave Michael 16 of her sweets, how many more sweets than Doreen did Michael then have?

12. Jenny had 63 marbles and Tony had 92. If Tony gave Jenny 45 of his marbles, how many more marbles than Tony did Jenny then have?

13. If $483 + 399 = 882$, what is $882 - 483$?

14. If $768 + 563 = 1331$, what is $788 + 563$?

15. The sum of two consecutive whole numbers is 107. What are the two numbers?

16. The numbers of three, adjacent, even-numbered houses total 102. Find the three house numbers.

Exercise 15

1. (*a*) Add this list of numbers.

Now look at the list
upside down and add it
up again.

What do you notice
about both answers?

618
891
169
908
986
816
⎯⎯
⎯⎯

(*b*) Write a question of your own that gives the same total
upside down as it does the right way up.

2. (*a*) Write a three-digit number
where the first and last
digits are different.

Reverse the digits.

Subtract the smaller number
from the larger number.

Reverse the digits of your
answer.

Add these last two numbers.

e.g. 316

613

$$\begin{array}{r} 613 \\ -316 \\ \hline 297 \end{array}$$

$$\begin{array}{r} 792 \\ +\ 297 \\ \hline 1089 \end{array}$$

(*b*) Repeat part (*a*) using some more three-digit numbers.
Write what you notice about your answers.

3. Investigate four-digit numbers in the same way as the three-
digit numbers in question 2.

4. Use all eight figures: 1, 2, 3, 4, 5, 6, 7, 8 to form two, four-digit
numbers. Choose the two numbers as follows.
   (*a*) The two numbers, when added, should give the largest
possible total. Find that total.

   (*b*) A different pair of numbers, when subtracted, should
give the largest possible difference. Find that difference.

5. (a) Find: $2+3+4+5+6+7+8+9$

(b) Find: $12+13+14+15+16+17+18+19$

(c) Find: $52+53+54+55+56+57+58+59$

(d) Find: $57+58+59+60+61+62+63+64$

6. Using all the digits from 1 to 9, in that order, once only, write down an addition that totals 144.

7. Using all the digits 9, 8, 7, 6, 5, 4, 3, 2, 1, in that order, and using + and −, try to obtain a question that has an answer of 100 (e.g. $98+7-6-54+32+1 = \underline{78}$, but 100 is needed).

8. Use the digits 1, 2, 3, 4, 5, 6, 7, 8, 9, in that order, and use + and −, to obtain a question that has an answer of 100.

9. Use the digits 9, 8, 7, 6, 5, 4, 3, 2, 1, in that order, and use + and −, to obtain a question that has an answer of 1000.

10. In a competition, the red team was thought to have beaten the blue team by 5 points. When the points were checked, it was found that some of the blue team's points had been awarded to the red team. If the blue team actually beat the red team by 21 points, how many points were wrongly awarded?

Exercise 16 ◼ M

Copy and complete the following number squares:

1.

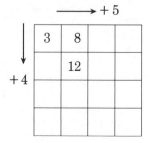

2.

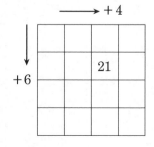

3. $\longrightarrow +12$

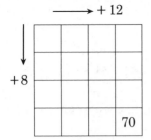

$+8$ ... 70

7. $\longrightarrow +7$

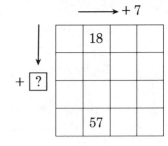

$+\boxed{?}$ ... 18 ... 57

4. $\longrightarrow +\boxed{?}$

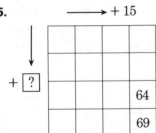

$+7$ ... 11 ... 20

8. $\longrightarrow +\boxed{?}$

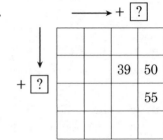

$+\boxed{?}$ ... 39 ... 50 ... 55

5. $\longrightarrow +15$

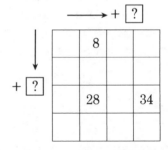

$+\boxed{?}$ ... 64 ... 69

9. $\longrightarrow +\boxed{?}$

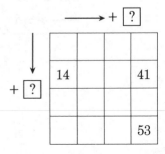

$+\boxed{?}$ ... 8 ... 28 ... 34

6. $\longrightarrow +\boxed{?}$

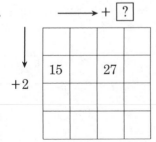

$+2$ ... 15 ... 27

10. $\longrightarrow +\boxed{?}$

$+\boxed{?}$ ... 14 ... 41 ... 53

11.

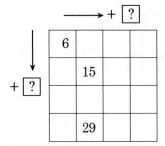

12.

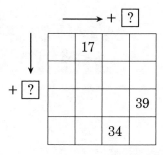

3 Multiplication and Division

Find the value of:

1. 600×2
2. 30×20
3. 50×30
4. 70×400
5. 60×300
6. 800×20
7. 700×50
8. 200×400
9. 90×4000
10. 3000×70
11. 600×8000
12. 5000×900
13. 9000×2000
14. 7000×8000
15. 3000×4000
16. $500 \times 80\,000$
17. $60\,000 \times 9000$
18. $700 \times 200\,000$
19. $6000 \times 70\,000$
20. $900\,000 \times 7000$
21. $50 \times 6\,000\,000$
22. $800\,000 \times 40\,000$
23. $400\,000 \times 60\,000$
24. $900\,000 \times 800\,000$
25. $8000 \div 20$
26. $\dfrac{90\,000}{300}$
27. $\dfrac{600\,000}{200}$
28. $\dfrac{2\,000\,000}{50}$
29. $3\,000\,000 \div 6000$
30. $\dfrac{100\,000\,000}{4000}$

Estimating

Exercise 2

Estimate the answers to the following questions. Work with one significant figure.

$e.g.$
$$586 \times 34$$
$$\approx 600 \times 30$$
$$= \underline{\underline{18\,000}}$$

30

1. 38×42
2. 57×23
3. 69×38
4. 476×32
5. 625×59
6. $590 \div 23$
7. $\dfrac{876}{28}$
8. $523 \div 51$
9. 737×864
10. $3829/19$
11. 766×1063
12. $8499 \div 17$
13. 650×491
14. $\dfrac{7615}{38}$
15. 721×406
16. $16\,312 \times 751$
17. $28\,106 \div 98$
18. $9683/169$
19. 4646×3592
20. $\dfrac{5938}{375}$

Exercise 3

1. About how much would I need to buy 29 stamps costing 18 p each?

2. A carton of milk costs 26 p. If someone buys two of these cartons each day, estimate the monthly milk bill.

3. A holiday costs £293.99 per adult. Estimate the total cost of the holiday for four adults.

4. There were 882 bottles in a warehouse. If they were packed in boxes of 18 bottles, estimate the number of boxes used.

5. Estimate the time taken to travel 192 miles at 38 m.p.h.

6. Estimate the number of weeks it would take to save £59.50 at £2.85 per week.

7. Estimate the cost of $18\,\text{m}^2$ of carpet at £9.35 per square metre.

8. Mr Charlton travelled the following distances during a particular week: 141 miles, 172 miles, 218 miles, 207 miles and 165 miles. Estimate the total distance he travelled in that week.

Exercise 4

Answer these:

1. 542×6
2. 7×384
3. 207×9
4. 5164×8
5. 2070×4
6. 517×30
7. 50×629
8. 124×32
9. 26×897

10. 483×17　　**12.** 574×208　　**14.** 768×730
11. 3082×41　　**13.** 396×504　　**15.** 456×216

Exercise 5

Answer these:

1. $4326 \div 7$　　　**6.** $15\,070 \div 5$　　　**11.** $28\,105 \div 35$
2. $1156 \div 4$　　　**7.** $18\,027 \div 3$　　　**12.** $40\,290 \div 51$
3. $8586 \div 6$　　　**8.** $35\,280 \div 7$　　　**13.** $53\,106 \div 53$
4. $3078 \div 9$　　　**9.** $864 \div 24$　　　**14.** $8386 \div 14$
5. $4056 \div 8$　　　**10.** $8514 \div 18$　　　**15.** $60\,836 \div 67$

Exercise 6

Copy the following and fill in the missing digits:

1.
```
    ? 2 ?
  ×     3
  ? 2 ? 5
```

2.
```
    6 5 7
  ×     ?
  ? ? ? 5
```

3.
```
    5 ? 4
  ×     ?
  ? 6 6 8
```

4.
```
  2) 6 8 ?
     ? ? 2
```

5.
```
        8 ? 9
  3) ? 6 0 ?
```

6.
```
  7) ? ? 5
     1 2 ?
```

7.
```
    ? 5 4
  ×     ?
  6 0 ? 2
```

8.
```
    ? 2 ?
  ×     4
  3 3 ? 4
```

9.

```
        5  4  6
  ?) 3 ? 2 ?
```

10.

```
        3 ? 6
     ×    2 ?
    ─────────
    ? ? 6 ?
    ? ? ? 0
    ─────────
    ? ? 0 ? 8
```

11.

```
     5  9
  ×     ?
  ────────
     2  3  6
```

12.

```
    ? ? ?
  ×       3
  ─────────
    1  7  0  1
```

13.

```
        9  8
  ×        ?
  ──────────
     8  8  2
```

14.

```
    ? ? ?
  ×     2  1
  ──────────
    1 0 9 8 3
```

15.

```
        5  6  2
  7) ? ? ? ?
```

16. $826 \div$? ? $= 14$

17. $32 \times$? $= 288$

18. ? ? $\times 39 = 1638$

Exercise 7

Write the units digit of the answer to each of these questions:

1. 62×17	**9.** 43×729	**17.** 5027×39
2. 29×34	**10.** 367×87	**18.** 413×197
3. 73×81	**11.** 165×79	**19.** 6060×38
4. 94×45	**12.** 48×81	**20.** 478×709
5. 65×816	**13.** 82×104	**21.** 394×296
6. 843×95	**14.** 2176×52	**22.** 649×19
7. 406×387	**15.** 358×168	**23.** 455×827
8. 718×56	**16.** 924×203	**24.** 3017×218

Exercise 8

Use quick methods to answer these:

A **1.** $2 \times 9 \times 5$ **4.** $35 \times 81 \times 2$
   2. $17 \times 5 \times 2$ **5.** $25 \times 97 \times 4$
   3. $9 \times 15 \times 2$ **6.** $64 \times 125 \times 8$

B *e.g. 1* 35×46 *e.g. 2* 24×13
             $= 70 \times 23$ $= 8 \times 39$
             $= 1610$ $= 312$

   1. 47×14 **7.** 54×45
   2. 15×36 **8.** 25×88
   3. 36×25 **9.** 63×33
   4. 16×78 **10.** 27×31
   5. 21×29 **11.** 125×84
   6. 32×17 **12.** 250×320

C *e.g.* 23×99
           $= 23 \times 100 - 23$ (23 lots of $100 - 23$ lots of 1)
           $= 2300 - 23$
           $= 2277$

   1. 99×37 **4.** 599×64
   2. 58×99 **5.** 25×799
   3. 76×299 **6.** 999×71

Exercise 9

For each question, select the one correct answer:

1. $67 \times 43 = \boxed{?}$
   A. 2880   B. 2881   C. 2421   D. 2420

2. $58 \times 24 = \boxed{?}$
   A. 1032   B. 1052   C. 1392   D. 732

3. $4 \times 79 \times 25 = \boxed{?}$

    A. 17 536   B. 1580   C. 7900   D. 79 000

4. $46 \times 72 = \boxed{?}$

    A. 23×36 B. 23×144 C. 92×144 D. 48×70

5. $3900 \times 230 = \boxed{?}$

    A. 87 900   B. 879 000   C. 89 700   D. 897 000

6. $12\,960\,000 \div 480 = \boxed{?}$

    A. 27   B. 270   C. 2700   D. 27 000

7. $56 \times 24 = \boxed{?}$

    A. 14×48 B. 112×48 C. 48×28 D. 28×12

8. $1728 \div 54 = \boxed{?}$

    A. $864 \div 108$ B. $864 \div 27$ C. $432 \div 27$ D. $3456 \div 27$

9. $16 \times 12 \times 26 \times 9 = \boxed{?}$

    A. $32 \times 24 \times 13 \times 3$ C. $64 \times 6 \times 13 \times 3$

    B. $48 \times 6 \times 52 \times 3$ D. $8 \times 36 \times 13 \times 3$

10. $820 \times 7500 = \boxed{?}$

    A. 6 150 000   B. 615 000   C. 61 500   D. 651 000

Exercise 10

$$\left.\begin{array}{l} 63 \times 48 = 3024 \\ \text{and} \quad 36 \times 84 = 3024 \end{array}\right\} \text{ the same answer}$$

Note   63 was changed to 36 and 48 was changed to 84.

Check that 69×32 gives the same answer as 96×23.

Use a calculator to help you to find some more two-digit numbers where this happens (i.e. by reversing the digits and then multiplying, the same answer is obtained).

Try to explain how to recognise that two, two-digit numbers give the same answer when reversed and multiplied.

Exercise 11

Copy and complete:

1. $4 \times 6 = 2 \times \boxed{?}$
2. $6 \times 10 = 3 \times \boxed{?}$
3. $4 \times 12 = 8 \times \boxed{?}$
4. $12 \times 7 = 4 \times \boxed{?}$
5. $5 \times 8 = \boxed{?} \times 10$
6. $12 \times 9 = \boxed{?} \times 4$
7. $\boxed{?} \times 18 = 4 \times 9$
8. $20 \times \boxed{?} = 4 \times 15$
9. $24 \div 6 = 8 \div \boxed{?}$
10. $64 \div 8 = 16 \div \boxed{?}$
11. $22 \div 2 = 66 \div \boxed{?}$
12. $54 \div 9 = \boxed{?} \div 3$
13. $48 \div 3 = \boxed{?} \div 12$
14. $60 \div \boxed{?} = 30 \div 5$
15. $25 \times 12 = 75 \times \boxed{?}$
16. $84 \times 48 = \boxed{?} \times 6$
17. $17 \times 52 = 68 \times \boxed{?}$
18. $301 \div 98 = \boxed{?} \div 14$
19. $104 \div 13 = \boxed{?} \div 78$
20. $66 \times 198 = 18 \times \boxed{?}$

Exercise 12

Copy these, but replace each box with the symbol $+$, $-$, $\times$, or $\div$ to make each calculation correct:

1. $6 \boxed{?} 4 \boxed{?} 9 = 15$
2. $9 \boxed{?} 3 \boxed{?} 5 = 17$
3. $18 \boxed{?} 6 \boxed{?} 2 = 14$
4. $12 \boxed{?} 2 \boxed{?} 5 = 19$
5. $26 \boxed{?} 2 \boxed{?} 7 = 20$
6. $6 \boxed{?} 2 \boxed{?} 8 = 24$
7. $30 \boxed{?} 6 \boxed{?} 9 = 27$
8. $13 \boxed{?} 4 \boxed{?} 24 = 28$
9. $16 \boxed{?} 4 \boxed{?} 8 = 12$
10. $48 \boxed{?} 24 \boxed{?} 12 = 12$
11. $9 \boxed{?} 8 \boxed{?} 2 = 36$
12. $28 \boxed{?} 4 \boxed{?} 10 = 17$
13. $7 \boxed{?} 8 = 28 \boxed{?} 2$
14. $4 \boxed{?} 12 = 32 \boxed{?} 2$
15. $6 \boxed{?} 5 = 48 \boxed{?} 18$
16. $14 \boxed{?} 3 = 36 \boxed{?} 6$
17. $60 \boxed{?} 5 = 6 \boxed{?} 6$
18. $12 \boxed{?} 6 = 9 \boxed{?} 8$
19. $4 \boxed{?} 6 \boxed{?} 8 = 32$
20. $16 \boxed{?} 2 \boxed{?} 7 = 11 \boxed{?} 4$
21. $24 \boxed{?} 4 \boxed{?} 6 = 7 \boxed{?} 2$
22. $3 \boxed{?} 9 \boxed{?} 3 = 6 \boxed{?} 5$
23. $(18 \boxed{?} 12) \boxed{?} 6 = 5$
24. $4 \boxed{?} (11 \boxed{?} 4) = 28$

Exercise 13

1. If $67 \times 29 = 1943$ find the value of:
  - (a) 670×290
  - (b) $6700 \times 29\,000$
  - (c) 2900×67
  - (d) $1943 \div 29$
  - (e) $1943 \div 67$
  - (f) $194\,300 \div 67$

2. If $260 \times 38\,000 = 9\,880\,000,$ find the value of:
  - (a) 26×38
  - (b) 380×260
  - (c) 2600×3800
  - (d) $9\,880\,000 \div 260$
  - (e) $9880 \div 38$
  - (f) $988\,000 \div 2600$

3. If $2548 \div 52 = 49,$ find the value of:
  - (a) 49×52
  - (b) $2548 \div 49$
  - (c) 520×490
  - (d) $4900 \times 52\,000$
  - (e) $25\,480 \div 52$
  - (f) $2\,548\,000 \div 490$

4. Given that $2294 \div 31 = 74,$ find the value of:
  - (a) 31×74
  - (b) 7400×310
  - (c) $74\,000 \times 3100$
  - (d) $2294 \div 74$
  - (e) $229\,400 \div 74$
  - (f) $229\,400 \div 310$

5. Given that $530 \times 8700 = 4\,611\,000,$ find the value of:
  - (a) 53×87
  - (b) $530 \times 87\,000$
  - (c) 8700×5300
  - (d) $4611 \div 53$
  - (e) $461\,100 \div 87$
  - (f) $4\,611\,000 \div 5300$

6. If $18 \times 96 = 1728,$ find the value of:
  - (a) 96×18
  - (b) $18\,000 \times 9600$
  - (c) 960×1800
  - (d) $17\,280 \div 96$
  - (e) $17\,280 \div 960$
  - (f) $172\,800 \div 180$

Exercise 14

1. I have 87 tablets. How many days should they last if I take three each day?

2. Fuses are sold in boxes of four. How many fuses will there be in 19 boxes?

37

3. A car averaged 38 m.p.h. for 3 h. How far did it travel?

4. There were 168 pupils in the first year. If they were in six equal-sized classes, how many were in each class?

5. If there were 125 g of sweets in a box, how many grams of sweets would there be in five of those boxes?

6. How many weeks are there in 119 days?

7. A piece of string of length 96 cm is cut into 8 cm lengths. How many pieces are obtained?

8. What would five 18 p stamps cost?

9. A shop sold 20 dozen eggs. How many was that?

10. 3480 tins were put into boxes and each box held 40 tins. How many boxes were used?

11. Some small screws are sold in packs of 24. A shop sold 14 packs. How many screws was that?

12. How many times can 17 be subtracted from 391?

13. Egg boxes hold half a dozen eggs each. If there were 523 eggs:
(*a*) How many boxes would be needed?
(*b*) How many eggs would be left over?

14. If 637 coloured pencils were packed into boxes of ten:
(*a*) How many boxes were used?
(*b*) How many pencils were left over?

15. If 519 coloured pencils were packed into boxes of 12:
(*a*) How many boxes were used?
(*b*) How many pencils were left over?

16. A 492 cm length of string was cut into 15 cm lengths:
(*a*) How many lengths were obtained?
(*b*) What length was left over?

Exercise 15   M

John Napier (1550–1617) was the son of a Scottish nobleman. He invented ways of calculating. One of the calculating aids he invented is known as Napier's Bones (or rods). They were used not only in Europe but also in China and Japan.

Copy these 'bones' on to squared paper or on to card.

Index	0	1	2	3	4	5	6	7	8	9
1	0/0	0/1	0/2	0/3	0/4	0/5	0/6	0/7	0/8	0/9
2	0/0	0/2	0/4	0/6	0/8	1/0	1/2	1/4	1/6	1/8
3	0/0	0/3	0/6	0/9	1/2	1/5	1/8	2/1	2/4	2/7
4	0/0	0/4	0/8	1/2	1/6	2/0	2/4	2/8	3/2	3/6
5	0/0	0/5	1/0	1/5	2/0	2/5	3/0	3/5	4/0	4/5
6	0/0	0/6	1/2	1/8	2/4	3/0	3/6	4/2	4/8	5/4
7	0/0	0/7	1/4	2/1	2/8	3/5	4/2	4/9	5/6	6/3
8	0/0	0/8	1/6	2/4	3/2	4/0	4/8	5/6	6/4	7/2
9	0/0	0/9	1/8	2/7	3/6	4/5	5/4	6/3	7/2	8/1

Now cut out each 'bone' (or rod) from your numbered set (as in the example).

You should finish with 11 strips (strips 0 to 9 plus an index strip).

4
0 / 4
0 / 8
1 / 2
1 / 6
2 / 0
2 / 4
2 / 8
3 / 2
3 / 6

Exercise 16

Use your 'bones' to try these examples:

e.g. 1 43×2

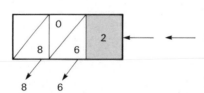

4	3	Index
0 / 4	0 / 3	1
0 / 8	0 / 6	2
1 / 2	0 / 9	3

e.g. 2 96×4

Now use your 'bones' to work these out:

A
1. 23×3
2. 4×12
3. 3×31
4. 21×4
5. 43×2

6. 40×8
7. 6×90
8. 37×2
9. 81×9
10. 5×17

11. 82×3
12. 87×6
13. 56×4
14. 4×59
15. 65×8

16. 7×67
17. 5×85
18. 72×9
19. 8×78
20. 41×7

B
1. 204×2
2. 341×2
3. 3×123
4. 4×202

5. 6×109
6. 312×4
7. 5×713
8. 569×8

9. 7×806
10. 8×480
11. 363×6
12. 4×921

13. 954×5
14. 6×455
15. 497×7
16. 9×319

4 More Work on Number and Money

Find the number that is exactly half-way between the two given numbers:

1. 8 and 16	**9.** 3 and 57	**17.** 295 and 101
2. 3 and 19	**10.** 44 and 6	**18.** 176 and 498
3. 15 and 27	**11.** 2 and 74	**19.** 239 and 545
4. 18 and 34	**12.** 93 and 11	**20.** 164 and 736
5. 0 and 34	**13.** 82 and 12	**21.** 377 and 893
6. 46 and 22	**14.** 127 and 31	**22.** 1243 and 3075
7. 39 and 21	**15.** 49 and 167	**23.** 2619 and 6827
8. 9 and 45	**16.** 158 and 282	**24.** 2906 and 7302

Exercise 2

1. Add 475, 216 and 384.

2. From 2084 take 1657.

3. Take 3895 from 6402.

4. What is the sum of 3429 and 5786?

5. Find the difference between 683 and 257.

6. Find the product of 826 and 7.

7. Find the product of 79 and 28.

8. Divide 16 120 by 8.

9. Divide 11 638 by 23.

10. Subtract 896 from the product of 9 and 713.

11. Add 2969 to the product of 18 and 34.

12. Add 764 to the sum of 2616 and 79.

13. Take 691 from the sum of 735 and 487.

14. Divide the sum of 3847 and 9228 by 25.

15. Multiply 409 by 51.

Exercise 3

1. Write 3094 s in minutes and seconds.

2. 485 pupils go on a school trip. If each coach holds 38 pupils, how many coaches are needed?

3. The product of three numbers is 14 355. If two of the numbers are 15 and 33, is the third number odd or even?

4. I have £135 made up of an equal number of £10 and £5 notes. How many of each have I got?

5. An additional 7 cm of string will give me a length that is 16 cm less than 85 cm. How long is the string I have got?

6. Find the units digit that is in the answer to the calculation $86 \times 39 \times 47$.

7. What is the difference between 12 times 79 and 10 times 79?

8. Calculate the distance from the surface of the Earth to the surface of the Moon, if the diameter of the Earth is 12 757 km and the Moon's diameter is 3476 km, and if the distance from the centre of the Earth to the centre of the Moon is 384 400 km.

9. A man has all the £5 notes numbered from 769 048 to 769 213 inclusive. How much is that?

10. Brian is 11 cm taller than Janet, but is 4 cm smaller than Alan. How much taller than Janet is Alan?

11. What is the remainder when 837 289 is divided by 25?

12. Find the two numbers nearest to 3000 that will divide exactly by 57.

13. The product of two consecutive numbers is 2070. What are the two numbers?

14. The product of two consecutive even numbers is 3024. Find them.

Exercise 4

1. What number, when divided by 57, gives a quotient* of 316?

2. What number, when divided by 78, gives a quotient of 243 and a remainder of 29?

3. By what number must I divide 462 to obtain a quotient of 14 and a remainder of 28?

4. Fifteen people went to the theatre and sat in the same row of consecutive, odd-numbered seats. If the first person sat in seat number 37, in what numbered seat could the last person be sitting?

5. Find the least number, which, when added to 487 will make the sum exactly divisible by 99.

6. In an election 37 462 people voted for two people. If the winning candidate won by 9784 votes, how many votes did the losing candidate get?

7. John and Pam, together, have a total of 319 marbles. If Pam and David's marbles total 293 and if there are 464 marbles altogether, how many marbles does each person have?

8. I have two strips of card. One is 628 mm long, while the other is 479 mm. If I gum them together to form a single strip, and if they overlap by 156 mm, find the length of the new strip.

9. How many digits would I write, if I listed all the natural numbers from 286 to 437 inclusive?

10. If I wrote all the natural numbers from 39 to 571 inclusive, how many digits would I have written altogether?

*See the glossary, p. 435.

Exercise 5

1. The numbers of five, adjacent, even-numbered houses add up to 930. What are the numbers of the houses?

2. In a game, a number of people stand evenly spaced in a circle, and are numbered consecutively from 1 upwards. Number 6 stands directly opposite number 19. How many people must there be?

3. How many people will there be if they stand evenly spaced in a circle and are numbered from 8 upwards, and if number 13 is opposite number 28?

4. If 24 people stand evenly spaced in a circle, and are numbered consecutively from 13 upwards, which numbered person is opposite number 21?

5. Find the sum of all the odd numbers from 1 to 99 inclusive.

6. Two buses set off on a journey together. There were twice as many people on the first bus as on the second. At the first stop, 13 people got off the first bus, while six people got on the second. Both buses now carried the same number of people. How many people started off on each bus?

7. (a) In the first division of the football league there are 22 football teams. If each team plays all the other teams twice, once at home and once away, during the year, how many games will be played altogether?

   (b) How many games would be played if there were 18 teams?

   (c) How many games would be played if there were 37 teams?

8. The distance around a rectangular piece of card (its *perimeter*) is 1260 mm. Find its dimensions if its length is twice its breadth.

Exercise 6

1. (*a*) Copy and complete the number pattern:

$$21 - 12 = 9$$
$$31 - 13 = \boxed{?}$$
$$41 - 14 = \boxed{?}$$
$$51 - 15 = \boxed{?}$$
$$\boxed{?} - \boxed{?} = \boxed{?}$$
$$\boxed{?} - \boxed{?} = \boxed{?}$$
$$\boxed{?} - \boxed{?} = \boxed{?}$$
$$91 - 19 = \boxed{?}$$

(*b*) What do you notice about the answers?

2. (*a*) Write a two-digit number where the first digit is greater than the second.
Write the number obtained when the digits are reversed.
Subtract the smaller number from the larger.
What is your answer?

(*b*) Now write as many subtraction questions as you can that use two 2-digit numbers and give the answer 36.

(*c*) Explain how to recognise when a subtraction question has an answer of 36.

3. Investigate other answers in the same way as the answer 36 in question 2.
Write about what you discover.

4. Do any of the answers not divide exactly by 9?

5. For questions that have the same answer, subtract the units digit from the tens digit if the tens digit is larger, or the tens digit from the units digit if the units digit is larger.
Write about what you notice.

Money

Exercise 7

A Look at each amount of money. If it is correctly written, copy it. If it is wrongly written, write it in the way you think it should be written.

1. £4	**9.** £0.07	**17.** £5.0
2. 6£	**10.** £0.3	**18.** £384
3. £2.84 p	**11.** 678 p	**19.** £3.6
4. £5.00	**12.** £0.43	**20.** £4 29 p
5. £23 p	**13.** £65.33 p	**21.** .56 p
6. £.72	**14.** £0.06 p	**22.** £74.00
7. 19 p	**15.** p 81	**23.** p. 57
8. 7 p	**16.** £0.90	**24.** £18.00 p

B Write in figures:

1. forty-four pounds
2. two pounds fifty-six
3. nine pounds eighty
4. seventy-one pounds thirteen
5. three pounds ninety-five
6. six pounds seven
7. fifty-two pounds ten
8. thirty-eight pounds
9. fifteen pounds sixty
10. twenty-three pounds six

C £8.75 is usually written as £8—75 on a cheque. Write each of these in the normal way.

1. £2—58	**4.** £3—36	**7.** £0—92
2. £19—23	**5.** £41—70	**8.** £38—51
3. £64—87	**6.** £9—05	**9.** £326—18

Write these as on a cheque:

10. £1.64	**12.** £5.19	**14.** £8.30
11. £79.81	**13.** £27.45	**15.** £85.06

Exercise 8

Throughout this exercise, the coins that may be used are: 1 p, 2 p, 5 p, 10 p, 20 p, 50 p and £1. Unless otherwise stated, you may use more than one of any coin.

1. Five coins have a total value of 20 p. Which coins could they be?

2. Four coins have a total value of 10 p. Which coins could they be?

3. Five coins have a total value of £1. Give three different lists of coins where this can happen.

4. Can three coins have a total value of 20 p?

5. Can three coins have a total value of 10 p?

6. Can three coins have a total value of 5 p?

7. Can three coins have a total value of 18 p?

8. List five coins that have a total value of £2.75.

9. List four coins that have a total value of £2.05.

10. List all possible ways of making up 10 p from the coins above.

11. List all possible ways of making up 30 p from the coins above, if no more than six coins are used at any one time in making the sum of 30 p.

12. If you have one each of any combination of the coins 5 p, 10 p, 20 p and 50 p, list all possible sums of money that can be made up using those coins.

Exercise 9

1. A shopkeeper bought a television set for £149.50 and then sold it for £209.95. How much profit did he make?

2. Mrs Dickson paid £34.99 for a dress in a sale. If the dress had been reduced by £8.50, what was its price before the sale?

3. Material costs £8.49 per metre. Find the cost of 4 m.

4. A meal for four people came to £19.40. If each person's choice cost the same, what was the cost per person?

5. If turkey costs 64 p per pound, find the cost of a 13 lb turkey.

6. Joyce spent £46.37 altogether at four shops. If she spent £7.56 at the first shop, £15.68 at the second and £9.85 at the third, how much did she spend at the fourth shop?

7. I gave a shopkeeper £10. He said that, to save change, if I gave him a further 27 p he would give me £1.50. How much did my goods cost?

8. How much per year is £123.46 per week?

9. How much per week is £5062.72 p.a. (per annum or per year)?

10. Find the amount taken, if 146 tickets were sold at £1.60 each.

11. A shopkeeper could buy five packs of cards for £5.95, to sell at £1.49 per pack. Find the profit made from selling 30 packs.

12. A washing machine costs £379.95 cash. It can be bought on HP (hire-purchase) for a deposit of £113.95, followed by 24 monthly payments of £13.15. How much extra is paid on HP?

Exercise 10

1. A shopkeeper sold five TV sets in a sale for £1249.80. If each set had been reduced by £49.99, how much more money would the shopkeeper have taken if the five sets were sold at their original price?

2. If 6 m of material costs £41.04, find the cost of 8 m.

3. If 6 m of material costs £41.82, find the cost of 12 m.

4. If 7 yd of material costs £41.72, what is the cost of 6 yd?

5. Which is the cheaper buy, 400 g at £3.88 or 300 g at £2.94?

6. Mrs Banks saves the same amount of money each week for several weeks. The weekly amount is over one pound and a whole number of pence. If she has saved £10.57 so far, for how many weeks has she been saving?

Exercise 11 M

Copy this number line:

Answer these using a calculator and mark your answers on your number line. (Mark a dot and label the position with the letter of that question.)

e.g. 1 $7 - 3 = 4$

e.g. 2 $5 - 8 = {}^-3$

(*a*) $12 - 5$
(*b*) $23 - 14$
(*c*) $47 - 33$
(*d*) $2 - 8$
(*e*) $4 - 13$
(*f*) $18 - 18$
(*g*) $4 - 16$
(*h*) $16 - 4$
(*i*) $39 - 29$
(*j*) $29 - 39$
(*k*) $13 - 27$
(*l*) $18 - 22$

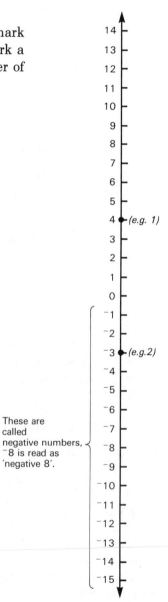

These are called negative numbers, ${}^-8$ is read as 'negative 8'.

Exercise 12

Copy these, but replace each box with $=$ or $\neq$ to make each statement correct. (You may use a calculator to help you.)

1. $6932 + 4785 \boxed{?} 4785 + 6932$
2. $704 - 398 \boxed{?} 398 - 704$
3. $546 \times 41 \boxed{?} 41 \times 546$
4. $1037 \div 17 \boxed{?} 17 \div 1037$
5. $6185 - 927 \boxed{?} 927 - 6185$
6. $73 \times 28 \boxed{?} 37 \times 82$
7. $68 \times 43 \boxed{?} 43 \times 68$
8. $983 \times 427 \boxed{?} 427 \times 983$

Exercise 13

A Answer these using a calculator:

1. $8240 + 6390$
2. $724 + 69 + 9046$
3. $5407 - 2916$
4. $78\,312 - 39\,478$
5. 106×351
6. 849×37
7. $3792 \div 79$
8. $123\,213 \div 201$

B Find out which of these are wrong. If an answer is wrong, find the correct answer with a calculator.

1. $689 + 342 = 1030$
2. $7615 + 947 = 8562$
3. $14\,029 + 8736 = 20\,760$
4. $907 - 648 = 259$
5. $7134 - 2937 = 4193$
6. $21\,006 - 8749 = 12\,258$
7. $342 \times 64 = 21\,886$
8. $504 \times 19 = 9076$
9. $26 \times 1037 = 26\,962$
10. $4312 \div 14 = 38$
11. $27\,820 \div 260 = 197$
12. $10\,816 \div 104 = 104$

C Use a calculator to help you with these:

1. In an election there were two candidates. Mrs Winner polled 39 327 votes while Mr Unwin polled 23 846 votes.

    (a) By how many votes did Mrs Winner win?

    (b) How many people voted altogether?

2. How many seconds are there in a year (365 days)?

3. Coloured pencils were packed into boxes of fifteen:
   (*a*) How many full boxes were made up out of 585 pencils?
   (*b*) How many full boxes were made up out of 414 pencils?
   (*c*) In part (*b*), how many pencils were left over?

Exercise 14

1. Use *only* the keys $\boxed{3}$, $\boxed{7}$, $\boxed{+}$, $\boxed{-}$, $\boxed{\times}$, $\boxed{\div}$ and $\boxed{=}$ as many times as you need. Try to obtain these answers. Show your methods.

   e.g. 1 $\boxed{7}$ $\boxed{+}$ $\boxed{7}$ $\boxed{+}$ $\boxed{3}$ $\boxed{+}$ $\boxed{3}$ $\boxed{+}$ $\boxed{3}$ $\boxed{=}$ 23
   or $\boxed{7}$ $\boxed{+}$ $\boxed{7}$ $\boxed{+}$ $\boxed{3}$ $\boxed{\times}$ $\boxed{3}$ $\boxed{=}$ 23 (This may not work on some calculators. Try it.)

   e.g. 2 $\boxed{3}$ $\boxed{\times}$ $\boxed{7}$ $\boxed{+}$ $\boxed{7}$ $\boxed{-}$ $\boxed{3}$ $\boxed{=}$ 25

   e.g. 3 $\boxed{3}$ $\boxed{7}$ $\boxed{+}$ $\boxed{3}$ $\boxed{7}$ $\boxed{-}$ $\boxed{3}$ $\boxed{=}$ 71

   (*a*) 13   (*b*) 24   (*c*) 46   (*d*) 59   (*e*) 106

2. Use *only* the keys $\boxed{5}$, $\boxed{9}$, $\boxed{+}$ and $\boxed{=}$ as many times as you need. Try to obtain these answers. Show your methods.
   (*a*) 23   (*b*) 24   (*c*) 31   (*d*) 73   (*e*) 114

3. Use *only* the keys $\boxed{7}$, $\boxed{8}$, $\boxed{+}$ and $\boxed{=}$ as many times as you need. List all possible *answers* up to 50 that can be obtained using only these four given keys.

4. Use *only* the keys $\boxed{4}$, $\boxed{6}$, $\boxed{+}$ and $\boxed{=}$ as many times as you need. Try to obtain these answers. Show your methods.
   (*a*) 52   (*b*) 59   (*c*) 74   (*d*) 58   (*e*) 98

5. Use *only* the keys $\boxed{3}$, $\boxed{5}$, $\boxed{+}$ and $\boxed{=}$ as many times as you need. List all possible ways of obtaining the answer 43.

6. Use *only* the keys $\boxed{3}$, $\boxed{4}$, $\boxed{5}$, $\boxed{7}$, $\boxed{+}$, $\boxed{-}$, $\boxed{\times}$, $\boxed{\div}$ and $\boxed{=}$. For each question, each key above may be depressed only once. Try to obtain these answers. Show your methods.
   (*a*) 19   (*b*) 31   (*c*) 17   (*d*) 91   (*e*) 62

Exercise 15

Use a calculator throughout this exercise:

1. Use only the number keys, the $\boxed{=}$ key and the operation keys $\boxed{+}$ and $\boxed{-}$. All these keys may be used as many times as you wish. ($\boxed{\times}$, $\boxed{\div}$ and other operation keys may not be used.) Try to find answers to the following. Show how you obtained the answers.

   (a) 8×3 (b) 6×794 (c) $28 \div 7$ (d) $413 \div 59$

2. Use any keys except $\boxed{8}$ or $\boxed{9}$. Try to find answers to the following. Show how you obtained the answers.

   (a) $458 + 375$ (d) 6×348 (g) 8×473
   (b) $639 + 459$ (e) $999 - 762$ (h) $864 \div 8$
   (c) $598 - 273$ (f) $999 - 489$ (i) $917 + 468$

3. Ask a friend to:
   (a) Key in his or her age on a calculator, e.g.   14
   (b) Multiply it by 25.   350
   (c) Add 36.   386
   (d) Multiply by 4.   1544
   (e) Add the number of the month of his or her birth
       (e.g. May = 5).   1549
   (f) Now take the calculator from your friend and
       subtract 144. The first two digits give the age and
       the last two digits give the month of birth.   1405
       The example shows the age to be 14 and the month
       to be May

4. Ask a friend to:
   (a) Key in his or her age on a calculator, e.g.   13
   (b) Multiply it by 5.   65
   (c) Add 12.   77
   (d) Multiply by 4.   308
   (e) Subtract 4.   304
   (f) Multiply by 5.   1520
   (g) Add the number of the month of his or her birth
       (e.g. May = 5).   1525
   (h) Multiply by 25.   38 125
   (i) Add 18.   38 143

(*j*) Multiply by 4.	152 572
(*k*) Add the date of his or her birthday (e.g. 27 May, so add 27).	152 599
(*l*) Subtract 50.	152 549
(*m*) Take the calculator from your friend. Subtract 22 022. The display shows age, month and 'date' of birth.	130 527

Exercise 16

Ask a friend to write down two numbers, one under the other, without you seeing them. (I suggest that the numbers be less than 15, e.g. 8 and 13.)

These two numbers should be added and the total should be written underneath the first two numbers (e.g. 8 + 13 = 21). The second and third numbers should be added to give the fourth number (13 + 21 = 34).

The third and fourth numbers should be added to give the fifth number. Your friend should continue this until there are 10 numbers.

You can now look at the list of ten numbers and quickly tell your friend the total!

(The total can be found by multiplying the seventh number in the list by 11. 144 × 11 = 1584.)

8
13
21
34
55
89
144
233
377
610

5 Drawing and Measuring

Exercise 1

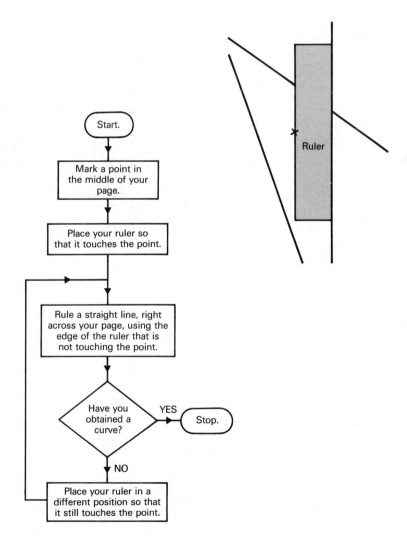

Exercise 2

A Copy this pattern. Join the numbers using straight lines so that the total is always 15.

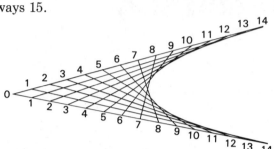

Copy some of these patterns:

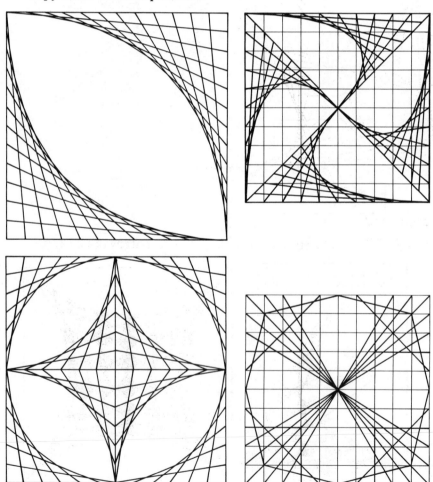

B Here is another curve stitching pattern.

Design one of your own.

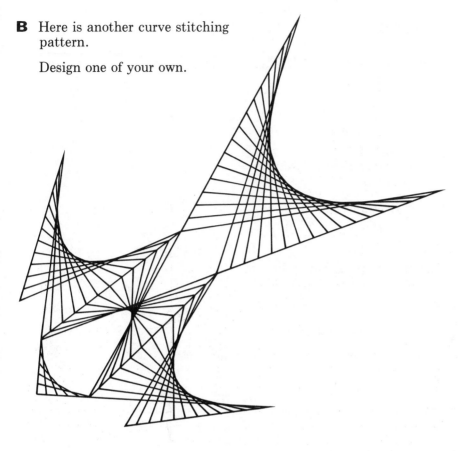

Exercise 3

You can colour in parts of your shapes to make patchwork patterns:

Exercise 4

Either use a piece of filter paper, or draw a circle and cut it out.

Mark a point, P, on your piece of paper close to the edge.

Fold the paper so that the edge (the circumference of the circle) touches the point, P. Carefully make a crease.

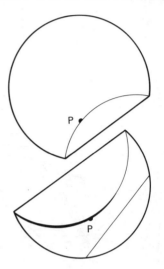

Unfold the paper and draw a line along the crease. (This is a chord of the circle.)

Fold your paper again and again and draw along the crease each time.

Notice the curve you have made.

Look up the word 'ellipse' in your dictionary.

Exercise 5

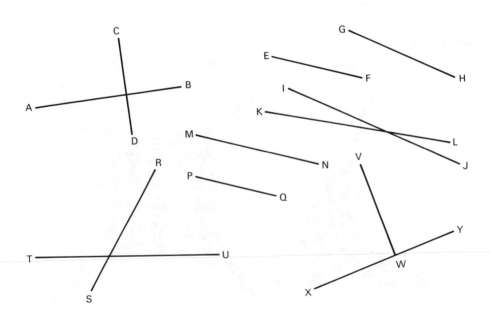

1. List the pairs of line segments that are perpendicular to each other.

2. List the pairs of line segments that intersect but are not perpendicular.

3. Which line segments are parallel?

4. Which line segment is parallel to one line and intersects another?

Exercise 6 M

Each time a new line is drawn it is drawn to intersect all the lines that are already there:

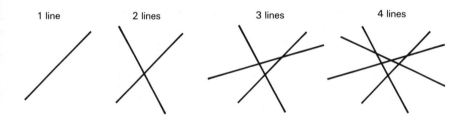

Copy and complete the following table. Look for patterns.

Number of lines	Number of points of intersection	Number of regions
1	0	2
2	1	4
3	3	7
⋮ 12		

Straight lines should be drawn to join each point to every other point. Three or more points should not form one straight line.

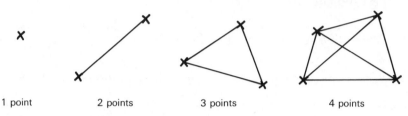

1 point   2 points   3 points   4 points

Copy and complete the table. Look for patterns.

Number of points	Number of lines
1	0
2	1
3	3
4	6
⋮ 12	

Draw circles and straight lines as follows: straight lines should be drawn to join each point to all the other points. No more than two lines should intersect at any one point inside each circle. Copy the table opposite. Use your drawings to help you to complete the table.

No. of points on the circle	No. of points of intersection (inside)	No. of lines	No. of regions
1	0	0	1
2	0	1	2
3	0	3	4
4	1	?	?
5	?	?	?
6	?	?	?

Exercise 9

To construct parallel lines:

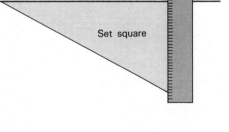

1. Mark a straight line on a piece of paper.

2. Mark a point through which you want to draw a line parallel to the first line.

3. Place one edge of your set square along the line, as shown.

4. Place your ruler so that it touches a different side of your set square.

5. Keep your ruler very still. Slide your set square along your ruler until it touches the point.

6. Draw a line along your set square to pass through the point. The line you have drawn should be parallel to your first line.

61

Exercise 10

To construct a straight line perpendicular to a given straight line:

1. Draw a straight line. Place your set square along the line as shown. Place your ruler along the other short edge of the set square.

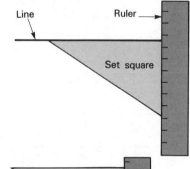

2. Keep your ruler very still. Slide your set square along the ruler as shown.

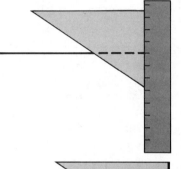

3. Remove the ruler. (Your set square now crosses the line.) Draw your answer line along the edge of the set square that was touching the ruler.

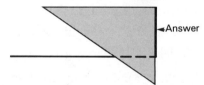

Exercise 11   An Illusion

The four thick black lines are really parallel. (Check by measuring.)

They do not look parallel.

It is an *illusion*.

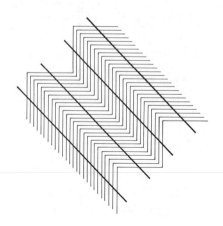

Exercise 12

The word 'line' refers to an infinite line (i.e. a line that is continuous in both directions).

Lines are said to *intersect* if they meet in a common point.

If a heavy mass is fastened to one end of a piece of thread and allowed to hang, the thread is said to be *vertical*.

A plane surface such as a wall is called a 'vertical plane'.

A line that follows the same direction as the horizon is *horizontal*.

A surface such as a table top or a floor is called a 'horizontal plane'.

Now answer the following questions (note that many of them require very careful thought, so take care):

1. Name some horizontal lines in the classroom.

2. Name some vertical lines in the classroom.

3. Name some horizontal planes in the classroom.

4. Name some vertical planes in the classroom.

5. Is it possible to draw a horizontal line on a vertical plane.

6. Is it possible to draw a vertical line on a horizontal plane?

7. Is it possible to draw a horizontal line on a plane that is neither horizontal nor vertical?

8. A certain plane is neither horizontal nor vertical. Is it possible to draw a vertical line on it?

9. If a plane surface contains a horizontal line, must that surface be a horizontal plane?

10. If a vertical line lies on a plane surface, must that surface be a vertical plane?

11. A horizontal plane contains a straight line. Must that line be horizontal?

12. A straight line lies on a vertical plane. Must that straight line be vertical?

13. Must two vertical lines point in the same direction?

14. Must two horizontal lines point in the same direction?

15. Is it possible to have two vertical lines that intersect?

16. Is it possible to have two intersecting horizontal lines?

17. Two horizontal lines lie in the same plane. Is it possible for those two lines not to cross each other?

18. A certain plane surface is not a horizontal plane. Is it possible to draw two intersecting horizontal lines on such a surface?

19. Two horizontal lines lie on a horizontal plane. Is it possible for two such lines not to intersect?

20. Two horizontal lines lie on a horizontal plane. Is it possible for these lines to intersect?

21. Two horizontal lines lie on a vertical plane. Can these two lines intersect?

22. Two horizontal lines lie on a plane surface. Must that surface be a horizontal plane?

23. Two intersecting horizontal lines lie on a plane surface. Must that surface be a horizontal plane?

Exercise 13

fathom, cubit, foot, span, hand, palm, digit, inch

These units of length have something to do with different parts of the body.

Find out what each word means (you may need to use a dictionary), write down the meaning, then draw a sketch of that part of the body.

Measure all the lengths on yourself.
(Use centimetres or millimetres.)   *e.g.*

Digit   21 mm

64

Metric Length

Exercise 14

kilometre (km), metre (m), centimetre (cm), millimetre (mm)

Which of the above units would you use to find:

1. the length of your shoe?

2. the length of the street where you live?

3. the length of a swimming bath?

4. the distance from London to Newcastle?

5. the width of one of your fingers?

6. the length of your pen?

7. the thickness of your exercise book?

8. the height of your chair seat?

9. the height of a doorway?

10. distances on a motorway (for road signs)?

Exercise 15

Use the distance ready reckoner on the next page to help with the answers to the following:

1. How far is it from Carlisle to Nottingham?

2. How far is it from Penzance to Edinburgh?

3. (a) Which journey is further, Southampton to Cambridge or Hull to Norwich?
   (b) By how many kilometres is it further?

4. Mrs Wood travelled from London to Gloucester and then to Aberdeen. How far did she travel altogether?

5. Mr Cardwell travelled from Liverpool to Nottingham, and then to Southampton. How far did he travel altogether?

The distances in the chart below are given in kilometres. Reading along the row for the first city and the column for the second gives the distance between them.

From \ To	Bristol	Cambridge	Cardiff	Carlisle	Dover	Edinburgh	Glasgow	Gloucester	Hull	Inverness	Liverpool	Manchester	Newcastle	Norwich	Nottingham	Oxford	Penzance	Perth	Preston	Southampton	York	London
Aberdeen	806	749	838	368	990	203	229	782	581	170	566	554	378	797	638	782	1110	133	504	898	522	856
Bristol		246	70	322	440	598	594	56	374	851	291	269	483	346	234	118	318	670	299	120	362	192
Cambridge			299	410	205	547	562	203	230	803	314	248	370	99	134	128	563	614	315	211	251	96
Cardiff				474	373	632	630	93	398	853	323	304	512	398	262	170	378	704	330	190	392	245
Carlisle					629	157	152	384	240	414	202	190	93	454	299	418	744	234	138	536	181	491
Dover						789	781	306	456	1035	475	453	587	272	339	222	586	854	483	232	469	125
Edinburgh							72	542	378	256	360	349	174	592	437	579	904	70	296	693	318	648
Glasgow								538	392	275	354	342	240	606	450	571	899	96	293	686	333	643
Gloucester									317	797	230	213	418	288	178	77	362	618	253	152	304	166
Hull										640	202	155	200	307	144	277	675	454	190	413	61	330
Inverness											610	597	432	846	691	829	1155	187	550	942	579	902
Liverpool												58	277	374	166	267	592	430	48	387	162	338
Manchester													230	294	115	245	573	418	53	370	115	318
Newcastle														414	259	416	781	246	210	518	141	448
Norwich															197	227	658	661	362	296	296	184
Nottingham																166	539	507	192	274	139	205
Oxford																	434	650	278	107	296	90
Penzance																		978	605	363	667	464
Perth																			371	763	394	605
Preston																				350	128	350
Southampton																					403	128
York																						334

All the distances in this table are in kilometres.

6. Mr Jones travelled from Inverness to Newcastle, then continued to Preston, and then Oxford. How far did he travel altogether?

7. Which is further, a journey from Oxford to Glasgow or a return journey from Bristol to Manchester?

8. Which is further, a return journey from Cardiff to Newcastle or a journey from Dover to Perth via Liverpool and York?

Exercise 16

1.

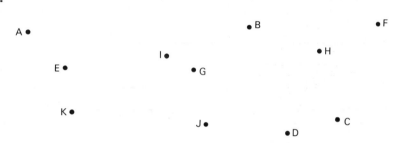

Measure these distances using millimetres:

(a) AB	(f) GK	(k) AE
(b) CE	(g) AC	(l) EH
(c) AF	(h) BK	(m) GI
(d) BF	(i) DJ	(n) BE
(e) CG	(j) AG	(o) EI

2. In the diagram for question 1, which distances are:
   (a) longer than EF?   (b) shorter than FH?

3. Draw straight lines having the given lengths:
   (a) 25 mm   (b) 97 mm   (c) 54 mm   (d) 31 mm   (e) 78 mm

4. How long is the given line? (Use the drawing of a ruler.)

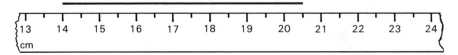

5. I measured a piece of wood with a broken ruler. I had to measure from the 7 cm mark. The ruler showed 25 cm. What was the correct length of the piece of wood?

Estimating Length

Exercise 17

Estimate, to the nearest centimetre, the length of each of the given lines. (DO NOT measure.)

1. ————————————————

2. —————————————————————

3. ————

4. ———————————————————

5. ————

6. ——————————————————————————

7. —————————————————————

8. ——————————

9. ——————————————————————

10. ——————————

Exercise 18

Estimate the length of the two grey lines, then measure them:

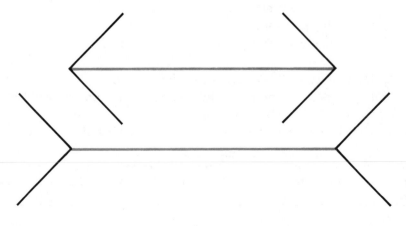

Copy the table given below:

	Item	Estimate	Accurate measurement
1.	My own height	?	?
2.	My size of waist	?	?
3.	The distance around my head	?	?
4.	The length of a school corridor	?	?
5.	The length of a classroom	?	?
6.	The width of a classroom	?	?
7.	The height of a classroom	?	?
8.	The height of a door	?	?
9.	The width of a doorway	?	?
10.	The length of a desk	?	?
11.	The width of a window	?	?
12.	The length of the school drive (Your teacher may suggest another distance.)	?	?

A Estimate each of the above and fill your estimates in the correct column of your table. Use metric units.

B Measure each of the above and complete the correct column of your table.

Exercise 20

A Measure the lines in Exercise 17 (p. 68) as accurately as possible using inches, and parts of an inch where necessary.

B Repeat Exercise 19, but this time, use imperial units.

Exercise 21   Further Estimations

1. How long is a bath towel?
   A. 1.2 m   B. 0.3 km   C. 500 cm   D. 3 m

2. How high is a doorway?
   A. 1 m   B. 2 m   C. 100 mm   D. 15 m

3. How long is a pen?
   A. 12 mm   B. 12 cm   C. 200 mm   D. 2 m

4. The *diameter* of the head of a drawing pin is:
   A. 3 mm   B. 0.4 cm   C. 8 mm   D. 1.2 cm

5. The *circumference* of a football is:
   A. 0.2 m   B. 25 cm   C. 50 cm   D. 75 cm

6. What would have a length of 100 m?
   A. an ordinary house   C. an association football pitch
   B. a tennis court   D. a cricket square

7. What would have a length of about 25 cm?
   A. a shoe   C. a paperclip
   B. a pair of scissors   D. a light bulb

8. What is most likely to be 2 mm thick?
   A. an encyclopaedia   C. a cake
   B. a pen   D. a match

9. What would have a diameter of 80 mm?
   A. a cricket ball   C. a saucer
   B. a football   D. a bucket

10. What would be 7.5 m high?
    A. a small boy   C. a house
    B. a classroom door   D. a church tower

70

1. A roll of material has 25 m on it. It needs to be cut into 3 m and 4 m lengths.

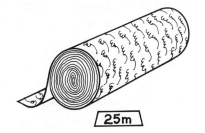

25m

Copy and complete the table to show how many of each can be cut off and the amount of waste.

Number of 3 m lengths	Number of 4 m lengths	Waste (m)
8	0	1
7	?	?
6	?	?
5	?	?
4	?	?
3	?	?
2	?	?
1	?	?

2. There are now two rolls of material. One has 25 m on it while the other has 37 m on it.

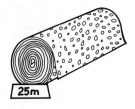

25m

37m

There are many different ways of cutting the rolls to give 3 m and 4 m lengths. Investigate the different ways of cutting the rolls so that the number of 3 m lengths equals the number of 4 m lengths. For each way discovered, work out the amount of waste.

e.g. Six 4 m lengths can be cut from the 25 m roll leaving 1 m waste. Two 4 m lengths and eight 3 m lengths can then be cut from the 37 m roll leaving 5 m waste. We now have eight of each length and 5 m + 1 m waste. Note that the 5 m piece left is waste. If we cut either a 3 m or a 4 m length from it, we shall not have the same number of 3 m and 4 m lengths.

3. Repeat question 2 for rolls having 25 m and 38 m on them.

4. Repeat question 2 for rolls having 26 m and 37 m on them.

5. Repeat question 2 for rolls having 34 m and 44 m on them.

6. Investigate other size rolls and other size lengths.

The Metric Steps

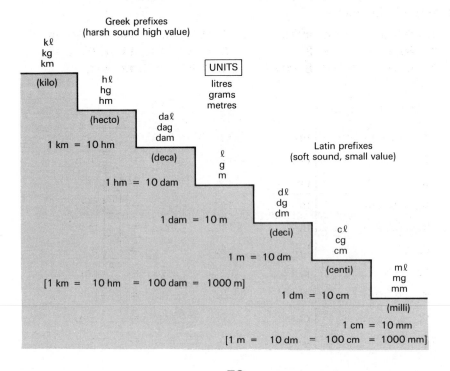

Exercise 23   Length Conversions

A Write in millimetres:

1. 4 cm	**4.** 2 m	**7.** 2.8 m	**10.** 0.9 cm
2. 7.5 cm	**5.** 0.6 cm	**8.** 47 cm	**11.** 68 cm
3. 16.2 cm	**6.** 3.5 m	**9.** 6.39 m	**12.** 0.71 m

B Write in centimetres:

1. 4 m	**4.** 3.6 m	**7.** 582 mm	**10.** 0.28 m
2. 60 mm	**5.** 7.9 m	**8.** 9 mm	**11.** 8.42 m
3. 84 mm	**6.** 0.7 m	**9.** 5.67 m	**12.** 3 km

C Write in metres:

1. 500 cm	**6.** 821 cm	**11.** 1806 cm	**16.** 498 mm
2. 396 cm	**7.** 9.2 km	**12.** 4723 mm	**17.** 0.04 km
3. 3 km	**8.** 7285 cm	**13.** 0.8 km	**18.** 0.022 km
4. 9 km	**9.** 6.93 km	**14.** 8293 mm	**19.** 56 cm
5. 4.6 km	**10.** 5.024 km	**15.** 0.76 km	**20.** 7 cm

D Write in kilometres:

1. 5000 m	**4.** 400 m	**7.** 29 300 m	**10.** 460 000 cm
2. 2800 m	**5.** 3750 m	**8.** 80 m	**11.** 72 000 cm
3. 1600 m	**6.** 80 000 m	**9.** 36 m	**12.** 45 m

E Copy and complete:

1. 6.5 cm = ? mm		**11.** 48 700 cm = ? km
2. 5.1 m = ? cm		**12.** 32 cm = ? mm
3. 39 mm = ? cm		**13.** 0.6 m = ? cm
4. 482 cm = ? m		**14.** 4.6 m = ? mm
5. 5.9 km = ? m		**15.** 2 cm = ? m
6. 4700 m = ? km		**16.** 3.77 m = ? mm
7. 3 m = ? mm		**17.** 5 km = ? cm
8. 0.8 cm = ? mm		**18.** 68 m = ? km
9. 615 mm = ? cm		**19.** 0.52 m = ? mm
10. 0.43 km = ? m		**20.** 0.064 km = ? m

Length and Perimeter

Exercise 24

1. A rectangular field is 94 m long. It is 78 m wide. Find the total length of fencing needed to fence around the field.

2. A rectangle with length 19 cm has a perimeter of 54 cm. Calculate its breadth.

3. The length of a rectangle is three times its breadth. If its length is 48 cm, calculate its perimeter.

4. The length of a rectangle is five times its breadth. If its perimeter is 120 cm, calculate its length.

5. The fencing from around the field shown was used to completely fence a rectangular field that was 103 m long.
   Calculate the breadth of the rectangular field.

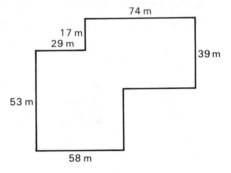

Exercise 25

1. The diagram shows a picture that has been framed. If the picture framing is 18 mm wide, and if the picture itself measures 485 mm by 340 mm, find:
   (a) the perimeter of the inside edge of the frame,
   (b) the perimeter of the outside edge of the frame.

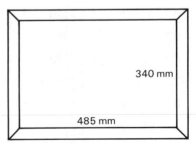

74

2. A rectangular room measures 18 ft by 13 ft:
   - (*a*) What is the perimeter of the room?
   - (*b*) If a carpet is placed in the room so that there is a border of uncovered floor 1 ft wide around it, calculate the perimeter of the carpet.

3. A rectangular room measures 8 m by 4.5 m. Another room is 1 m shorter in length than this first room, but it has the same perimeter. Calculate the breadth of this second room.

4. A strip of paper measures 200 cm by 2 cm:

2 cm

200 cm

2 cm

   - (*a*) What is the perimeter of the strip of paper?
   - (*b*) A 2 cm square piece of paper is cut off the end of this 200 cm strip. What is the perimeter of this 2 cm square?
   - (*c*) What is the perimeter of the strip of paper that is left after the 2 cm square has been cut off?
   - (*d*) What is the perimeter of the strip of paper that is left after five 2 cm squares have been cut off the original strip?

Perimeter and Graphs

Exercise 26 ▰▰▰▰▰▰▰▰▰▰▰▰▰▰▰▰▰▰▰ **M**

1. What is the length of the perimeter of an equilateral triangle where each side is:
   - (*a*) 1 cm?
   - (*c*) 3 cm?
   - (*e*) 5 cm?
   - (*b*) 2 cm?
   - (*d*) 4 cm?
   - (*f*) 6 cm?

2. Copy and complete the following diagram (you may use the answers above):

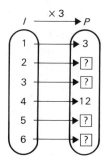

3. Make a table from question 2. Note that you can draw up the table in different ways. Choose and use the method you prefer.

Length of side, l (cm)	1	2	3	4	5	6
Perimeter, P (cm)	3	?	?	12	?	?

Length of side, l (cm)	Perimeter, P (cm)
1	3
2	?
3	?
4	12
5	?
6	?

4. Now plot a graph of the perimeter against the length of side.
[Suggested scale: 2 cm to 1 unit on the length axis (horizontal axis) and 1 cm to 1 unit on the perimeter axis (vertical axis).]
Join all the points carefully.

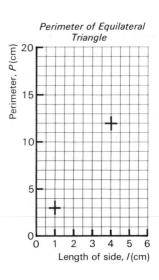

Perimeter of Equilateral Triangle

76

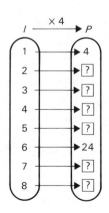
1. As in Exercise 26, copy and complete the given mapping diagram for a square of side l cm and perimeter P cm:

2. Now make a table, then plot a graph.
   (Use a scale of 2 cm to 1 unit on the length axis, and use 1 cm to 2 units on the perimeter axis.)

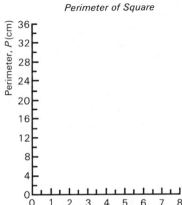

Perimeter of Square

Problems on Length

Exercise 28

1. A gas fire of length 740 mm is fixed against a straight wall in a lounge. If the gas fire is in the central position on that wall, and if the wall is 5.6 m long, what will be the length of space on either side of the fire?

2. Three books are on a bookshelf, placed together. The boards of the covers of these books are each 2 mm thick, while 15 pages of the books are together 1 mm thick. If the first book has 270 pages, the second book 190 pages, and the third book 335 pages, how much space on the shelf do the three books use?

3. A man, having a pace of 750 mm, sets off walking from the same place as a woman, who has a pace of 625 mm. If they walk in the same direction, and each take 280 paces, how far ahead will the man then be?

4. A piece of paper is used to wrap a box of length 300 mm, width 210 mm and height 80 mm. When the paper is wrapped around the box's length it overlaps itself by 50 mm. Similarly, the overlap in the other direction is also 50 mm. What are the dimensions of the piece of paper?

5. A piece of wood of length 8 m is cut into pieces that are each 640 mm long. After the last piece has been cut, what length of wood is left over?

6. A train travels at an average speed of 96 km/h. Find the distance travelled if the journey took 4 h.

7. Find the perimeter, in metres, of a rectangle having a length of 782 mm and a width of 579 mm.

8. There are two pieces of wood. One is 800 mm long and the other is 600 mm long. The two pieces are to be cut into a total of six smaller pieces. The new pieces are to have lengths of 350 mm, 290 mm, 260 mm, 190 mm, 170 mm and 140 mm. How would you cut the pieces?

Exercise 29

1. A man can run a distance of 1 km in 3 min. How long would it take him to run 400 m at the same speed?

2. Seven buttons are to be sewn on to a piece of material that is 200 mm long. If each of the two end buttons are sewn with their centres 16 mm from each end of the material, and if the buttons are to be equally spaced, what is the distance between the centres of adjacent buttons?

3. A rectangular piece of garden, 5.07 m by 3.51 m, is to be paved using paving stones that are 780 mm square. How many whole stones are needed for the length? How many whole stones are needed for the breadth? If the edge pieces are cut from whole stones without damage, how many paving stones need to be bought to do the required paving?

More Metric Units

Exercise 30

kilometre (km)   litre (ℓ)   kilogram (kg)
metre (m)   centilitre (cℓ)   gram (g)
centimetre (cm)   millilitre (mℓ)
millimetre (mm)

Choose, from the metric units above, the unit you would use to measure the following:

1. the height of a tall man,

2. the amount of medicine in a small bottle,

3. how heavy an adult is,

4. the amount of beer in a barrel,

5. how heavy a packet of nuts is,

6. the distance from Liverpool to London,

7. how heavy a 10 p coin is,

8. the amount of petrol put in a car,

9. the length of a garden,

10. how heavy your luggage is,

11. the amount of water in a bucket,

12. how heavy a packet of tea is,

13. the amount of shampoo in a bottle,

14. the length of curtain material,

15. the length (or breadth) of a book,

16. a dose of medicine,

Exercise 31

Copy and complete the following:

1.	6 km = $\boxed{?}$ m		**13.**	5 cℓ = $\boxed{?}$ mℓ
2.	6 kg = $\boxed{?}$ g		**14.**	40 mℓ = $\boxed{?}$ cℓ
3.	7 m = $\boxed{?}$ mm		**15.**	820 mℓ = $\boxed{?}$ cℓ
4.	7 ℓ = $\boxed{?}$ mℓ		**16.**	7.6 km = $\boxed{?}$ m
5.	7 g = $\boxed{?}$ mg		**17.**	7.6 kg = $\boxed{?}$ g
6.	9000 g = $\boxed{?}$ kg		**18.**	9500 g = $\boxed{?}$ kg
7.	5000 mℓ = $\boxed{?}$ ℓ		**19.**	2.58 kg = $\boxed{?}$ g
8.	2000 mg = $\boxed{?}$ g		**20.**	6.3 ℓ = $\boxed{?}$ mℓ
9.	3 m = $\boxed{?}$ cm		**21.**	6.3 ℓ = $\boxed{?}$ cℓ
10.	3 ℓ = $\boxed{?}$ cℓ		**22.**	7100 mℓ = $\boxed{?}$ ℓ
11.	400 cℓ = $\boxed{?}$ ℓ		**23.**	7100 cℓ = $\boxed{?}$ ℓ
12.	5 cm = $\boxed{?}$ mm		**24.**	16.9 ℓ = $\boxed{?}$ mℓ

Exercise 32

A Write in millilitres:

1. 6 cℓ	**4.** 5 ℓ	**7.** 3.6 ℓ	**10.** 0.1 cℓ
2. 2.5 cℓ	**5.** 0.7 cℓ	**8.** 38 cℓ	**11.** 89 cℓ
3. 14.3 cℓ	**6.** 8.5 ℓ	**9.** 2.56 ℓ	**12.** 0.26 ℓ

B Write in centilitres

1. 7 ℓ	**4.** 2.9 ℓ	**7.** 342 mℓ	**10.** 0.31 ℓ
2. 50 mℓ	**5.** 6.4 ℓ	**8.** 7 mℓ	**11.** 7.93 ℓ
3. 42 mℓ	**6.** 0.8 ℓ	**9.** 8.47 ℓ	**12.** 2 kℓ

C Write in litres

1. 300 cℓ	**4.** 1.9 kℓ	**7.** 7600 mℓ	**10.** 328 mℓ
2. 849 cℓ	**5.** 8165 cℓ	**8.** 2984 mℓ	**11.** 42 mℓ
3. 7 cℓ	**6.** 2.98 kℓ	**9.** 0.38 kℓ	**12.** 63 540 mℓ

D Write in grams

1. 200 cg	**4.** 6.5 kg	**7.** 3865 mg	**10.** 0.4 kg
2. 457 cg	**5.** 34 kg	**8.** 5.842 kg	**11.** 291 mg
3. 8 kg	**6.** 2.16 kg	**9.** 2987 cg	**12.** 0.073 kg

E Write in kilograms

1. 4000 g	**4.** 1640 g	**7.** 48 g	**10.** 72 000 g
2. 7600 g	**5.** 70 000 g	**8.** 58 700 g	**11.** 69 360 g
3. 900 g	**6.** 26 000 g	**9.** 984 000 mg	**12.** 708 g

F Copy and complete:

1. 2.9 cℓ = ? mℓ	**16.** 41 cm = ? mm
2. 6.7 ℓ = ? mℓ	**17.** 0.7 ℓ = ? mℓ
3. 2.6 g = ? mg	**18.** 2 kg = ? mg
4. 9.6 kℓ = ? ℓ	**19.** 3.8 m = ? mm
5. 49 mg = ? cg	**20.** 42 g = ? kg
6. 37 mℓ = ? cℓ	**21.** 806 g = ? kg
7. 184 cℓ = ? ℓ	**22.** 0.73 m = ? mm
8. 6200 g = ? kg	**23.** 0.29 ℓ = ? mℓ
9. 4 g = ? mg	**24.** 0.06 ℓ = ? mℓ
10. 0.1 cℓ = ? mℓ	**25.** 0.025 kg = ? g
11. 324 mℓ = ? cℓ	**26.** 145 g = ? kg
12. 0.54 kℓ = ? ℓ	**27.** 9 g = ? kg
13. 0.54 kg = ? g	**28.** 29 mℓ = ? ℓ
14. 0.54 km = ? m	**29.** 7.06 km = ? cm
15. 39 500 mg = ? kg	**30.** 0.054 ℓ = ? mℓ

Exercise 33

1. How many 250 mℓ bottles can be filled from 6 ℓ?

2. How many 125 g packets of sweets can be made up from:
   (a) 8 kg?   (b) 14 kg?

3. If I fill six 250 mℓ glasses with lemonade and a further five 300 mℓ glasses, how many litres do I use altogether?

4. If I fill four 420 mℓ glasses from 2.5 ℓ of milk, how many millilitres are left?

5. Sweets weighing 1.75 kg are shared equally amongst ten people. How many grams will each person receive?

6. After walking 5.75 km, I have a further 500 m to travel on foot. What is the total distance I will have walked when the journey is completed? (Give the answer in kilometres.)

7. I have five packets of biscuits of the same mass, each holding 15 biscuits. If the total mass of the five packets is 2.25 kg, what is the mass of one biscuit?

8. How many litres of wine will I use if I fill 15 glasses, where each glass holds 150 mℓ?

9. If 250 mℓ of shaving cream has a mass of 200 mg, what is the mass of 3 ℓ of shaving cream?

10. I have two different sizes of glasses, 350 mℓ glasses and 250 mℓ glasses. I have 2 ℓ of orange juice that I want to pour into these glasses, without any juice being left over, to fill them all completely. How many of each size of glass must I use?

6 Circles

Exercise 1

Copy and learn the names relating to a circle:

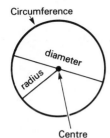

centre (Greek *kentron* = a sharp point)

circumference (Latin *circumferre* = to carry round)

diameter (Greek *dia* = through, + *metron* = measure)

radius (plural — *radii*) (Latin = spoke of a wheel)

arc (Latin *arcus* = bow or arch)

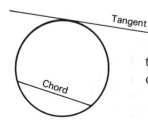

tangent (Latin *tangere* = to touch)
chord (Greek *khorde* = string)

We use two radii to make a *sector*:

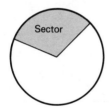

We use a chord to make a *segment*:

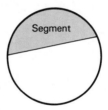

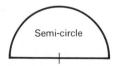

A *semi-circle* is half a circle. We use a diameter to make a semi-circle.

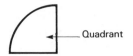

A *quadrant* is a quarter of a circle. We use two radii to make a quadrant.

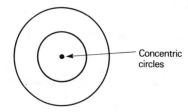

Concentric circles are circles that have the same centre.

Exercise 2

1. Carefully copy the circle pattern shown:

2. Here is another circle pattern idea:

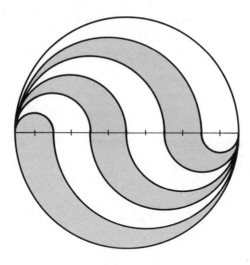

Now make some of your own.

Exercise 3

1. Why are most tins cylindrical?

2. Why are many castle towers cylindrical?

Exercise 4

1. (*a*) Draw any circle.
   (*b*) Mark a point on the circle.
   (*c*) Without altering your
        pair of compasses, place
        the point on the marked
        point and then draw a
        small arc to cross the
        circle.

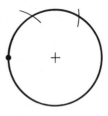

   (*d*) With centre on this new position, mark another small arc to
        cross the circle again.
   (*e*) Repeat this until you return to your starting point.

2. Into how many parts do these arcs divide the circle?

3. (*a*) Join the arcs in order going around the circle, and starting and finishing at the same position.
   (*b*) What is the name of the shape you have drawn?

Exercise 5

Copy these, or try some of your own:

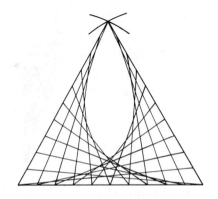

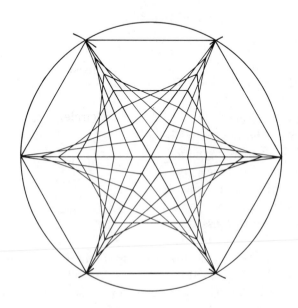

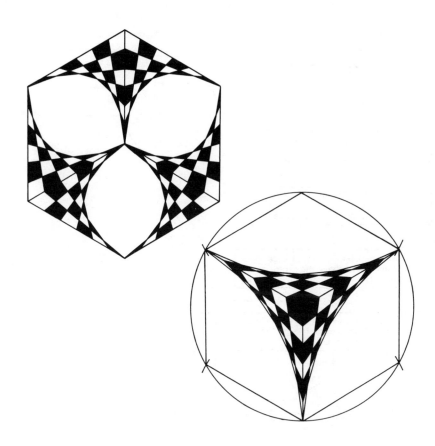

Exercise 6

1. Mark a point on your page. (You need at least 5 cm space to each side and above and below this point.)

2. With centre the marked point, draw a circle of radius 25 mm. This circle will be called the *base circle*.

3. With centre on the base circle, draw another circle of radius 25 mm.

4. With centre at a different position on the base circle, draw another circle of radius 25 mm.

5. Repeat step 4 over and over again, until an interesting pattern is obtained. (The more circles you draw, the better the final shape obtained will be.)

Exercise 7

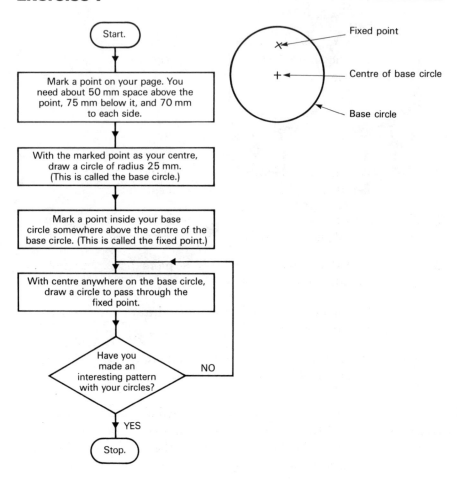

Exercise 8

1. Mark a point on your page. You need about 45 mm space above the point, 80 mm below it and 70 mm to each side.

2. With this point as your centre, draw a circle of radius 25 mm. (This is called the base circle.)

3. Mark a point on the base circle at the top. (This is called the fixed point.)

4. With centre anywhere on the base circle, draw a circle to pass through the fixed point.

5. Repeat step 4 over and over again until an interesting pattern is obtained. (The more circles you draw, the better your final pattern will be.)

Exercise 9

A 1. Mark a point on your page. You need about 60 mm space above the point, 110 mm below it and 80 mm to each side.

2. With this point as your centre, draw a circle of radius 25 mm. (This is called the base circle.)

3. Mark a point above this base circle and no more than 25 mm from it. (This is called the fixed point.)

4. With centre anywhere on the base circle, draw a circle to pass through the fixed point.

5. Repeat step 4 over and over again. (The more circles you draw, the better your final pattern will be.)

B Draw a base circle of radius 25 mm. (You need about 60 mm space above its centre, 110 mm below it and 80 mm to each side.) Mark a point 25 mm above this base circle (call it the fixed point). Now continue as in part A, steps 4–5.

C Draw a base circle of radius 15 mm. (You need about 50 mm space above its centre, 80 mm below it, and 65 mm to each side.) Mark a fixed point above this base circle between 15 mm and 30 mm from it. (If k mm = distance of the fixed point from the base circle, then radius $< k$ mm $<$ diameter of the base circle.) Now continue as in part A, steps 4–5.

D Draw a base circle of radius 15 mm. (You need about 65 mm space above its centre, 95 mm below it and 80 mm to each side.) Mark a fixed point above this base circle between 30 mm and 45 mm from the circle. Now continue as in part A steps 4–5.

E Look up the words 'cardioid' and 'limaçon' in a dictionary. Write down their meanings.

Arches

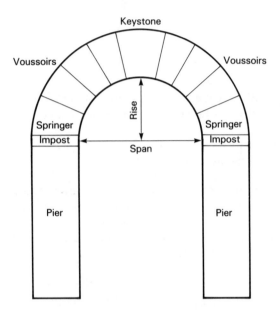

The roofs of the earliest buildings were supported by slabs of timber or stone laid upon and between two columns. However, stone slabs are easily cracked by heavy weights built on top of them, and wooden beams are really only suitable for small buildings. Arches came into use because they enabled larger weights to be built above them. This allowed buildings to be built with higher roofs and also allowed wider gaps to be spanned.

The Romans used arches in many structures. Their arches were round. Arch shapes have changed through the ages. It is possible to guess the approximate age of a structure by the shape of its arch.

Saxon (449–1066) arches were semi-circular.

Norman (1066–1189) arches were also semi-circular, but recessed sub-arches were used; the arches were highly decorated. *Transitional Norman* showed a gradual change to the pointed arches of *Gothic* architecture (12th–16th century).

Early English (13th century) arches were pointed, with deep-cut mouldings and circular piers. *Decorated* (14th century) arches were also pointed, with more but shallower mouldings. *Perpendicular* (15th century) arches were pointed but more obtuse, often using a four-centred arch.

Renaissance (14th–16th century) showed a gradual change back to the round classical-style arches.

Arches are made using wedge-shaped blocks placed one on top of the other in such a way that the two sides eventually meet at the top.

The various parts of an arch have special names, as shown. The most important stone in an arch is the *keystone*. Without it, the arch would collapse. It is the last piece of the arch to be inserted.

Arches have been built since about 4000 BC.

Exercise 10

A Carefully copy these arches and those on the next page:

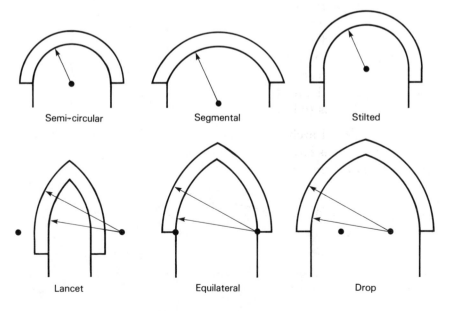

Semi-circular   Segmental   Stilted

Lancet   Equilateral   Drop

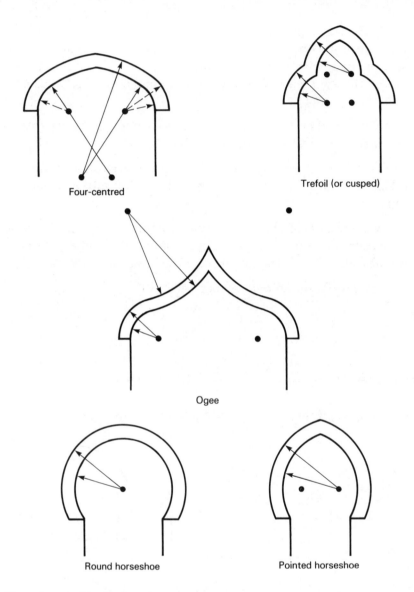

Four-centred

Trefoil (or cusped)

Ogee

Round horseshoe

Pointed horseshoe

B Here is an elliptical arch:

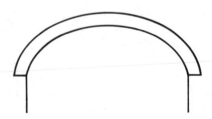

The following diagram shows how an *ellipse* can be constructed. Lines are drawn in any direction from the common centre to meet both circles.

Where a line meets the smaller circle, draw a horizontal line and where the same line meets the outer circle draw a vertical. Each point created in this way, where a horizontal and vertical line meet, gives a point on the ellipse. (In the following diagram, only half an ellipse is shown.) Use this method, or any other method you can discover, to construct an ellipse.

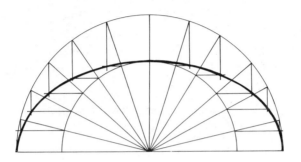

Exercise 11   To Bisect a Straight Line

1. On a piece of paper, draw a straight line that you want to bisect.

2. Open a pair of compasses so that the radius is bigger than half the length of your straight line.

3. Place the point of your pair of compasses at one end of your line. Draw arcs above and below your line.

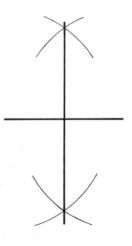

4. Now place the point of your pair of compasses at the other end of your line. Draw two more arcs, one above and one below the line. These arcs should cross your first arcs to give two points.

5. Join these two points with a straight line. This line should bisect your first line. It is called the *perpendicular bisector* of the line.

93

Exercise 12　To Bisect a Straight Line with a Ruler and without Measuring

1. Position the ruler as shown, such that each edge of the ruler touches an end of the line. Draw along each edge of the ruler, above and below the given line.

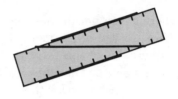

2. Repeat step 1 with the ruler pointing in a different direction, as shown in the second diagram.

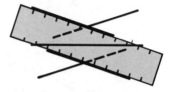

3. The perpendicular bisector can now be drawn by joining the two points of intersection.

Exercise 13

1. Draw a circle with radius 25 mm. Draw a chord of length 40 mm inside this circle. How far is the chord from the centre of the circle?

2. Draw two concentric circles. Let the radii be 35 mm and 20 mm. Now draw one straight line to be a chord of the larger circle and a tangent to the smaller circle. How long is the line?

3. Draw a circle with a diameter of 68 mm. Draw a second circle to touch the first circle. The centre of the second circle should lie outside the first circle, and its radius should be 17 mm. Draw three *common tangents* to the two circles. Two of the common tangents have the same length, how long are they? (That is, find the distance from where they touch one circle to where they touch the other circle.)

4. Try to draw pairs of circles that have exactly:
   (a) no common tangents,
   (b) one common tangent,
   (c) two common tangents,
   (d) four common tangents.

Exercise 14

A **1.** Construct △ABC where AB = 60 mm, BC = 35 mm and AC = 45 mm. On AB, mark a point D such that AD = 25 mm. Measure CD.

2. Construct △PQR where PQ = 84 mm, RP = 59 mm and QR = 46 mm. If S is the mid-point of PQ, how long is RS?

3. Construct △XYZ such that XY = YZ = 54 mm and XZ = 32 mm. What sort of triangle is △XYZ?

4. Construct △JKL such that JK = 82 mm, KL = 51 mm and JL = 23 mm. What do you notice?

5. Construct △LMN such that all three sides equal 62 mm. What sort of triangle is △LMN?

6. Construct △UVW where UV = 64 mm, VW = 70 mm, and UW = 58 mm. Mark the mid-points of these sides, labelling them X, Y and Z respectively.
How long is: (*a*) XY?   (*b*) YZ?   (*c*) XZ?

7. Copy the given figure. How long is BD?

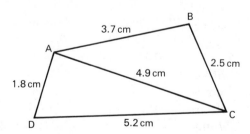

8. Construct quadrilateral ABCD where DC = 64 mm, AD = 35 mm, AC = 61 mm, AB = 30 mm and CB = 51 mm. How long is BD?

B **1.** Construct △JKL such that KL = 85 mm, JK = 45 mm and JL = 80 mm. Bisect KL and let the bisector meet JL at point M. How long is KM?

2. In $\triangle$CDE, CD = 68 mm, DE = 60 mm, CE = 50 mm. F lies on CD such that CF = 34 mm. Draw FG parallel to CE where G lies on DE.

(a) How long is DG?   (b) How long is CG?

Exercise 15

1. Draw a circle with a radius of 38 mm. Draw two non-parallel chords of this circle. Construct the perpendicular bisectors of both chords.

Where do these perpendicular bisectors meet?

2. Draw a circle with a diameter of 54 mm. Draw a diameter AB. Produce AB to C where CB = 43 mm. Draw a straight line CE of length 90 mm so that E lies on the circle.

If D lies on CE and on the circle, find the length of chord DE.

3. The straight line, ST, is 84 mm long, while SU is 58 mm and TU is 66 mm. Construct $\triangle$STU.

The straight line, VW, where V lies on SU and W lies on TU, is parallel to ST, and SV = 40 mm.

If the perpendicular bisector of ST meets VW at X, how long is TX?

4. The straight line MN is 75 mm in length. Draw MN, then construct its perpendicular bisector. If P is the mid-point of MN, then PQ = 27 mm where Q lies on the perpendicular bisector of MN. Using a set square and a ruler, draw QR parallel to MN such that QR = 48 mm.

How long is MR?

5. Draw a straight line, CD, 95 mm in length. Using a pair of compasses, bisect CD and label its mid-point, X. P and Q lie on the perpendicular bisector of CD and are on opposite sides of CD, such that PX = QX = 35 mm. Draw PC, PD, QC, and QD.

Now measure PC, PD, QC, and QD. What do you notice about these lengths?

7 Factors, Multiples and Primes

Exercise 1   M

A What is special about the last digit of any number that is exactly divisible by:

1. 2?   **2.** 10?   **3.** 5?

B Divisibility by 3

Copy and complete the table.

Number	Divisible by 3	Sum of the digits	Digital root*
27	YES	2 + 7 = 9	9
56	NO	5 + 6 = 11	1 + 1 = 2
42	?	?	?
69	?	6 + 9 = 15	1 + 5 = 6
51	?	?	?
127	?	?	?
265	?	?	?
408	?	?	?
197	?	?	?
374	?	?	?
639	?	?	?
568	?	?	?
885	?	?	?
924	?	?	?
682	?	?	?

1. What do you notice about the digital root* for each number that is exactly divisible by 3?

2. Divide each third-column entry (the sum of the digits) by 3. What do you notice about all such divisions when the number is exactly divisible by 3?

*See the glossary, p. 433.

C Divisibility by 4

Copy and complete the table.

Number	Divisible by 4?	Last two digits	Number	Divisible by 4?	Last two digits
36	YES	36	918	?	?
46	NO	46	734	?	?
190	?	?	744	?	?
420	?	?	872	?	?
348	?	?	1460	?	?
613	?	?	6338	?	38
724	?	?	9094	?	?
508	?	?	7184	?	?

For each number, divide the last two digits (in the third column) by 4. What do you notice about the results of these divisions when the number is exactly divisible by 4?

D Divisibility by 9

Copy and complete the table.

Look at the single-digit number found and written in the last column. What do you notice about this value when the given number is exactly divisible by 9? Divide each answer in the third column (sum of the digits) by 9. What do you notice about these divisions when the given number is exactly divisible by 9?

Number	Divisible by 9?	Sum of the digits	Digital root
63	YES	6 + 3 = 9	9
75	NO	7 + 5 = 12	1 + 2 = 3
96	?	9 + 6 = 15	1 + 5 = 6
147	?	1 + 4 + 7 = 12	1 + 2 = 3
162	?	?	?
297	?	?	?
403	?	?	?
576	?	?	?
2997	?	?	?
3822	?	?	?
4042	?	?	?
5813	?	?	?
6701	?	?	?
6986	?	?	?
27 558	?	?	?
74 898	?	?	?
82 051	?	?	?

E Divisibility by 8

Copy and complete the table.

Divide each third-column value by 8 (i.e. the last three digits of each given number). What do you notice about the results of each division when the given number is exactly divisible by 8?

Number	Divisible by 8?	Last three digits
152	YES	152
216	?	216
242	?	?
1344	?	344
4396	?	?
7896	?	?
1987	NO	?
2728	?	?
6432	?	?
3680	?	?
5756	?	756
21 576	?	?
39 184	?	184
78 986	?	?
146 968	?	?
402 780	?	?

F Divisibility by 6

Copy and complete the table.

Look carefully at your answers in the table and write what you notice.

Number	Divisible by 6?	Divisible by 2?	Divisible by 3?
54	YES	YES	?
78	YES	?	YES
86	?	?	?
93	?	NO	?
254	?	?	?
561	?	?	?
732	?	?	?
894	?	?	YES
2986	?	?	?
3426	?	?	?
7830	?	?	?
4587	?	NO	?
24 976	?	?	?
48 357	?	?	?
78 858	?	?	?
53 378	?	?	?

Notes on Divisibility

Divisibility by	Notes
2	A number is exactly divisible by 2 if it is an *even* number. Its last digit is 0, 2, 4, 6 or 8.
3	A number is exactly divisible by 3 if the sum of its digits is exactly divisible by 3. Alternatively, a number is exactly divisible by 3 if its digital root is 3, 6 or 9.
4	A number is exactly divisible by 4 if its last two digits are exactly divisible by 4.
5	A number is exactly divisible by 5 if its units digit is 0 or 5.
6	A number is exactly divisible by 6 if it satisfies the conditions for both 2 and 3, that is, it ends in 0, 2, 4, 6 or 8 *and* the sum of its digits is exactly divisible by 3.
8	A number is exactly divisible by 8 if its last three digits divide exactly by 8.
9	A number is exactly divisible by 9 if the sum of its digits is exactly divisible by 9. Alternatively, a number is exactly divisible by 9 if its digital root is 9.
10	A number is exactly divisible by 10 if its units digit is 0.

Exercise 2   M

Test the given numbers for divisibility by 2, 3, 4, 5, 6, 8, 9 and 10:

1. 21 852	**5.** 10 400	**9.** 9424
2. 1617	**6.** 46 200	**10.** 53 973
3. 63 146	**7.** 83 250	**11.** 45 315
4. 24 185	**8.** 2538	**12.** 77 256

Exercise 3

Find the missing digits such that there is no remainder for each of these divisions. If there is more than one answer to a question, list all possible solutions.

1. $80\,79a \div 5$
2. $764m \div 2$
3. $39\,25w \div 4$
4. $21\,6y4 \div 4$
5. $354\,k72 \div 9$

6. $97\,2c6 \div 8$
7. $90\,3d6 \div 8$
8. $41\,x51 \div 3$
9. $13l\,562 \div 6$
10. $52\,61i \div 6$

Exercise 4

A 1. (a) Divide 4738 by 9 and write the remainder.
  (b) Find the digital root* of 4738.
  (c) Compare the digital root with the remainder and write what you notice.
  (d) Test other numbers to find their remainders when divided by 9. Find the digital root of each number.
  (e) Explain how to find, without dividing, the remainder when any number is divided by 9.

2. Investigate how to find remainders without dividing when numbers are being divided by:

(a) 3
(b) 10
(c) 5

(d) 100
(e) 25
(f) 50

(g) 2
(h) 4
(i) 8

B Without dividing fully, find the remainder, if any, from each division:

1. $27\,389 \div 2$
2. $4692 \div 10$
3. $51\,735 \div 10$
4. $29\,168 \div 5$
5. $30\,619 \div 5$
6. $17\,621 \div 9$

7. $34\,285 \div 9$
8. $21\,782 \div 3$
9. $2847 \div 4$
10. $19\,638 \div 4$
11. $72\,648 \div 8$
12. $38\,719 \div 8$

13. $54\,278 \div 8$
14. $61\,237 \div 100$
15. $90\,806 \div 100$
16. $35\,284 \div 50$
17. $18\,639 \div 50$
18. $54\,790 \div 25$

*See the glossary, p. 433.

101

Exercise 5

1. Write all the divisors* of 36.

2. Find all the divisors of 140.

3. Find all the divisors of 94 that give a remainder of 4.

4. Find all the divisors of 107 that give a remainder of 3.

5. How many whole numbers less than 100 are not exactly divisible by 9?

6. Write the numbers that lie between 100 and 200 that divide exactly by 9 and have a units digit of 8.

7. Find the smallest three-digit number that is exactly divisible by 9.

8. Write all the even divisors of 120.

9. Write all the odd divisors of 210.

10. Write the first three numbers that divide exactly by:
    (a) both 3 and 5,   (b) both 3 and 6.

11. One divisor of 95 is 5. Find another divisor of 95, other than 1 or 95.

12. How many numbers from 600 to 800 inclusive are exactly divisible by all the divisors 2, 5 and 9?

13. How many whole numbers from 200 to 300 inclusive are not exactly divisible by both 4 and 9?

14. A five-digit number has the digits 6, 8, two 2s and one other digit. For each question, write down the *smallest* possible number that uses all five digits (you will need to work out for each question which other digit to use). The five-digit number must be exactly divisible by:
    (a) 2   (b) 3   (c) 4   (d) 5   (e) 6   (f) 8   (g) 9

*See the glossary under 'quotient', p. 435.

Factors

$$63 = 7 \times 9$$

We say that 7 and 9 are *factors* of 63.

63 has been written as the product of two factors. Also, $3 \times 21 = 63$ and $1 \times 63 = 63$. To find *all* the factors of 63, *all* possible products are needed.

The factors of 63 are $\{1, 63, 3, 21, 7, 9\}$.

Exercise 6

Find the factors of:

1. 10	**5.** 12	**9.** 26	**13.** 81	**17.** 207
2. 14	**6.** 20	**10.** 32	**14.** 100	**18.** 245
3. 28	**7.** 9	**11.** 24	**15.** 75	**19.** 315
4. 21	**8.** 30	**12.** 42	**16.** 105	**20.** 348

Exercise 7   M

Copy and complete:

1. 'is a factor of'

3. 'is a factor of'

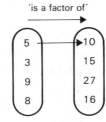

2. 'is a divisor of'

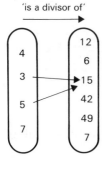

4. 'is a factor of'

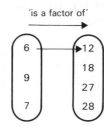

5.

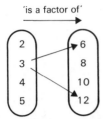

'is a factor of'

6.

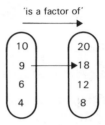

'is a factor of'

Exercise 8

1. Write all the odd numbers that are factors of 84.

2. Write all the even numbers that are factors of 132.

3. Write three numbers that have 7 as a factor.

4. Write three numbers that do not have any even factors.

5. (*a*) Write the first three numbers that have both 2 and 7 as factors.

   (*b*) Write the first three numbers that have both 3 and 10 as factors.

   (*c*) Write the first three numbers that have both 5 and 10 as factors.

6. (*a*) What is the largest factor of 78, other than 78 itself?

   (*b*) What is the largest factor of 507, other than 507 itself?

7. What is the largest odd number that is a factor of 252?

8. What is the largest even number that is a factor of 770, other than 770 itself?

9. One factor of 133 is 7, find another factor other than 133 or 1.

10. One of the factors of 851 is 23. Find another factor, other than 1, or the number 851 itself.

11. Find the largest three-digit number that has 6 as one of its factors.

12. List all the numbers between 290 and 310 that have a factor of 9.

13. The difference between two factors of 819 is 8. Find the two factors.

14. When 8 is added to a certain number it becomes a factor of 945. When 2 is subtracted from the same number it also becomes a factor of 945. Find the two possible numbers.

Multiples

Since 28 is in the 7-times table (the *multiplication* table for 7), 28 is a *multiple* of 7. Note that 28 is also a multiple of 4.

28 is in fact a multiple of 1, 28, 2, 14, 4 and 7.

Exercise 9

1. Write down six multiples of:
   (*a*) 4   (*b*) 9   (*c*) 15   (*d*) 12   (*e*) 25

2. Give the multiples of 7 that lie between 80 and 100.

3. (*a*) List the multiples of 3 that are less than 50.
   (*b*) List the multiples of 4 that are less than 50.
   (*c*) List the multiples of 12 that are less than 50.
   (*d*) How could you use the answers to parts (*a*) and (*b*) to help you to find the multiples of 12 that are less than 50?

4. (*a*) List the multiples of 4 that lie between 63 and 127.
   (*b*) List the multiples of 5 that lie between 63 and 127.
   (*c*) Use your answers to parts (*a*) and (*b*) to help you to find the multiples of 20 that lie between 63 and 127.

5. What is the smallest number that should be added to 263 to make it a multiple of 15?

6. Find the smallest number, which, when multipled by 6, becomes a multiple of 20.

7. By what number should 28 be multiplied to make it into a multiple of 42? (Give the smallest number.)

8. If 37*2 is a multiple of 9, find the missing digit.

9. A total of 153 bottles are to be stored in boxes. These are two sizes of box, boxes that hold 15 bottles and boxes that hold only 8 bottles. How many of each size of box are required if no bottles are to be left over, and no space is left in either box?

10. Find a number between 90 and 120 that is 4 more than a multiple of 6, and 3 less than a multiple of 5.

Exercise 10

1. If 26*54 is a multiple of 18, find the missing digit.

2. By what number should 56 be multipled to make it into a multiple of 35? (Give the smallest number.)

3. Find the smallest number that is a multiple of 25 and is also a multiple of 30.

4. Find the difference between the smallest and the largest multiples of 21 that lie between 350 and 450.

5. When a certain number of jelly babies is shared equally amongst either 6, 8 or 15 people, there are none left over; however, when shared amongst 7 people, 1 jelly baby remains. Find the smallest number of jelly babies for which this will happen.

Exercise 11   Factors and Multiples

1. Write down all multiples of 8 that lie between 57 and 85.

2. Write down all numbers between 40 and 70 that are 5 less than a multiple of 11.

3. How many two-digit numbers are there that are multiples of 15?

4. Write all the multiples of 4 that lie between 2375 and 2400.

5. Find the multiple of 26 that is nearest to 600.

6. Find the smallest number that needs to be added to 627 to give a multiple of 17.

7. What is the smallest number that needs to be added to 3648 to give a number that is a multiple of 8?

8. What is the smallest three-digit number that has 75 as a factor?

9. Find the largest, even three-digit number that is a multiple of 9.

10. Write down a number between 460 and 470 that is 3 less than a multiple of 6.

11. Find all the possible numbers, other than 3, that are factors of 273 and also multiples of 3.

12. Find the missing digits so that:
    (a) $23\,18*$ is a multiple of 9.
    (b) $50\,2*4$ is a multiple of 6.

13. If $46\,3*5$ is a multiple of 25, find possible values of the missing digit.

14. Find the smallest number that is 3 more than a multiple of 7, and 5 less than a multiple of 13.

15. What is the smallest four-digit number that is a multiple of 17?

Prime Numbers

Exercise 12 ━━━━━━━━━━━━━━━━━━━━━━━━━ M

Eratosthenes, an astronomer who lived in Greece about 275–195 BC, devised a method for finding prime numbers. It is known as 'the sieve of Eratosthenes'.

A *prime number* is a number that can only be divided exactly by itself and 1. (*Note* 1 is not a prime number.)

e.g. To find all the prime numbers up to 100:

1. Write all the numbers from 1 to 100 in the way shown.

2. Cross out the number 1 since *1 is not a prime number.*

3. 2 is the first prime, so do not cross it out, but cross out all the multiples of 2 (4, 6, 8, etc.).

~~1~~	2	3	~~4~~	5	~~6~~	7	~~8~~	~~9~~	~~10~~
11	~~12~~	13	~~14~~	~~15~~	~~16~~	17	~~18~~	19	~~20~~
~~21~~	~~22~~	23	~~24~~	25	~~26~~	~~27~~	~~28~~	29	~~30~~
31	~~32~~	~~33~~	~~34~~	35	~~36~~	37	~~38~~	39	~~40~~
41	~~42~~	43	~~44~~	45	~~46~~	47	~~48~~	~~49~~	~~50~~
~~51~~	~~52~~	53	~~54~~	55	~~56~~	57	~~58~~	59	~~60~~
61	~~62~~	~~63~~	~~64~~	65	~~66~~	67	~~68~~	~~69~~	~~70~~
71	~~72~~	73	~~74~~	~~75~~	~~76~~	~~77~~	~~78~~	79	~~80~~
~~81~~	~~82~~	83	~~84~~	~~85~~	~~86~~	~~87~~	~~88~~	89	~~90~~
~~91~~	~~92~~	~~93~~	~~94~~	~~95~~	~~96~~	97	~~98~~	~~99~~	~~100~~

4. The next number, after 2, that has not been crossed out, is 3. Leave it, but cross out all multiples of 3 (the first few of these have been done for you).

5. The next number, after 3, that has not been crossed out, is 5. Leave it, but cross out all other multiples of 5.

6. Repeat this process until there are no further multiples left to be crossed out.

7. List the remaining numbers. They are all the *prime numbers* that are less than 100.

8. How many prime numbers are there that are less than 100?

9 How many prime numbers do you think there are between 100 and 200? Check your answer.

10. How many prime numbers are there between 200 and 300?

Exercise 13   M

Instead of using a 10 by 10 number square for the sieve of Eratosthenes, arrange the numbers as shown.

As before:

1. Cross out 1 (not prime).

2. Leave 2. Cross out all the multiples of 2. (The first few of these have been done for you.)

3. Leave 3, but cross out all the multiples of 3.

4. Leave the next number that has not been crossed out (i.e. 5) but cross out all its multiples.

5. Repeat step 4 as far as necessary.

1	2	3	4	5	6
7	8	9	10	11	12
13	14	15	16	17	18
19	20	21	22	23	24
25	26	27	28	29	30
31	32	33	34	35	36
37	38	39	40	41	42
43	44	45	46	47	48
49	50	51	52	53	54
55	56	57	58	59	60
61	62	63	64	65	66
67	68	69	70	71	72
73	74	75	76	77	78
79	80	81	82	83	84
85	86	87	88	89	90
91	92	93	94	95	96
97	98	99	100	101	102

The numbers that have not been crossed out are the *prime numbers*. Note how easy it is to see them (they are only in certain columns). Try this for other arrangements (say 8 across, or 12, or 9).

Exercise 14

1. Write three two-digit prime numbers that have a units digit of 7.

2. A two-digit prime number is less than 70. The sum of its digits is 7. Find two such prime numbers.

3. List all the prime numbers that are factors of:
(*a*) 36   (*b*) 105   (*c*) 252   (*d*) 693

4. List all the two-digit prime numbers that remain prime when their digits are reversed.

5. The sums of the digits of five different, 2-digit prime numbers are also two-digit prime numbers. Find these five primes.

6. The sum of two prime numbers is 36. Find both, if one of them is a factor of 143.

7. Find, where possible, all the pairs of prime numbers where the sum of the two primes is:
(*a*) 20   (*c*) 30   (*e*) 29   (*g*) 41
(*b*) 24   (*d*) 25   (*f*) 49   (*h*) 43

8. Find, where possible, several pairs of prime numbers such that the difference between the two primes is:
(*a*) 10   (*c*) 30   (*e*) 3   (*g*) 7   (*i*) 11
(*b*) 18   (*d*) 46   (*f*) 5   (*h*) 9   (*j*) 13

9. A certain prime number is a factor of 924. When this prime is subtracted from another prime, the answer is 24. Find both prime numbers.

10. (*a*) List the factors of 825.
(*b*) Which of the factors in part (*a*) are prime?

Exercise 15   Prime Factors

1. (*a*) What are the factors of 90?
(*b*) Which of these factors of 90 are prime?

2. Give the prime factors of 48.

3. What are the prime factors of 140?

4. Write the prime factors of 168.

5. Which of the following numbers are prime factors of 56?
2, 3, 4, 5, 6, 7, 8, 14, 16, 24, 28, 56

6. Find a two-digit prime factor of 13 545.

7. A certain prime number is a factor of 5525. The same number is also a prime factor of 3927. Find it.

8. What is the smallest number that has each of the prime numbers 2, 3, 5 and 7 as its factors?

Exercise 16 **M**

Copy the diagram.

On your copy, write the numbers 1, 2, 3, 4, 5, 6 and 7.

One number should be in each area.

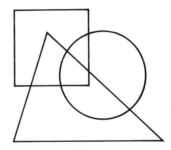

Follow these rules.

1. The sum of the numbers in the circle should be a multiple of 5.

2. The sum of the numbers in the square should be a multiple of 3.

3. The sum of the numbers in the triangle is prime.

HCF and LCM

The factors of 36 are {1, 2, 3, 4, 6, 9, 12, 18, 36}.

These can be shown as:

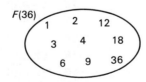

111

The factors of 54 are {1, 2, 3, 6, 9, 18, 27, 54}.

These can be shown as:

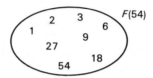

The two sets of factors overlap:

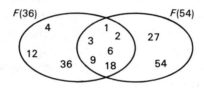

Since {1, 2, 3, 6, 9, 18} are factors of both 36 and 54, they are called *common factors*.

The *highest* of these factors is 18, so 18 is called the HCF of 36 and 54 (HCF stands for 'highest common factor').

It is sometimes called the 'greatest common divisor'.

Exercise 17

Find the highest common factors of:

1. 8 and 10
2. 12 and 9
3. 12 and 16
4. 15 and 20
5. 40 and 32
6. 36 and 48
7. 45 and 63
8. 28 and 40

9. 54 and 90
10. 49 and 56
11. 39 and 52
12. 48 and 72
13. 150 and 120
14. 42 and 98
15. 60 and 105
16. 112 and 32

17.	84 and 147	21.	36, 27 and 63
18.	74 and 58	22.	48, 96 and 73
19.	154 and 117	23.	75, 125 and 200
20.	18, 24 and 42	24.	52, 26 and 78

Exercise 18

1. (a) List the multiples of 3 that are less than 80.
   (b) List the multiples of 5 that are less than 80.
   (c) List the numbers that are multiples of both 3 and 5 (that is, the common multiples of 3 and 5) that are less than 80.
   (d) What is the lowest common multiple of 3 and 5? (It is sometimes referred to as the *least common multiple* or simply as the *LCM*.)

2. (a) List the multiples of 4 that are less than 80.
   (b) List the multiples of 6 that are less than 80.
   (c) List the common multiples of 4 and 6 that are less than 80.
   (d) What is the lowest common multiple of 4 and 6?

3. (a) List the multiples of 12 that are less than 100.
   (b) List the multiples of 16 that are less than 100.
   (c) List the common multiples of 12 and 16 that are less than 100.
   (d) What is the LCM of 12 and 16?

Exercise 19

Find the LCM (lowest or least common multiple) of the following:

1.	3 and 7	9.	14 and 35	17.	39 and 52
2.	6 and 9	10.	9 and 45	18.	75 and 125
3.	4 and 8	11.	21 and 35	19.	4, 6 and 12
4.	10 and 15	12.	24 and 30	20.	3, 5 and 7
5.	6 and 5	13.	24 and 20	21.	6, 9 and 12
6.	6 and 8	14.	15 and 25	22.	7, 8 and 12
7.	7 and 10	15.	16 and 18	23.	10, 12 and 15
8.	14 and 10	16.	14 and 42	24.	24, 12 and 16

113

1	2	3	4	5	6	7	8	9	10
11	12	13	14	15	16	17	18	19	20
21	22	23	24	25	26	27	28	29	30
31	32	33	34	35	36	37	38	39	40
41	42	43	44	45	46	47	48	49	50
51	52	53	54	55	56	57	58	59	60
61	62	63	64	65	66	67	68	69	70
71	72	73	74	75	76	77	78	79	80
81	82	83	84	85	86	87	88	89	90
91	92	93	94	95	96	97	98	99	100

Use a 100-number square as shown.

Cross out all multiples of 2 using vertical (|) lines.

Cross out all multiples of 3 using diagonal (/) lines.

Cross out all multiples of 4 using horizontal (–) lines.

Cross out all multiples of 5 using diagonal (\) lines.

(Some of these crossings out have already been done.)

Look carefully at the crossed-out numbers, then cover the number square before answering these questions:

1. Which numbers are crossed out with a $+$?

2. Which numbers are crossed out with a $\times$?

3. Which numbers are crossed out with a $\not/$?

4. What is the first number that is crossed out by three marks?

5. What is the first number that is crossed out by four marks?

6. Where possible, list the numbers that are crossed out by *only* the given mark:
   (a) \   (b) /   (c) —   (d) |

7. What sort of mark will cross out the following numbers? (Draw the mark.)
   (a) 8   (c) 36   (e) 39   (g) 90
   (b) 20   (d) 84   (f) 75   (h) 64

8. If the number square continued beyond 100, by what sort of mark would the following be crossed out?

(a) 150   (c) 126   (e) 328   (g) 125   (i) 495
(b) 144   (d) 202   (f) 180   (h) 560   (j) 423

Exercise 21   M

1. Copy and complete the table:

First number x	Second number y	HCF	LCM	HCF $\times$ LCM	Product of the two numbers $x \times y$
6	15		30		
32	48	16			
8	24			192	
20	50				
39	24				
35	12				
72	108				
96	60				
63	45				
98	42				

2. What do you notice about your answers in the last two columns of the table?

3. Copy and complete: $x \times y = \text{HCF} \times \boxed{?}$

4. The HCF of two numbers is 6, while the LCM is 72. If one of the numbers is 24, find the other number.

5. Is it true that the product of the HCF and the LCM of any three numbers is equal to the product of the three numbers?

115

Exercise 22

1. The HCF of 192 and 216 is 24. What is the LCM of the same two numbers?

2. The LCM of 48 and 60 is 240. Find the HCF.

3. The LCM of two numbers is 504 while their HCF is 21. The two numbers are 63 and 16?. Unfortunately, a digit has been smudged. What should it be?

4. (a) What is the HCF of 52 and 65?
   (b) What is the LCM of 52 and 65?

Exercise 23

1. A light is flashed every 20 s, while a second light is flashed every 25 s. If they flash at the same time now, after how many seconds will they once again flash together?

2. Two bells begin to toll at the same time. If the first bell tolls every 6 s while the second bell tolls every 10 s, after how many seconds will they again toll together?

3. I belong to two societies. Both meet on a Tuesday. One meets every 6 weeks, while the other meets every 4 weeks. After how many weeks will there be a clash?

4. A man and a woman set off walking together at the same speed and in step with each other for their first pace. If the man's pace is 3 ft while the woman's pace is 2 ft, how far will they walk before they are in step again?

5. Two people set off walking together and their paces are 90 cm and 80 cm. Find the distance walked, in metres, before they are once again in step, if they were in step when they first started and if they were walking at the same speed.

6. Three bells begin to toll at the same time. If they toll at intervals of 4, 6 and 10 seconds respectively, after how many seconds will they next toll together?

7. Three friends have a day out together. If Laura has a day off every 4 days, while Christine has a day off every 5 days, and Mary a day off every 6 days, in how many days time will Laura, Christine and Mary be able to spend the day together?

8. A gearwheel with 25 teeth drives a second wheel with 30 teeth. When they first begin to turn two particular teeth touch. Find the number of times each wheel turns before the same two teeth are together in the same position again.

9. A boy has less than 50 marbles. When he puts his marbles into nine equal groups or into 12 equal groups, five marbles are left over. How many marbles must he have?

Exercise 24 ▬▬▬▬▬▬▬▬▬▬▬▬▬▬▬▬▬ **M**

Copy and complete:

A

Across
3. Three times 4 down
5. A prime number between 70 and 80

Down
1. An even number less than 20
2. A multiple of 9 that is less than 700
4. See 3 across

B

Across
1. Ten less than the sum of 2 down, 3 down and 5 across
4. A multiple of 5 that is divisible by 9
5. A multiple of 7

Down
2. Seven times 5 across, but not divisible by ten
3. A multiple of 5

C

Across
1. A prime number
3. A prime number that is greater than 70
5. Two less than nine times 5 down
6. Two times 1 down

Down
1. A multiple of 19
2. Seven times 1 across
4. Eight times 6 across
5. See 5 across

Exercise 25   Sequences

A Copy the following sequences and fill in the missing numbers:

1. 6, 12, 18, 24, ?, 36, 42, ?

2. 3, 7, 11, 15, 19, ?, ?, 31

3. 69, 61, 53, ?, ?, 29, 21, 13

4. 2, 3, 6, 11, 18, ?, 38, ?

5. 1, 2, 6, 13, ?, 36, 52, ?

6. 2, 5, 11, 20, ?, 47, ?, 86

7. 192, 96, 48, ?, 12, ?, 3

8. 2, 6, 18, ?, 162, ?, 1458

9. 2, 7, 4, 9, 6, 11, ?, 13, 10, ?

10. 105, ?, 69, 54, 41, 30, 21, ?, 9, 6

11. 2, 4, 7, 9, 12, 14, 17, ?, 22, 24, ?

12. 5, 6, 8, 12, 20, ?, ?, 132

13. 1, 8, ?, 64, 125, ?, 343, 512, 729, 1000

14. 134, 245, 356, ?, 578, ?

15. 910, 821, 732, ?, 554, ?, 376, 287, 198

B Copy the following sequences and in each case underline the one term that is incorrect:

1. 29, 25, 21, 17, 15, 9, 5

2. 1, 2, 4, 7, 11, 17, 22, 29

3. 1, 2, 4, 8, 18, 32, 64

118

4. 2, 4, 8, 16, 22, 32, 44, 58, 74, 92

5. 6, 9, 14, 21, 30, 39, 54, 69, 86

C Find the missing number in each sequence:

1. 3, 8, $\boxed{?}$, 24

2. 18, 11, 6, $\boxed{?}$, 2

3. 5, 9, 17, 33, $\boxed{?}$

4. 40, 24, $\boxed{?}$, 12, 10, 9

5. 51, 49, 53, 45, $\boxed{?}$

Rectangular Numbers

Any number that can be shown as a rectangular pattern of dots is called a *rectangular number*.

12 is a rectangular number:

12 can also be shown as:

Note that ● ● ● ● is the same as:

7 is not a rectangular number. ● ● ● ● ● ● ●

A straight line of dots is *not* called a rectangle.

119

Exercise 26

A Draw dot patterns to show which of these numbers are rectangular numbers:

1. 6   **2.** 13   **3.** 14   **4.** 24   **5.** 25   **6.** 27

B Show the number 30 as a rectangular dot pattern in as many different ways as possible.

C **1.** List the first 15 numbers that are not rectangular numbers (miss 1; start with 2, 3, 5, 7, and so on).

    2. What are these non-rectangular numbers called?

Square Numbers

Square numbers are numbers that can be shown as a square of dots. 16 is a square number:

We also call the number 1 a square number.

Exercise 27

A Show which of these are square numbers by drawing a square pattern of dots:

1. 4   **2.** 8   **3.** 9   **4.** 24   **5.** 36

B **1.** Write down the first eight square numbers.

    2. What is the tenth square number?

    3. What is the twelfth square number?

    4. Find the fifteenth square number.

    5. Find the twentieth square number.

Exercise 28

Copy and complete these, then give the next three steps:

1. (a)
$$1 = 1$$
$$1 + 2 + 1 = 4$$
$$1 + 2 + 3 + 2 + 1 = 9$$
$$1 + 2 + 3 + 4 + 3 + 2 + 1 = \boxed{?}$$

(c)
$$1 = 1$$
$$1 + 3 = 4$$
$$1 + 3 + 5 = 9$$
$$1 + 3 + 5 + 7 = \boxed{?}$$

(b)
$$1 \times 1 = 1$$
$$2 \times 2 = 4$$
$$3 \times 3 = 9$$
$$4 \times 4 = \boxed{?}$$
$$5 \times 5 = \boxed{?}$$

2. Question 1 (c) may help with these questions:
(a) What is the sum of the first 10 odd numbers?
(b) What is the sum of the first 15 odd numbers?
(c) What is the sum of the first 20 odd numbers?

Exercise 29 **M**

$$1 = 1$$
$$1 + 3 = 4$$
$$1 + 3 + 5 = 9$$
$$1 + 3 + 5 + 7 = 16$$
etc.

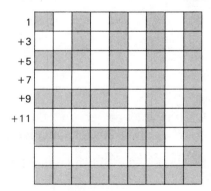

The diagrams above show how the odd numbers can be added to give the square numbers.

Copy the diagrams and show the next step in each case.

121

Exercise 30

Plot a graph to show the square numbers.

Draw a pair of axes as shown. (Suggested scale: 2 cm to 1 unit on the horizontal axis, 2 cm to 5 units on the vertical axis.)

A point has been plotted to show that the fifth square number is 25 (i.e. $5 \times 5 = 25$ which is written as $5^2 = 25$).

Do not forget to give your graph a title.

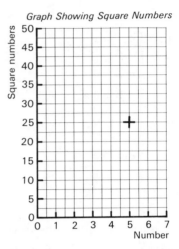

Graph Showing Square Numbers

Exercise 31   Triangular Numbers

Here are the first five triangular numbers:

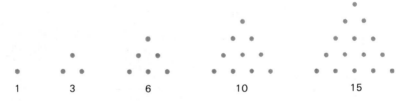

1. Draw a dot pattern to show the sixth triangular number. What is the sixth triangular number?

2. What is the eighth triangular number? Draw its dot pattern.

3. Which of these numbers are triangular numbers?
    19, 36, 46, 66, 78, 105, 121, 136

4. List the first 17 triangular numbers. Underneath each one, print O if it is odd and E if it is even. The first five of these are:

    1 3 6 10 15
    O O E E O

What do you notice about your answers?

122

5. Copy this number pattern.
Give the next three rows of the pattern.

$$1 = 1$$
$$1 + 2 = 3$$
$$1 + 2 + 3 = 6$$
$$1 + 2 + 3 + 4 = 10$$
$$1 + 2 + 3 + 4 + 5 = 15$$
etc.

What sort of numbers are obtained in the answers?

Exercise 32

```
•          •            •              •                  •
1        x  x         x  x           x  x               x  x
      1 + 2 = 3     o  o  o        o  o  o            o  o  o
                 1 + 2 + 3 = 6   +  +  +  +          +  +  +  +
                              1 + 2 + 3 + 4 = 10   *  *  *  *  *
                                               1 + 2 + 3 + 4 + 5 = 15
```

The above patterns show that the sum of consecutive numbers gives the triangular numbers.

A Copy these and give the next three steps:

$$2 = 2$$
$$2 + 4 = 6$$
$$2 + 4 + 6 = 12$$
$$2 + 4 + 6 + 8 = 20$$
$$2 + 4 + 6 + 8 + 10 = 30$$
etc.

Now divide each of your answers by 2.
What do you notice about the numbers you obtained?

		e.g. 1	e.g. 2
B **1.**	Select any triangular number.	6	15
2.	Double it.	12	30
3.	Note your answer.		

	e.g. 1	*e.g. 2*
4. Note which triangular number you selected.	third	fifth

5. If the third triangular number was selected, find 12   30
3 × 4. If the ninth triangular number was selected,
find 9 × 10, and so on.

6. Compare your answer with that obtained in
step 2.

7. Try this again using a different triangular
number.

8. What do you notice about the answers obtained
in steps 2 and 5?

Exercise 33

A Find the difference between successive triangular numbers.
Copy these. Give the next five steps.

1   3   6   10   15   21   ?   ?   ?   ?   ?

2   3   4   5   6   ?   ?   ?   ?   ?

$3 \times 10 = 30$

B   1   3   6   10   15   21

$5 \times 6 = 30$

	e.g.
1. Write any triangular number.	3
2. Miss the next triangular number.	
3. Write the one following that.	10
4. Multiply the two numbers together and note the answer.	$3 \times 10 = 30$
5. Now write the triangular number that you missed out.	6
6. Subtract 1.	5
7. Multiply these two numbers.	$5 \times 6 = 30$

8. Repeat these steps using different triangular numbers.

9. In each case, what do you notice about the answers obtained in steps 4 and 7?

C Plot a graph to show the first six triangular numbers.

The fifth triangular number (i.e. 15) has been shown on the graph.

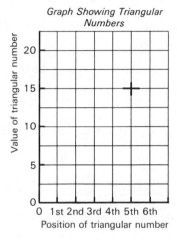

Graph Showing Triangular Numbers

Exercise 34 M

Part of a multiplication square is shown:

Copy it.

⊗	1	2	3	4	5	6	7	8	9	10
1	①									
2	2	4								
3	③	⑥	9							
4	4	8	12	16						
5	5	10	15	20	25					
6	6	12	18	24	30	36				
7	7	14	21	28	35	42	49			
8	8	16	24	32	40	48	56	64		
9	9	18	27	36	45	54	63	72	81	
10	10	20	30	40	50	60	70	80	90	100

125

Ring the number 1 (as shown).

Now ring several numbers by following these rules:

1. Move two down. Ring the number (as shown).

2. Move one across. Ring the number (as shown).

Repeat steps 1 and 2 over and over again until you can go no further.

What sort of numbers have been ringed?

Miscellaneous Exercises

Exercise 35

1. Copy these and show the next three steps.

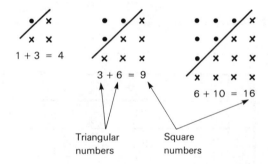

$1 + 3 = 4$

$3 + 6 = 9$

$6 + 10 = 16$

Triangular numbers

Square numbers

2. Select any triangular number.

Multiply it by 8.

Add 1.

What sort of number have you obtained?

Repeat this for other triangular numbers.

3. Try to find two square numbers, which, when added, give another square number. (Find three different answers.)

4. Try to find two triangular numbers, which, when added, give another triangular number.

5. How many prime triangular numbers can you find?

6. Number 1 is a square number and also a triangular number.

Try to find some more numbers that are both square numbers and triangular numbers.

7. $\{1, 4, 10, 15, 25, 36, 43, 51\}$

Look at the given set of numbers. Which of the numbers are
(*a*) rectangular numbers?
(*b*) square numbers?
(*c*) triangular numbers?

Exercise 36

Copy and complete these when necessary, then give the next three steps:

1.
$$1 \times 9 = \qquad 9$$
$$21 \times 9 = \qquad 189$$
$$321 \times 9 = \qquad 2889$$
$$4321 \times 9 = 38\,889$$
etc.

2.
$$11 \times 9 = \;\; 99$$
$$21 \times 9 = 189$$
$$31 \times 9 = 279$$
$$41 \times 9 = 369$$
etc.

3.
$$1 \times 8 + 1 = \qquad 9$$
$$12 \times 8 + 2 = \qquad 98$$
$$123 \times 8 + 3 = \qquad 987$$
$$1234 \times 8 + 4 = 9876$$
etc.

4.
$$3 \times 9 = \qquad 27$$
$$33 \times 9 = \qquad 297$$
$$333 \times 9 = \qquad 2997$$
$$3333 \times 9 = 29\,997$$
etc.

5.
$$1 \times 1 \times 1 = 1$$
$$2 \times 2 \times 2 = 3 + 5$$
$$3 \times 3 \times 3 = 7 + 9 + 11$$
$$4 \times 4 \times 4 = 13 + 15 + 17 + 19$$
etc.

6.
$$1 \times 1 = \qquad 1$$
$$11 \times 11 = \qquad 121$$
$$111 \times 111 = \qquad 12321$$
$$1111 \times 1111 = 1234321$$
etc.

7.
$$1 \times 8 = 10 - 2$$
$$2 \times 8 = 20 - 4$$
$$3 \times 8 = 30 - 6$$
$$4 \times 8 = 40 - 8$$
etc.

8.
$$3 \times 37 = 111$$
$$6 \times 37 = \boxed{?}$$
$$9 \times 37 = \boxed{?}$$
$$12 \times 37 = \boxed{?}$$
etc.

9.

$$6 \times 6 = 36$$
$$66 \times 66 = 4356$$
$$666 \times 666 = 443\,556$$
$$6666 \times 6666 = 44\,435\,556$$

etc.

10.

$$\frac{22 \times 22}{1 + 2 + 1} = \boxed{?}$$

$$\frac{333 \times 333}{1 + 2 + 3 + 2 + 1} = \boxed{?}$$

$$\frac{4444 \times 4444}{1 + 2 + 3 + 4 + 3 + 2 + 1} = \boxed{?}$$

etc.

Exercise 37

The following anagrams are of mathematical words. Find the words and, for each one, either state its meaning or draw a sketch to illustrate it.

1. CAR
2. FOR CATS
3. NICER TEST
4. TILER
5. GNAT NET
6. DAD NOT II
7. DREAM TIE
8. TREK O MILE
9. REAL PALL
10. MEGS TEN
11. CUT BRATS
12. RIPER MEET
13. M RIPE
14. CC MICE RUN FREE
15. L ZORINO HAT
16. RIPE LAND PURE C
17. TERM E
18. LIVE CART
19. IV DIED
20. SEC ROT
21. PIT MULE L
22. U SAID R
23. MY PULL IT
24. CL RICE
25. ROD HC

8 Fractions and Decimals

fraction

Latin *frangere* = to break or fracture

$$\frac{2}{3}$$

2 ← *num*erator (number)

3 ← *denom*inator (French *le nom* = the name)

two-thirds   'Thirds' is the family *name* of the fraction.

Exercise 1 M

Copy these shapes. Shade each as asked.

1. Shade $\frac{3}{4}$.

2. Shade $\frac{1}{3}$.

3. Shade $\frac{5}{6}$.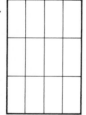

4. Shade $\frac{5}{8}$.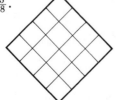

5. Shade $\frac{2}{5}$.

6. Shade $\frac{3}{8}$.

7. Shade $\frac{4}{5}$.

8. Shade $\frac{2}{3}$.

129

Exercise 2 ▌M

Copy these blocks. Divide each block into the correct number of parts so that you can shade the given fractions. Make your parts as nearly equal as you can. On each of your blocks, only shade the first part. Question 8 has been done for you.

WHOLE

1. Shade the whole.

2. Shade $\frac{1}{2}$.

3. Shade $\frac{1}{3}$.

4. Shade $\frac{1}{4}$.

5. Shade $\frac{1}{5}$.

6. Shade $\frac{1}{6}$.

7. Shade $\frac{1}{7}$.

8. Shade $\frac{1}{8}$.

9. Shade $\frac{1}{9}$.

10. Shade $\frac{1}{10}$.

11. Shade $\frac{1}{11}$.

12. Shade $\frac{1}{12}$.

Exercise 3

1.
2.
3.
4.
5.
6.

What fraction of each of the above equal-sized rectangles has been shaded?

Exercise 4

A Write in figures:

1. one-half
2. two-thirds
3. one-quarter
4. five-sixths
5. three-eighths

6. nine-tenths
7. seven-sixteenths
8. thirteen-twentieths
9. thirty-one fortieths
10. twenty-nine hundredths

B Write in words:

1. $\dfrac{1}{3}$ 3. $\dfrac{2}{5}$ 5. $\dfrac{7}{10}$ 7. $\dfrac{9}{16}$

2. $\dfrac{3}{4}$ 4. $\dfrac{5}{8}$ 6. $\dfrac{11}{12}$ 8. $\dfrac{73}{100}$

C Write the *numerator* of each of these fractions:

1. $\dfrac{4}{5}$ 2. $\dfrac{57}{100}$ 3. $\dfrac{6}{10}$ 4. $\dfrac{14}{16}$ 5. $\dfrac{21}{32}$

D Write the *denominator* of each of these fractions:

1. $\dfrac{3}{4}$ 2. $\dfrac{7}{10}$ 3. $\dfrac{5}{8}$ 4. $\dfrac{23}{100}$ 5. $\dfrac{9}{16}$

131

Exercise 5

A

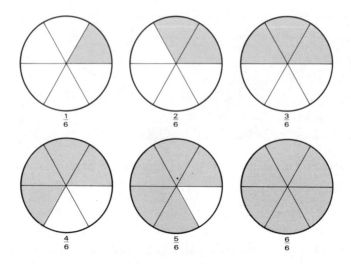

1. Why are the denominators all alike?

2. Why are the numerators all different?

B Draw a line:
   1. 60 mm long, and divide it into quarters,

   2. 60 mm long, and divide it into fifths,

   3. 80 mm long, and divide it into tenths,

   4. 40 mm long, and divide it into eighths,

   5. 108 mm long, and divide it into twelfths.

C Draw a rectangle 78 mm long and 35 mm wide. Divide the rectangle into six columns and five rows.

   1. Into how many small rectangles has the large rectangle been divided?

   2. What are the dimensions of the small rectangles?

   3. Shade $\frac{3}{5}$ of the large rectangle.

Exercise 6

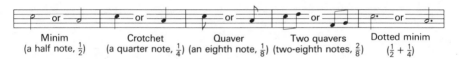

Minim	Crotchet	Quaver	Two quavers	Dotted minim
(a half note, $\frac{1}{2}$)	(a quarter note, $\frac{1}{4}$)	(an eighth note, $\frac{1}{8}$)	(two-eighth notes, $\frac{2}{8}$)	($\frac{1}{2} + \frac{1}{4}$)

Copy the music and divide it into bars:

A Four quarter notes (crotchets) fill each bar (or any combinations of notes that are equivalent to four quarter notes).

B Three quarter notes fill each bar (or any combinations of notes that are equivalent to three quarter notes).

Equivalent Fractions

Exercise 7

Copy these and fill in the missing numbers:

A 1. $\dfrac{1}{2} = \dfrac{1}{2} \times \dfrac{3}{3} = \dfrac{\boxed{?}}{6}$

2. $\dfrac{3}{4} = \dfrac{3}{4} \times \dfrac{2}{2} = \dfrac{6}{\boxed{?}}$

3. $\dfrac{5}{8} = \dfrac{5 \times 4}{8 \times 4} = \dfrac{\boxed{?}}{32}$

4. $\dfrac{3}{5} = \dfrac{3 \times 6}{5 \times 6} = \dfrac{18}{\boxed{?}}$

5. $\dfrac{2}{6} = \dfrac{2}{6} \times \dfrac{4}{4} = \dfrac{8}{\boxed{?}}$

6. $\dfrac{5}{6} = \dfrac{5}{6} \times \dfrac{\boxed{?}}{10} = \dfrac{50}{\boxed{?}}$

7. $\dfrac{7}{8} = \dfrac{7 \times \boxed{?}}{8 \times \boxed{?}} = \dfrac{35}{40}$

8. $\dfrac{8}{10} = \dfrac{8}{10} \times \dfrac{\boxed{?}}{5} = \dfrac{\boxed{?}}{\boxed{?}}$

133

9. $\dfrac{2}{3} = \dfrac{2}{3} \times \dfrac{\boxed{?}}{\boxed{?}} = \dfrac{16}{\boxed{?}}$

10. $\dfrac{7}{12} = \dfrac{7}{12} \times \dfrac{3}{3} = \dfrac{\boxed{?}}{\boxed{?}}$

B 1. $\dfrac{6}{12} = \dfrac{6 \div 6}{12 \div 6} = \dfrac{1}{\boxed{?}}$

6. $\dfrac{54}{66} = \dfrac{54 \div 6}{66 \div 6} = \dfrac{\boxed{?}}{11}$

2. $\dfrac{8}{12} = \dfrac{8 \div 4}{12 \div 4} = \dfrac{\boxed{?}}{3}$

7. $\dfrac{45}{72} = \dfrac{45}{72} \div \dfrac{9}{\boxed{?}} = \dfrac{\boxed{?}}{8}$

3. $\dfrac{12}{27} = \dfrac{12}{27} \div \dfrac{3}{3} = \dfrac{4}{\boxed{?}}$

8. $\dfrac{35}{56} = \dfrac{35}{56} \div \dfrac{\boxed{?}}{\boxed{?}} = \dfrac{5}{8}$

4. $\dfrac{15}{55} = \dfrac{15}{55} \div \dfrac{\boxed{?}}{5} = \dfrac{3}{\boxed{?}}$

9. $\dfrac{32}{64} = \dfrac{32 \div \boxed{?}}{64 \div \boxed{?}} = \dfrac{1}{2}$

5. $\dfrac{40}{48} = \dfrac{40 \div \boxed{?}}{48 \div \boxed{?}} = \dfrac{5}{6}$

10. $\dfrac{48}{84} = \dfrac{48}{84} \div \dfrac{12}{12} = \dfrac{\boxed{?}}{\boxed{?}}$

Exercise 8

Copy and complete to make sets of equivalent fractions:

1. $\dfrac{3}{10} = \dfrac{\boxed{?}}{20} = \dfrac{15}{\boxed{?}} = \dfrac{\boxed{?}}{40} = \dfrac{\boxed{?}}{120} = \dfrac{33}{\boxed{?}}$

2. $\dfrac{5}{6} = \dfrac{10}{\boxed{?}} = \dfrac{\boxed{?}}{18} = \dfrac{25}{\boxed{?}} = \dfrac{\boxed{?}}{60} = \dfrac{\boxed{?}}{90}$

3. $\dfrac{18}{42} = \dfrac{3}{\boxed{?}} = \dfrac{\boxed{?}}{28} = \dfrac{\boxed{?}}{84} = \dfrac{9}{\boxed{?}} = \dfrac{6}{\boxed{?}}$

4. $\dfrac{8}{48} = \dfrac{4}{\boxed{?}} = \dfrac{\boxed{?}}{96} = \dfrac{\boxed{?}}{240} = \dfrac{24}{\boxed{?}} = \dfrac{1}{\boxed{?}}$

5. $\dfrac{20}{32} = \dfrac{10}{\boxed{?}} = \dfrac{5}{\boxed{?}} = \dfrac{\boxed{?}}{80} = \dfrac{25}{\boxed{?}} = \dfrac{\boxed{?}}{96}$

134

Exercise 9

Copy these fractions. Fill in the missing numbers to make the fractions equivalent.

1. $\dfrac{3}{4} = \dfrac{\boxed{?}}{12}$

2. $\dfrac{3}{9} = \dfrac{1}{\boxed{?}}$

3. $\dfrac{3}{9} = \dfrac{\boxed{?}}{27}$

4. $\dfrac{12}{15} = \dfrac{\boxed{?}}{5}$

5. $\dfrac{18}{30} = \dfrac{3}{\boxed{?}}$

6. $\dfrac{26}{39} = \dfrac{2}{\boxed{?}}$

7. $\dfrac{2}{3} = \dfrac{28}{\boxed{?}}$

8. $\dfrac{33}{36} = \dfrac{\boxed{?}}{12}$

9. $\dfrac{7}{10} = \dfrac{\boxed{?}}{40}$

10. $\dfrac{8}{26} = \dfrac{4}{\boxed{?}}$

11. $\dfrac{12}{28} = \dfrac{\boxed{?}}{7}$

12. $\dfrac{2}{3} = \dfrac{\boxed{?}}{27}$

13. $\dfrac{600}{800} = \dfrac{\boxed{?}}{4}$

14. $\dfrac{5}{8} = \dfrac{10}{\boxed{?}}$

15. $\dfrac{21}{28} = \dfrac{\boxed{?}}{4}$

16. $\dfrac{1}{4} = \dfrac{\boxed{?}}{52}$

17. $\dfrac{35}{63} = \dfrac{\boxed{?}}{9}$

18. $\dfrac{48}{126} = \dfrac{8}{\boxed{?}}$

19. $\dfrac{52}{104} = \dfrac{\boxed{?}}{2}$

20. $\dfrac{27}{72} = \dfrac{\boxed{?}}{8}$

21. $\dfrac{6}{11} = \dfrac{54}{\boxed{?}}$

22. $\dfrac{100}{105} = \dfrac{20}{\boxed{?}}$

23. $\dfrac{54}{84} = \dfrac{9}{\boxed{?}}$

24. $\dfrac{72}{84} = \dfrac{\boxed{?}}{7}$

Exercise 10

Simplify these fractions (i.e. give the simplest equivalent fraction in each case). *Note*   Some books say 'cancel', or 'simplify by cancelling'.

1. $\dfrac{8}{16}$

2. $\dfrac{15}{20}$

3. $\dfrac{12}{18}$

4. $\dfrac{12}{42}$

5. $\dfrac{14}{42}$

6. $\dfrac{25}{45}$ **11.** $\dfrac{90}{165}$ **16.** $\dfrac{54}{114}$ **21.** $\dfrac{88}{660}$ **26.** $\dfrac{270}{378}$

7. $\dfrac{40}{56}$ **12.** $\dfrac{34}{51}$ **17.** $\dfrac{84}{132}$ **22.** $\dfrac{84}{189}$ **27.** $\dfrac{525}{840}$

8. $\dfrac{39}{52}$ **13.** $\dfrac{360}{450}$ **18.** $\dfrac{121}{132}$ **23.** $\dfrac{136}{152}$ **28.** $\dfrac{375}{975}$

9. $\dfrac{44}{55}$ **14.** $\dfrac{150}{200}$ **19.** $\dfrac{126}{144}$ **24.** $\dfrac{91}{154}$ **29.** $\dfrac{234}{342}$

10. $\dfrac{90}{144}$ **15.** $\dfrac{63}{108}$ **20.** $\dfrac{57}{95}$ **25.** $\dfrac{143}{165}$ **30.** $\dfrac{936}{1521}$

Mixed Numbers and Improper Fractions

Exercise 11

The shaded circles show that $\frac{5}{3} = 1\frac{2}{3}$.

an improper fraction   a mixed number

A Write these mixed numbers as improper fractions:

1. $1\frac{1}{3}$ **6.** $3\frac{4}{5}$ **11.** $7\frac{3}{8}$ **16.** $12\frac{2}{5}$ **21.** $2\frac{43}{100}$

2. $1\frac{3}{5}$ **7.** $6\frac{1}{2}$ **12.** $5\frac{7}{9}$ **17.** $1\frac{11}{16}$ **22.** $4\frac{9}{16}$

3. $2\frac{3}{4}$ **8.** $7\frac{2}{3}$ **13.** $11\frac{5}{6}$ **18.** $6\frac{2}{15}$ **23.** $9\frac{5}{12}$

4. $4\frac{5}{6}$ **9.** $8\frac{3}{4}$ **14.** $6\frac{5}{7}$ **19.** $8\frac{7}{8}$ **24.** $7\frac{13}{16}$

5. $2\frac{7}{10}$ **10.** $9\frac{2}{5}$ **15.** $3\frac{11}{12}$ **20.** $14\frac{3}{4}$ **25.** $6\frac{29}{32}$

B Write these improper fractions as mixed numbers:

1. $\dfrac{5}{4}$ **3.** $\dfrac{19}{6}$ **5.** $\dfrac{20}{3}$ **7.** $\dfrac{39}{10}$ **9.** $\dfrac{31}{8}$

2. $\dfrac{13}{5}$ **4.** $\dfrac{21}{8}$ **6.** $\dfrac{17}{2}$ **8.** $\dfrac{31}{4}$ **10.** $\dfrac{43}{9}$

11. $\dfrac{32}{7}$ **14.** $\dfrac{93}{10}$ **17.** $\dfrac{121}{8}$ **20.** $\dfrac{73}{15}$ **23.** $\dfrac{53}{16}$

12. $\dfrac{44}{5}$ **15.** $\dfrac{75}{8}$ **18.** $\dfrac{67}{12}$ **21.** $\dfrac{95}{12}$ **24.** $\dfrac{95}{16}$

13. $\dfrac{37}{3}$ **16.** $\dfrac{62}{9}$ **19.** $\dfrac{85}{4}$ **22.** $\dfrac{573}{100}$ **25.** $\dfrac{145}{32}$

Comparing Fractions

Exercise 12   M

Copy the graph on the next page which shows fractions. It is called a *Farey lattice*.

Try to work out how it was made.

1. One straight line shows the fractions $\left\{\frac{1}{2}, \frac{2}{4}, \frac{3}{6}, \frac{4}{8}, \frac{5}{10}, \frac{6}{12}, \text{etc.}\right\}$. What do you notice about these fractions?

2. $\dfrac{4}{6} = \dfrac{2}{3}$ Find $\frac{4}{6}$ and $\frac{2}{3}$ on your Farey lattice.

What do you notice?

3. $\dfrac{1}{5} = \dfrac{\boxed{?}}{10} = \dfrac{3}{\boxed{?}} = \dfrac{4}{\boxed{?}} = \dfrac{\boxed{?}}{25}$

Find these fractions on your graph.
What do you notice?

4. $\dfrac{4}{5} = \dfrac{8}{10}$ Show $\frac{4}{5}$ and $\frac{8}{10}$ on your graph.

Draw a straight line from the origin to pass through $\frac{8}{10}$. (The *origin* is the point where the two axes meet. The *axes* are the two numbered lines.)

Do you need to draw a different straight line to join the origin to the fraction $\frac{4}{5}$?

5. Use your graph to help you to list two more fractions that are equivalent to $\frac{4}{5}$.

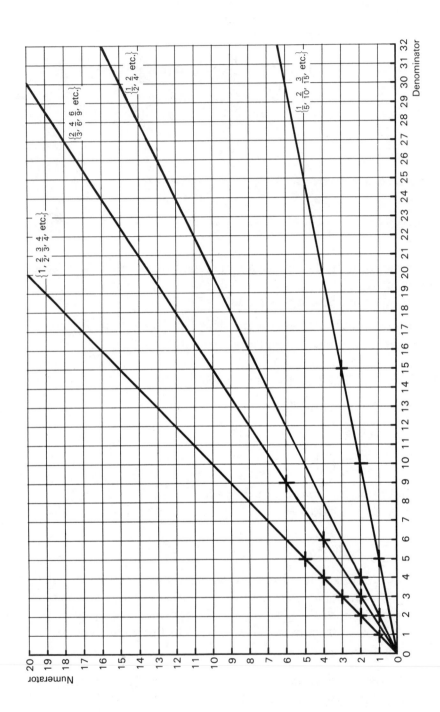

6. (*a*) Which fraction is bigger, $\frac{3}{4}$ or $\frac{1}{2}$?

(*b*) Draw a straight line from the origin to pass through $\frac{3}{4}$.

(*c*) Which line is steeper, the line that passes through $\frac{3}{4}$, or the line that passes through $\frac{1}{2}$?

7. (*a*) Which line is steeper, the line that passes through $\frac{2}{3}$, or the line that passes through $\frac{1}{2}$?

(*b*) Which fraction is bigger, $\frac{2}{3}$ or $\frac{1}{2}$?

8. Use your graph to find out whether these statements are true or false:

(*a*) $\dfrac{6}{9} = \dfrac{10}{15}$ (*e*) $\dfrac{4}{5} < \dfrac{7}{8}$ (*i*) $\dfrac{6}{15} = \dfrac{8}{20}$

(*b*) $\dfrac{3}{8} > \dfrac{2}{5}$ (*f*) $\dfrac{5}{7} > \dfrac{9}{13}$ (*j*) $\dfrac{14}{18} = \dfrac{10}{12}$

(*c*) $\dfrac{7}{10} < \dfrac{4}{6}$ (*g*) $\dfrac{3}{11} < \dfrac{2}{7}$ (*k*) $\dfrac{5}{11} < \dfrac{7}{15}$

(*d*) $\dfrac{9}{15} = \dfrac{3}{5}$ (*h*) $\dfrac{3}{5} > \dfrac{11}{18}$ (*l*) $\dfrac{5}{11} > \dfrac{7}{16}$

Exercise 13

Use your fraction graph for these:

1. Does $\frac{10}{10} = \frac{3}{3}$?   **6.** Does $\frac{10}{12} = \frac{15}{18}$?

2. Is $\frac{9}{4} > \frac{5}{4}$?   **7.** Is $\frac{14}{4} < \frac{10}{3}$

3. Is $\frac{4}{9} > \frac{4}{5}$?   **8.** Is $\frac{9}{16} < \frac{7}{12}$?

4. Is $\frac{4}{11} > \frac{3}{8}$?   **9.** Is $\frac{13}{15} > \frac{17}{20}$?

5. Is $\frac{11}{4} > \frac{8}{3}$?   **10.** Is $\frac{7}{10} < \frac{11}{15}$?

Exercise 14

A Which is bigger:

1. $\frac{1}{3}$ or $\frac{1}{4}$?   **6.** $\frac{5}{6}$ or $\frac{5}{7}$?   **11.** one-half or one-third?

2. $\frac{1}{9}$ or $\frac{1}{10}$?   **7.** $\frac{13}{25}$ or $\frac{13}{15}$?   **12.** five-ninths or five-eighths?

3. $\frac{1}{12}$ or $\frac{1}{10}$?   **8.** $\frac{4}{3}$ or $\frac{3}{4}$?   **13.** two-fifths or two-thirds?

4. $\frac{7}{16}$ or $\frac{7}{15}$?   **9.** $\frac{5}{12}$ or $\frac{5}{16}$?   **14.** three-quarters or three-fifths?

5. $\frac{8}{15}$ or $\frac{9}{15}$?   **10.** $\frac{11}{25}$ or $\frac{11}{20}$?   **15.** four-sevenths or four-fifths?

B **1.** Nick divided his bar of chocolate into quarters. Kim divided the same size of bar into sixths.
   (*a*) Who had the bigger pieces?
   (*b*) Who had the most pieces?

2. Lucy ate $\frac{3}{8}$ of a cake. Roy ate $\frac{5}{8}$ of the same size of cake. Who ate the least cake?

3. Emma spent $\frac{7}{9}$ of her money. Ravi spent $\frac{7}{12}$ of the same amount of money. Who spent the most?

Exercise 15

1. (*a*) Which is *larger*, $\frac{1}{6}$ or $\frac{1}{7}$?
   (*b*) Which is *smaller*, $\frac{5}{6}$ or $\frac{6}{7}$?

2. (*a*) Which is *larger*, $\frac{1}{10}$ or $\frac{1}{8}$?
   (*b*) Which is *smaller*, $\frac{9}{12}$ or $\frac{7}{8}$?

3. (*a*) Which is *larger*, $\frac{1}{4}$ or $\frac{1}{15}$?
   (*b*) Which is *smaller*, $\frac{3}{4}$ or $\frac{14}{15}$?

Which is *smaller*:

4. $\frac{3}{4}$ or $\frac{9}{10}$?   **7.** $\frac{14}{15}$ or $\frac{15}{16}$?   **10.** $\frac{6}{7}$ or $\frac{11}{12}$?

5. $\frac{5}{6}$ or $\frac{4}{5}$?   **8.** $\frac{15}{16}$ or $\frac{7}{8}$?   **11.** $\frac{7}{8}$ or $\frac{14}{15}$?

6. $\frac{11}{12}$ or $\frac{8}{9}$?   **9.** $\frac{15}{16}$ or $\frac{5}{6}$?   **12.** $\frac{9}{10}$ or $\frac{24}{25}$?

Exercise 16

Answer these:

1. (*a*) $\dfrac{3}{8} = \dfrac{\boxed{?}}{16}$ (*b*) Which is *larger*, $\frac{3}{8}$ or $\frac{7}{16}$?

2. (*a*) $\dfrac{3}{4} = \dfrac{\boxed{?}}{12}$ (*b*) $\dfrac{2}{3} = \dfrac{\boxed{?}}{12}$ (*c*) Which is *larger*, $\frac{3}{4}$ or $\frac{2}{3}$?

3. (*a*) $\dfrac{5}{8} = \dfrac{\boxed{?}}{24}$ (*b*) $\dfrac{2}{3} = \dfrac{\boxed{?}}{24}$ (*c*) Which is *smaller*, $\frac{5}{8}$ or $\frac{2}{3}$?

Which is *larger:*

4. $\frac{9}{16}$ or $\frac{5}{8}$?   **7.** $\frac{5}{8}$ or $\frac{3}{5}$?   **10.** $\frac{21}{25}$ or $\frac{17}{20}$?

5. $\frac{3}{5}$ or $\frac{7}{10}$?   **8.** $\frac{5}{12}$ or $\frac{3}{8}$?   **11.** $\frac{3}{10}$ or $\frac{4}{15}$?

6. $\frac{3}{4}$ or $\frac{7}{10}$?   **9.** $\frac{5}{12}$ or $\frac{7}{16}$?   **12.** $\frac{11}{16}$ or $\frac{2}{3}$?

Exercise 17

A Check whether a statement is true or false by multiplying both sides by the product of the two denominators and then cancelling:

e.g. 1 $\qquad \dfrac{3}{8} < \dfrac{5}{12}$ $\qquad$ *e.g. 2* $\qquad \dfrac{11}{20} > \dfrac{9}{16}$

$$\cancel{8} \times 12 \times \frac{3}{\cancel{8}} < 8 \times \cancel{12} \times \frac{5}{\cancel{12}} \qquad \cancel{20} \times 16 \times \frac{11}{\cancel{20}} > 20 \times \cancel{16} \times \frac{9}{\cancel{16}}$$

$$12 \times 3 < 8 \times 5 \qquad\qquad 16 \times 11 > 20 \times 9$$

$$36 < 40 \qquad\qquad\qquad 176 > 180$$

$$\underline{\underline{\text{True}}} \qquad\qquad\qquad \underline{\underline{\text{False}}}$$

1. $\dfrac{1}{4} < \dfrac{4}{15}$ **5.** $\dfrac{3}{8} > \dfrac{4}{10}$ **9.** $\dfrac{2}{9} < \dfrac{3}{16}$

2. $\dfrac{5}{12} < \dfrac{2}{5}$ **6.** $\dfrac{1}{3} < \dfrac{3}{8}$ **10.** $\dfrac{3}{4} > \dfrac{8}{11}$

3. $\dfrac{4}{6} > \dfrac{5}{8}$ **7.** $\dfrac{5}{12} > \dfrac{4}{9}$ **11.** $\dfrac{14}{25} > \dfrac{9}{16}$

4. $\dfrac{3}{10} > \dfrac{7}{25}$ **8.** $\dfrac{7}{15} < \dfrac{9}{20}$ **12.** $\dfrac{7}{16} < \dfrac{9}{20}$

B Copy these fractions. Put a sign, $<$, $>$ or $=$, in place of each question mark to make the statements true:

e.g. 1 $\qquad \dfrac{3}{7} \boxed{?} \dfrac{2}{5}$ $\qquad$ *e.g. 2* $\qquad \dfrac{5}{8} \boxed{?} \dfrac{10}{16}$

$$\text{Since } 5 \times 3 > 7 \times 2 \qquad\qquad \text{Since } 16 \times 5 = 8 \times 10$$

$$\underline{\dfrac{3}{7} > \dfrac{2}{5}} \qquad\qquad\qquad \underline{\dfrac{5}{8} = \dfrac{10}{16}}$$

$$e.g.\ 3 \qquad \frac{6}{9}\ \boxed{?}\ \frac{8}{12} \qquad e.g.\ 4 \qquad \frac{11}{16}\ \boxed{?}\ \frac{7}{10}$$

Since $12 \times 6 = 9 \times 8$ $\qquad$ Since $10 \times 11 < 16 \times 7$

$$\frac{6}{9} = \frac{8}{12} \qquad\qquad\qquad \frac{11}{16} < \frac{7}{10}$$

1. $\dfrac{2}{3}\ \boxed{?}\ \dfrac{7}{10}$ $\qquad\qquad$ **7.** $\dfrac{9}{14}\ \boxed{?}\ \dfrac{7}{12}$

2. $\dfrac{3}{7}\ \boxed{?}\ \dfrac{4}{9}$ $\qquad\qquad$ **8.** $\dfrac{7}{10}\ \boxed{?}\ \dfrac{9}{13}$

3. $\dfrac{7}{9}\ \boxed{?}\ \dfrac{3}{4}$ $\qquad\qquad$ **9.** $\dfrac{8}{15}\ \boxed{?}\ \dfrac{5}{9}$

4. $\dfrac{1}{5}\ \boxed{?}\ \dfrac{3}{16}$ $\qquad\qquad$ **10.** $\dfrac{11}{21}\ \boxed{?}\ \dfrac{9}{17}$

5. $\dfrac{4}{5}\ \boxed{?}\ \dfrac{7}{9}$ $\qquad\qquad$ **11.** $\dfrac{3}{8}\ \boxed{?}\ \dfrac{37}{100}$

6. $\dfrac{6}{8}\ \boxed{?}\ \dfrac{9}{12}$ $\qquad\qquad$ **12.** $\dfrac{13}{25}\ \boxed{?}\ \dfrac{17}{32}$

Exercise 18

1. A firm made a bar of chocolate called 'Fours or Fives' because it could be shared equally between either four or five people (without breaking any square of chocolate):
   (a) How many squares could the bar of chocolate have?
   (b) What is the smallest number of squares it could have?

2. Since the firm believed that people should share, they made another bar called 'Threes or Fours':
   (a) How many chocolate squares could it have?
   (b) What is the smallest number of squares it could have?

3. What is the smallest number of squares a bar called 'Threes or Sixes' could have?

4. What is the smallest number of squares a bar called 'Sixes or Eights' could have?

Exercise 19

1. Write a fraction that is bigger than $\frac{1}{5}$ but less than $\frac{1}{3}$.

2. Write a fraction that is bigger than $\frac{1}{4}$ but less than $\frac{1}{3}$.

3. Write a fraction that lies between $\frac{1}{8}$ and $\frac{1}{7}$.

4. Give a fraction that lies between $\frac{5}{8}$ and $\frac{5}{7}$.

5. Give a fraction that lies between $\frac{7}{9}$ and $\frac{7}{10}$.

6. Give a fraction that lies between $\frac{5}{8}$ and $\frac{13}{20}$.

Exercise 20

Partition the given set of fractions into the three subsets:

$L = \{$fractions less than 1$\}$ $E = \{$fractions equivalent to 1$\}$

$G = \{$fractions greater than 1$\}$

$$\left\{\frac{2}{3}, \ \frac{5}{5}, \ \frac{5}{8}, \ \frac{9}{5}, \ \frac{8}{3}, \ \frac{16}{16}, \ \frac{56}{100}, \ \frac{3}{5}, \ \frac{1}{10}, \ \frac{84}{20}, \ \frac{9}{9}, \ \frac{29}{32}, \ \frac{20}{25}\right\}$$

Set out your answers like this:

1. $L = \{$fractions less than 1$\} = \left\{\frac{2}{3}, \qquad\right\}$

2. $E = \{$fractions equivalent to 1$\} = \left\{\frac{5}{5}, \qquad\right\}$

3. $G = \{$fractions greater than 1$\} = \left\{\frac{9}{5}, \qquad\right\}$

Decimals

Exercise 21

A Write in centimetres: *e.g.* $48\,\text{mm} = \underline{\underline{4.8\,\text{cm}}}$

1. 39 mm	**4.** 62 mm	**7.** 85 mm	**10.** 26 mm
2. 57 mm	**5.** 13 mm	**8.** 78 mm	**11.** 5 mm
3. 24 mm	**6.** 41 mm	**9.** 97 mm	**12.** 1 mm

Note   One millimetre is one-tenth of a centimetre.

$$1\,\text{mm} = 0.1\,\text{cm}$$
$$\text{one-tenth} = \frac{1}{10} = 0.1$$

143

B Write in order of size, *smallest* first:

1. 0.8 cm, 1.7 cm, 4.2 cm, 0.3 cm, 0.9 cm, 2.5 cm
2. 6 mm, 0.4 cm, 1.9 cm, 26 mm, 5 mm, 0.7 cm
3. 0.6, 0.2, 0.8, 1.3, 0.5, 1.4, 0.4, 0.3, 0.9

C Write, using the pound sign:

e.g. 34 p = £0.34

1. 38 p	**4.** 23 p	**7.** 78 p	**10.** 52 p
2. 65 p	**5.** 56 p	**8.** 19 p	**11.** 8 p
3. 97 p	**6.** 49 p	**9.** 83 p	**12.** 1 p

Note One penny is one-hundredth of a pound.

$$1 \, p = £0.01$$

$$\text{one hundredth} = 0.01 = \frac{1}{100}$$

D Write in order of size, *largest* first:

1. £0.27, £0.46, £1.82, £0.19, £2.75, £0.37
2. £0.49, £0.64, 58 p, 28 p, £0.71, 50 p, £0.14
3. 0.37, 0.14, 0.57, 0.72, 0.04, 0.40, 0.1, 0.02

You can use a calculator to find out if two fractions are equal or if one is bigger than the other. Calculators use decimals (short for *decimal fractions*).

The fractions we have been using are called *vulgar fractions* or *common fractions*.

0.6 is a decimal
↑
This is called a *decimal point*

To find the decimal value of the fraction $\frac{5}{8}$, we key in :

5 ÷ 8 =

Try it.

What is your decimal answer? It should be 0.625.

Exercise 22

Change these common fractions to decimals using a calculator:

1. $\dfrac{1}{10}$ **4.** $\dfrac{2}{100}$ **7.** $\dfrac{32}{100}$ **10.** $\dfrac{49}{1000}$

2. $\dfrac{6}{10}$ **5.** $\dfrac{7}{100}$ **8.** $\dfrac{3}{1000}$ **11.** $\dfrac{546}{1000}$

3. $\dfrac{9}{10}$ **6.** $\dfrac{67}{100}$ **9.** $\dfrac{8}{1000}$ **12.** $\dfrac{802}{1000}$

Look carefully at the questions and answers.
Work out how to find the answers without a calculator.

Exercise 23

Write in words the value of each underlined digit:

e.g. 1   5̲2   five tens
e.g. 2   2.74̲   four-hundredths

(*Words:* thousands, hundreds, tens, units, tenths, hundredths, thousandths)

1. 42̲3   **6.** 5̲613   **11.** 0.41̲2   **16.** 384.2̲8
2. 6̲84   **7.** 4.01̲   **12.** 0.026̲   **17.** 107.061̲
3. 0.3̲   **8.** 39̲   **13.** 1̲.54   **18.** 29.007̲
4. 26.8̲   **9.** 0.75̲   **14.** 64.7̲8   **19.** 3.6̲02
5. 2.17̲   **10.** 0.168̲   **15.** 4̲29.2   **20.** 12.34̲9

History of Decimals

When decimals were first used, the decimal point did not exist.

Consider the decimal number 3.142.

Jemshid Al Kashi, a Persian mathematician who is believed to have died in 1436, would have written 3   142 (he would have left a space).

Pellos, an Italian, would have written 3.142 in 1492. However, he did not fully understand its significance.

In 1530, Christoff Rudolff, a German, would have written 3|142. Rudolff understood how to use decimals. Others, at that time, did not understand his work.

Simon Stevin (or Stevinus), a Belgian, would have written 3 ⓪ 1 ① 4 ② 2 ③ in 1585.

Jost Bürgi, from Switzerland, in 1592 would have written 3,142 or 3.142 or 3142. (He could not make up his mind!)

William Oughtred, from England, would have written 3|142 in 1631.

Adriaen Metius (1571–1635) would have written 3°:1'4"2''' or 3|1'4"2'''.

John Napier used the notation 3,1'4"2''' in 1617, the year in which he died. In the same year his friend Henry Briggs is believed to have used the decimal point.

Frans Van Schooten, a Dutchman, used the notation 3142... ③ in 1657.

Even today there is no agreement. In the United Kingdom and in the United States a decimal point is used, while in Europe a comma is used.

Exercise 24

A Change these common fractions to decimals using a calculator:

1. $\dfrac{1}{5}$	**6.** $\dfrac{7}{8}$	**11.** $\dfrac{1}{25}$	**16.** $\dfrac{24}{25}$	**21.** $\dfrac{29}{40}$
2. $\dfrac{3}{5}$	**7.** $\dfrac{1}{20}$	**12.** $\dfrac{7}{25}$	**17.** $\dfrac{1}{16}$	**22.** $\dfrac{2}{3}$
3. $\dfrac{1}{2}$	**8.** $\dfrac{9}{20}$	**13.** $\dfrac{9}{25}$	**18.** $\dfrac{9}{16}$	**23.** $\dfrac{1}{6}$
4. $\dfrac{3}{4}$	**9.** $\dfrac{11}{20}$	**14.** $\dfrac{13}{25}$	**19.** $\dfrac{11}{16}$	**24.** $\dfrac{3}{7}$
5. $\dfrac{5}{8}$	**10.** $\dfrac{17}{20}$	**15.** $\dfrac{18}{25}$	**20.** $\dfrac{17}{40}$	**25.** $\dfrac{6}{7}$

B Change these fractions to decimals *without using a calculator:*

1. $\dfrac{2}{5}$ **4.** $\dfrac{3}{8}$ **7.** $\dfrac{19}{20}$ **10.** $\dfrac{5}{16}$ **13.** $\dfrac{5}{6}$

2. $\dfrac{1}{4}$ **5.** $\dfrac{3}{20}$ **8.** $\dfrac{17}{25}$ **11.** $\dfrac{13}{16}$ **14.** $\dfrac{1}{7}$

3. $\dfrac{1}{8}$ **6.** $\dfrac{7}{20}$ **9.** $\dfrac{2}{25}$ **12.** $\dfrac{1}{3}$ **15.** $\dfrac{5}{7}$

C Change to decimals:

1. $1\frac{3}{10}$ **4.** $2\frac{3}{4}$ **7.** $9\frac{13}{20}$ **10.** $6\frac{4}{9}$

2. $3\frac{4}{5}$ **5.** $5\frac{7}{8}$ **8.** $2\frac{3}{25}$ **11.** $3\frac{5}{12}$

3. $4\frac{1}{2}$ **6.** $3\frac{3}{8}$ **9.** $4\frac{7}{16}$ **12.** $2\frac{4}{7}$

Exercise 25

Change these decimals to common fractions in their simplest form:

1. 0.9	**9.** 0.42	**17.** 0.125
2. 0.7	**10.** 0.18	**18.** 0.625
3. 0.8	**11.** 0.44	**19.** (*a*) 0.6
4. 0.5	**12.** 0.16	(*b*) 0.06
5. 0.23	**13.** 0.92	(*c*) 0.006
6. 0.75	**14.** 2.62	**20.** (*a*) 0.25
7. 0.65	**15.** 5.86	(*b*) 0.025
8. 0.55	**16.** 3.24	(*c*) 0.0025

Exercise 26

To what value is the arrow pointing?
Give each answer as a decimal.

1.

2.

147

3.

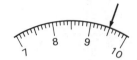

8.

4.

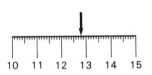

9.

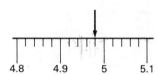

5.

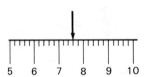

10.

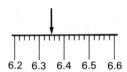

6.

11.

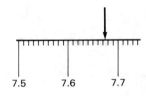

7.

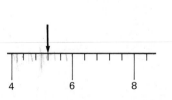

12.

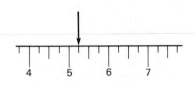

148

Carefully copy each of these scales.
Only some of the points have been numbered.
Number all the points on your drawings.

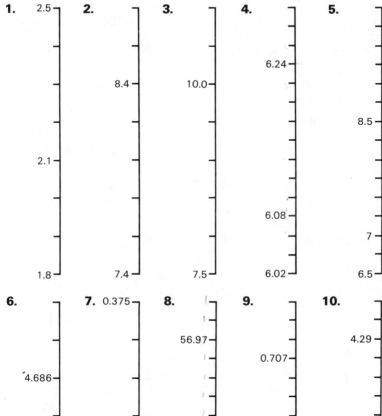

1. 2.5 … 2.1 … 1.8

2. 8.4 … 7.4

3. 10.0 … 7.5

4. 6.24 … 6.08 … 6.02

5. 8.5 … 7 … 6.5

6. 4.686 … 4.674

7. 0.375 … 0.340

8. 56.97 … 56.75

9. 0.707 … 0.647

10. 4.29 … 3.85

Exercise 28

It is possible to use a graph to change common fractions to decimals. Make a copy of the graph below, use a scale of 1 cm to 1 unit on the denominator axis and 2 cm to 1 unit on the numerator axis.

The graph shows that $\frac{1}{2} = 0.5$, $\frac{4}{5} = 0.8$, $\frac{1}{8} = 0.125$ and $\frac{2}{7} = 0.285$.

Use your graph to change these to decimals:

1. $\frac{1}{5}$ **4.** $\frac{3}{4}$ **7.** $\frac{7}{16}$ **10.** Try to find:

2. $\frac{3}{5}$ **5.** $\frac{5}{8}$ **8.** $\frac{2}{9}$ (a) $\frac{13}{20}$ (c) $\frac{12}{15}$

3. $\frac{9}{10}$ **6.** $\frac{7}{8}$ **9.** $\frac{4}{7}$ (b) $\frac{12}{25}$ (d) $\frac{11}{16}$

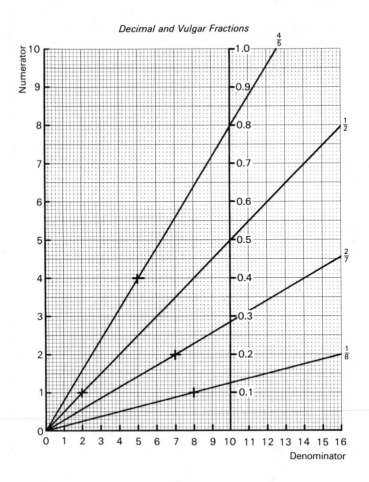

Decimal and Vulgar Fractions

150

Fractions of Quantities

Exercise 29

{half, third, quarter, fifth, sixth, seventh, eighth, ninth, tenth}

Copy these sentences and complete each by filling in the missing word. Select the missing word from the set of words above. (The same missing word may be used in more than one sentence.)

1. One $\boxed{?}$ of an hour is 15 min.

2. There are 20 s in one $\boxed{?}$ of a minute.

3. 200 mm is one $\boxed{?}$ of a metre.

4. There are 12 h in a $\boxed{?}$ of a day.

5. There are 250 m in a $\boxed{?}$ of a kilometre.

6. There are 10 min in one $\boxed{?}$ of an hour.

7. 6 s is one $\boxed{?}$ of a minute.

8. 125 mℓ is one $\boxed{?}$ of a litre.

Exercise 30

1. (*a*) Find one-quarter of 28 books.
(*b*) Find three-quarters of 28 books.

2. (*a*) Find $\frac{1}{5}$ of 45 sheets of paper.
(*b*) Find $\frac{4}{5}$ of 45 sheets of paper.

3. (*a*) Find $\frac{1}{8}$ of 32 sweets.
(*b*) What is five-eighths of 32 sweets?
(*c*) What is $\frac{7}{8}$ of 32 sweets?

4. Find $\frac{2}{3}$ of 42 stamps.

151

5. What is $\frac{1}{6}$ of 72 m?

6. What is $\frac{4}{7}$ of 56 lb?

7. Find $\frac{9}{10}$ of 70 kg.

8. Find $\frac{5}{6}$ of 360°.

9. What is $\frac{3}{8}$ of 112 yd?

10. What is $\frac{7}{12}$ of 96 in?

11. What is $\frac{13}{20}$ of 240 min?

12. Find $\frac{5}{9}$ of 117 days.

13. Find $\frac{7}{16}$ of 144 m.

14. Find $\frac{13}{16}$ of 368 marbles.

15. Find $\frac{21}{32}$ of £224.

Exercise 31

1. Find $\frac{1}{2}$ cm in millimetres.

2. Write $\frac{3}{4}$ h in minutes.

3. Write $\frac{4}{5}$ min in seconds.

4. Find $\frac{3}{8}$ km in metres.

5. What is $\frac{5}{6}$ of a day in hours?

6. What is $\frac{2}{3}$ of 2 h in minutes?

7. Write $\frac{2}{5}$ of £2 in pence.

8. Find $\frac{7}{10}$ of 3 h in minutes.

9. Find $\frac{9}{16}$ of 4 ℓ in millilitres.

10. How many centimetres are there in $\frac{11}{12}$ of 3 m?

11. How many weeks are there in $\frac{5}{8}$ of 2 years?

12. Find $\frac{3}{5}$ of 10 ft in inches (12 in $=$ 1 ft)

Exercise 32

The *pie chart* shows the sports enjoyed by 84 people:

1. What fraction liked swimming?

2. What fraction liked squash?

3. What fraction liked tennis?

4. What fraction liked badminton?

5. How many liked swimming?

6. How many liked squash?

7. How many liked tennis?

8. How many liked badminton?

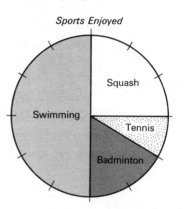

Sports Enjoyed

Exercise 33

1. A rectangle measures 12 cm by 7 cm. Draw the rectangle with sides of half-size.

2. A triangle has sides of lengths 69 mm, 102 mm and 81 mm. Construct a triangle with sides $\frac{2}{3}$ of these sizes.

3. In △PQR, PQ $=$ 84 mm. QR $=\frac{3}{4}$ of PQ and PR $=\frac{7}{9}$ of QR. Construct this triangle.

4. Draw a circle of radius 36 mm. Divide the circle into six equal parts (draw the six radii). Label the points where the radii meet the circle as A, B, C, D, E and F (anticlockwise). Let the centre of

153

the circle be point O. Mark points on each radius in turn (A_1 on OA, B_1 on OB, and so on) such that:

$$OA_1 = \tfrac{1}{6}OA \qquad OC_1 = \tfrac{1}{2}OC \qquad OE_1 = \tfrac{5}{6}OE$$
$$OB_1 = \tfrac{1}{3}OB \qquad OD_1 = \tfrac{2}{3}OD \qquad OF_1 = OF$$

Join A_1 to B_1 to C_1 to D_1 to E_1 to F_1.

Exercise 34

The graph below can be used to find fractions of a kilometre. Try to find out how it works. Make a copy of this graph. Use a scale of 1 cm to 1 unit on the denominator axis and 2 cm to 1 unit on the numerator axis.

Fractions of a Kilometre

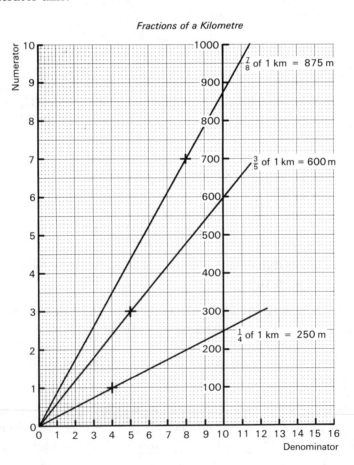

1. Now use your graph to find these fractions of a kilometre (in metres):

(a) $\dfrac{3}{4}$ (c) $\dfrac{3}{10}$ (e) $\dfrac{9}{16}$

(b) $\dfrac{4}{5}$ (d) $\dfrac{3}{8}$ (f) $\dfrac{5}{12}$

2. Try to draw a graph that will help you to find fractions of £1, in pence.

3. Try to draw a graph that will help you to find fractions of an hour in minutes. (This time, the answer line should not be drawn at the number 10 in the denominator. Try to think of the best place for this answer line.)

Exercise 35

e.g. 1   To find $\frac{3}{8}$ of 136 using a calculator,

key in: $\boxed{3}\ \boxed{\div}\ \boxed{8}\ \boxed{\times}\ \boxed{1}\ \boxed{3}\ \boxed{6}\ \boxed{=}$

Try it.

Sometimes you may not obtain a sensible answer. Try this:

e.g. 2 $\frac{4}{7}$ of 175, $\boxed{4}\ \boxed{\div}\ \boxed{7}\ \boxed{\times}\ \boxed{1}\ \boxed{7}\ \boxed{5}\ \boxed{=}$

My calculator gives 99.999 987. (Some calculators may give slightly different answers.) A sensible answer would be 100. Try it on your calculator.

Work these out on a calculator. Give sensible answers.

1. $\frac{5}{8}$ of 216 pages,   5. $\frac{5}{6}$ of 4218 matches,

2. $\frac{4}{7}$ of 294 eggs,   6. $\frac{13}{16}$ of 2016 jars,

3. $\frac{2}{9}$ of 873 tins,   7. $\frac{11}{12}$ of 5724 trees,

4. $\frac{2}{3}$ of 708 cartons,   8. $\frac{8}{15}$ of 225 bushes.

The correct answers to the questions in Exercise 35 may be obtained by working in a different order. Example 2 may be worked out as follows:

e.g. 2 $\frac{4}{7}$ of 175   *Answer*

Method 1   Key in: $\boxed{1}\,\boxed{7}\,\boxed{5}\,\boxed{\div}\,\boxed{7}\,\boxed{\times}\,\boxed{4}\,\boxed{=}$ 100

Method 2   Key in: $\boxed{4}\,\boxed{\times}\,\boxed{1}\,\boxed{7}\,\boxed{5}\,\boxed{\div}\,\boxed{7}\,\boxed{=}$ 100

Answer Exercise 35 again. This time, use Method 1 for the odd numbers and Method 2 for the even numbers.

1. About two-thirds the mass of an adult is water. How many litres of water are there in the body of an adult who has a mass of 78 kg? (1 ℓ of water has a mass of 1 kg.)

2. The petrol tank in a car is $\frac{7}{8}$ full. How many litres does it contain if it holds 56 ℓ when full?

3. Which is the most, $\frac{5}{12}$ of £300 or $\frac{3}{16}$ of £664?

4. Maria travelled $\frac{3}{4}$ of her journey of 276 km by train. How far was that?

5. Eric cycled $\frac{13}{15}$ of 105 km, while Sunil cycled $\frac{7}{9}$ of 126 km. Who cycled further, and by how many kilometres?

6. If $\frac{5}{8}$ of the 672 patients were under 35 years of age, how many was that?

7. Brass is an alloy made of $\frac{3}{5}$ copper and $\frac{2}{5}$ zinc. If the mass of 50 brass screws is 115 g, how heavy is the zinc that is in them?

8. There are 2640 children living in a certain town. $\frac{5}{16}$ attend secondary school, $\frac{8}{15}$ attend primary school and the rest do not go to school.
   (*a*) How many do not attend school?
   (*b*) If $\frac{9}{16}$ of the primary school children are girls, how many are boys?

9. Martin gave $\frac{7}{9}$ of his stamps away. If he had 3519 stamps to start with, how many were left?

10. After travelling four-sevenths of a journey of 273 km, how far had I yet to travel?

Exercise 38

1. Liz had 2376 stamps. She gave $\frac{3}{8}$ of these to her friend, Mary, and $\frac{2}{3}$ of the remainder to her brother. How many did she have left?

2. Mrs Jones receives £288 per month. How much would she receive per month if this amount was increased by five-sixteenths?

3. Clive lost $\frac{1}{5}$ of his money. If he lost £13, how much did he start with?

4. If, in spending $\frac{2}{3}$ of my money, I spent £24, how much money did I start with?

5. My petrol tank is $\frac{5}{8}$ full. If I have 30 ℓ left, find the capacity of my tank.

6. If $\frac{4}{7}$ of the pupils in a school were girls and there were 432 boys, how many pupils were there altogether?

7. If $\frac{2}{3}$ of the population of a town number 5700, how many people live in that town?

8. Dilip cycles for 3 h at 18 km/h. Paul walks $\frac{5}{6}$ of this distance and it takes him 9 h. How fast does Paul walk?

9. I started with a full tank of petrol. I used $\frac{3}{5}$ of this on a journey of 378 km, and had 18 ℓ left.
(a) How much petrol does my car's tank hold when full?
(b) How many kilometres will my car travel on 1 ℓ of petrol?

157

10. The petrol tank of a car holds 48ℓ, while petrol consumption is 14 km per litre. At the start of a journey the tank is $\frac{7}{8}$ full.

(*a*) After travelling 378 km, how many litres will be left?

(*b*) Find the total distance the car will have travelled when it runs out of petrol.

11. In a class, $\frac{3}{5}$ of the pupils were girls. $\frac{1}{4}$ of the boys in the class were absent. $\frac{2}{15}$ of the whole class were absent. There were 9 boys present. How many girls were present?

12. Wendy spent $\frac{1}{3}$ of her pocket money, while Sam spent $\frac{2}{3}$ of his. Could Wendy have spent more than Sam? Explain your answer.

9 Angles

Exercise 1

Use any piece of paper. Tear a piece into any shape.

Using only two folds, make a right-angle with your piece of paper.

The two lines on this diagram may help.

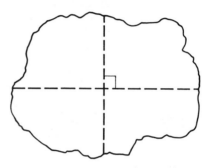

Exercise 2

For each question, write whether the angle is an acute angle, an obtuse angle, a reflex angle, a right-angle or a straight angle:

1.

4.

7.

2.

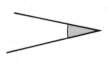

5.

8.

3.

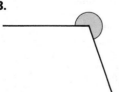

6.

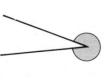

9.

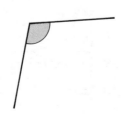

159

10.

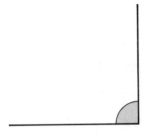

Note   Question 10 is not a left-angle!

Exercise 3 **M**

Use the map of Garstangle opposite. Copy the table and write the type of angle through which you turn (acute angle, obtuse angle, reflex angle or right-angle) if:

	You are at the	You face the	You turn	You now face the	Type of angle
1.	crescent	post office	anticlockwise	school	?
2.	church	inn	anticlockwise	station	?
3.	railway bridge	farm	clockwise	embankment	?
4.	castle ruins	river	anticlockwise	crescent	?
5.	crossroads	church	clockwise	school	?
6.	farm	marsh	anticlockwise	crossroads	?
7.	garage	station	clockwise	castle ruins	?
8.	green	garage	clockwise	cul-de-sac	?
9.	post office	cul-de-sac	clockwise	river	?
10.	marsh	embankment	anticlockwise	railway bridge	?

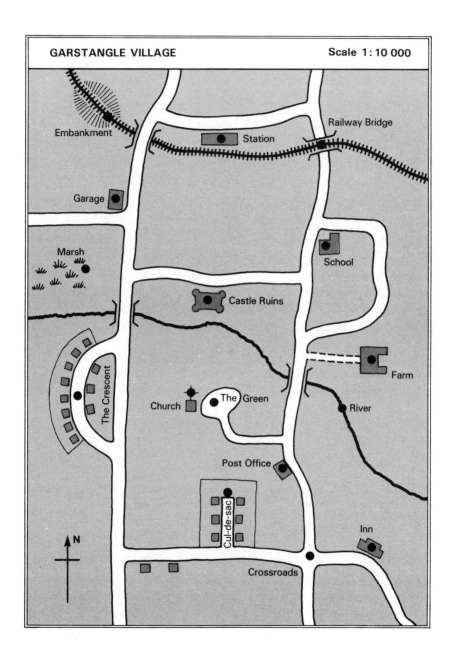

GARSTANGLE VILLAGE   Scale 1:10 000

Embankment

Station

Railway Bridge

Garage

Marsh

School

Castle Ruins

Farm

The Crescent

Church

The Green

River

Post Office

Cul-de-sac

Inn

N

Crossroads

Exercise 4

Copy these. For each question, rotate the line QR about R. Mark a dot, S, such that angle QRS is a right-angle (S shows the new position of Q).

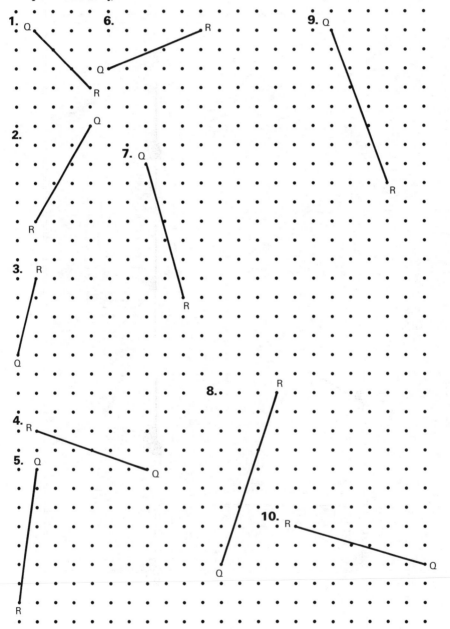

Exercise 5

Write, for each drawing, what fraction of a full turn it shows:

1.

2.

3.

4.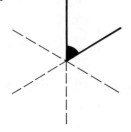

5.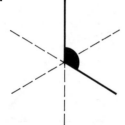

6.

7.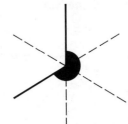

8.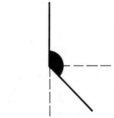

9.

10.

History

There are 360° in a full turn.

Why divide a full turn into 360 equal parts? Why not use some easier number such as 100?

It was possibly divided into 360 parts because thousands of years ago the Greeks and the Sumerians divided their year into 360 days. Each degree would be the daily amount of turning as the Earth followed its path around the Sun.

Exercise 6

A full turn is 360°.

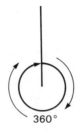

360°

How many degrees are there in:

1. $\frac{1}{2}$ turn?   **7.** $\frac{5}{6}$ turn?   **13.** $\frac{7}{12}$ turn?   **19.** $\frac{1}{360}$ turn?

2. $\frac{1}{4}$ turn?   **8.** $\frac{1}{10}$ turn?   **14.** $\frac{3}{20}$ turn?   **20.** $\frac{113}{360}$ turn?

3. $\frac{3}{4}$ turn?   **9.** $\frac{9}{10}$ turn?   **15.** $\frac{23}{30}$ turn?   **21.** 2 turns?

4. $\frac{1}{3}$ turn?   **10.** $\frac{1}{5}$ turn?   **16.** $\frac{9}{40}$ turn?   **22.** 5 turns?

5. $\frac{2}{3}$ turn?   **11.** $\frac{3}{5}$ turn?   **17.** $\frac{11}{24}$ turn?   **23.** 8 turns?

6. $\frac{1}{6}$ turn?   **12.** $\frac{1}{12}$ turn?   **18.** $\frac{19}{24}$ turn?   **24.** 200 turns?

Exercise 7

Estimate the number of degrees in each of these angles:

1.

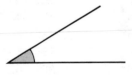

2.

3.

164

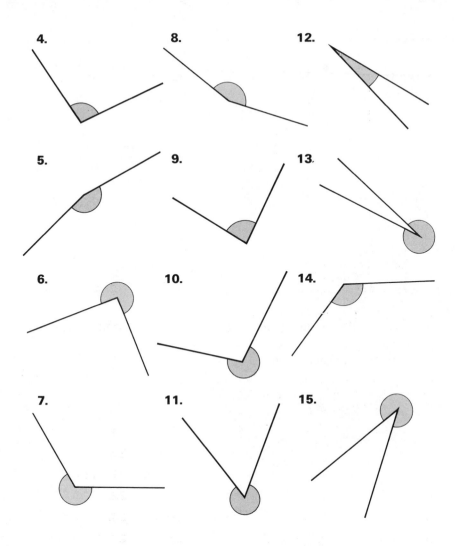

4. **8.** **12.**

5. **9.** **13.**

6. **10.** **14.**

7. **11.** **15.**

Exercise 8

Without using a protractor, try to draw two straight lines to show these angles. (Label each angle.)

1. 45°	**6.** 270°	**11.** 215°	**16.** 120°
2. 135°	**7.** 200°	**12.** 75°	**17.** 345°
3. 60°	**8.** 25°	**13.** 125°	**18.** 235°
4. 80°	**9.** 315°	**14.** 290°	**19.** 185°
5. 150°	**10.** 105°	**15.** 10°	**20.** 55°

Exercise 9

Write the correct name (acute angle, obtuse angle, reflex angle or right-angle) for each of the following angles:

1. 36°	**7.** 115°	**13.** 8°
2. 172°	**8.** 82°	**14.** 89°
3. 49°	**9.** 270°	**15.** 277°
4. 352°	**10.** 90°	**16.** 205°
5. 183°	**11.** 123°	
6. 260°	**12.** 99°	

Exercise 10

1. Measure this angle by placing the zero line of your protractor along QR.
Read the anticlockwise scale.

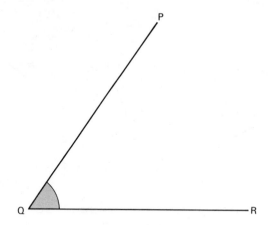

2. Now measure the angle again. This time, place the zero line of your protractor along PQ.
Read the clockwise scale.

3. What do you notice about the answers to questions 1 and 2?

Measure these angles. (Estimate each angle first. Your estimate should help you to decide which scale to use on your protractor.)

A

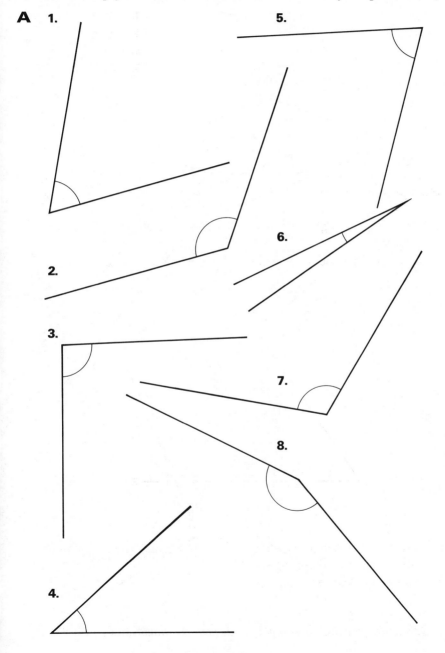

1.

2.

3.

4.

5.

6.

7.

8.

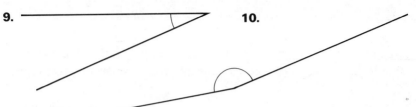

9.

10.

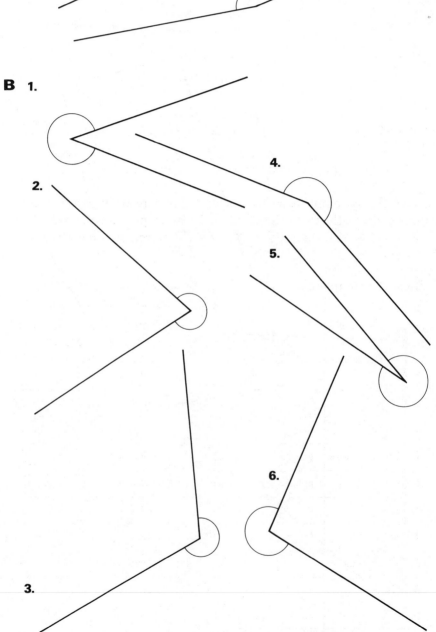

B **1.**

2.

4.

5.

6.

3.

7.

8.

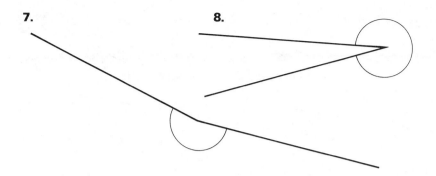

Exercise 12

Use the map of Garstangle on p. 161.

A Through how many degrees do you turn if you are at the castle ruins, you point north, then you turn clockwise to point to each of the named places on the map? (An angle is required for each place on the map.)

B Copy and complete the following table:

	You are at the	You face the	You turn to face the	You turn	Number of degrees
1.	post office	crescent	station	clockwise	?
2.	church	inn	embankment	anticlockwise	?
3.	school	farm	marsh	?	106°
4.	railway bridge	garage	?	anticlockwise	80°
5.	crossroads	green	cul-de-sac	clockwise	?
6.	crescent	?	farm	clockwise	77°
7.	cul-de-sac	inn	?	anticlockwise	132°
8.	castle ruins	?	railway bridge	anticlockwise	248°
9.	river	?	church	anticlockwise	309°
10.	?	castle ruins	embankment	clockwise	22°

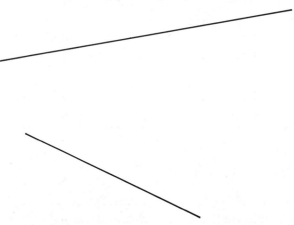
Trace these two lines. Without extending them until they intersect, find a method of measuring the angle between them.

When drawing angles, measure them as accurately as you can.

If a space ship flies on a straight course to the Moon (a journey of about 240 000 miles or 384 000 km) but is 1° out when it takes off, it will miss the Moon by over 4000 miles (over 6400 km).

Exercise 14

Carefully and accurately draw and label angles of the following sizes:

1. 40°	**4.** 12°	**7.** 138°	**10.** 64°	**13.** 36°
2. 25°	**5.** 86°	**8.** 99°	**11.** 142°	**14.** 109°
3. 71°	**6.** 155°	**9.** 163°	**12.** 174°	**15.** 57°

| **16.** 240° | **18.** 198° | **20.** 222° | **22.** 296° | **24.** 187° |
| **17.** 305° | **19.** 346° | **21.** 329° | **23.** 231° | **25.** 254° |

Exercise 15

Copy and complete the following curve stitching patterns, or make up your own pattern where a circle needs to be divided into a number of equal parts.

In question 1, there are two *concentric* circles and there are twice as many points on the outer circle than on the inner circle.

1.

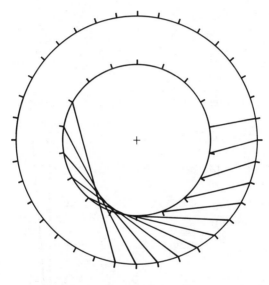

2.

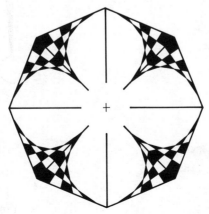

3. Join the numbers using your 2-times table:

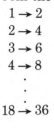

$1 \rightarrow 2$
$2 \rightarrow 4$
$3 \rightarrow 6$
$4 \rightarrow 8$
$\vdots$
$18 \rightarrow 36$

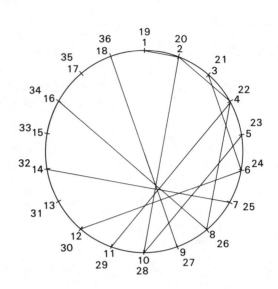

Exercise 16

Greek letters are often used to stand for angles.
We shall use the letters α, β and θ (alpha, beta and theta).

Calculate the missing angles. DO NOT measure.

1.

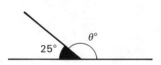

2.

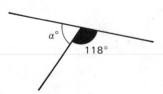

3.

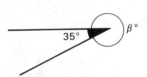

4.

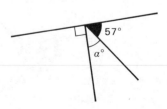

172

5.

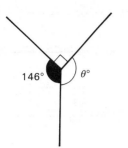

146° θ°

8.

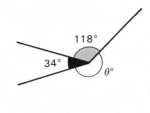

118° 34° θ°

6.

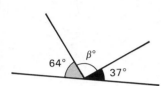

64° β° 37°

9.

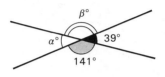

β° α° 39° 141°

7.

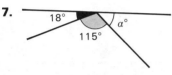

18° 115° α°

10.

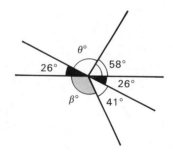

θ° 26° 58° 26° β° 41°

Exercise 17

When two straight lines intersect (as in the diagram), the two angles that lie opposite each other are called *vertically opposite angles.*

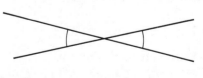

On separate diagrams, draw three pairs of intersecting lines. (All three drawings should be different.)

On each drawing, measure a pair of vertically opposite angles. Write what you notice about vertically opposite angles.

Calculate the missing angles. (Look for vertically opposite angles.)

1.

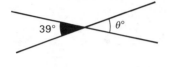

4.

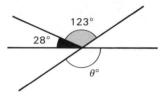

2.

5.

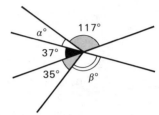

3.

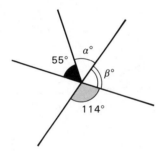

6.

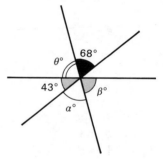

To Bisect an Angle

Exercise 19

Draw any angle ABC.

With centre B, and any radius, draw an arc to cut AB at D and to cut BC at E.

Check that your pair of compasses is set to a radius that is greater than $\frac{1}{2}$DE.

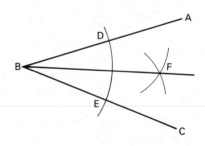

174

With centre at D, draw an arc between the arms and away from B.

With centre at E, using the *same* radius, draw another arc to cut the previous one at F.

Draw a straight line from B, through F.

This straight line, BF, *bisects* angle ABC.

Exercise 20

In Chapter 6, Exercise 12 (p. 94) a line was bisected using a pencil and ruler.

Draw any angle. Now try to find a method of bisecting the angle using only a pencil and ruler (the ruler must not be used for measuring).

Exercise 21

1. A wheel is turned through 284°. Through how many more degrees must it be turned to complete one revolution?

2. A piece of sheet metal is to be folded to form a right-angle. (The diagram shows three folds of 30° each.) How many degrees are needed for each fold if:
   (*a*) five folds are needed?
   (*b*) four folds are needed?

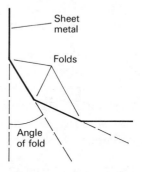

3. The Earth rotates once (through 360°) on its axis in 24 h. Through how many degrees does it turn in:
   (*a*) 8 h?   (*b*) 1 h?   (*c*) 4 min?   (*d*) 28 min?   (*e*) 52 min?

4. Some kitchen scales will weigh up to 4 kg. In weighing 4 kg, the pointer turns through 360°.
   (*a*) Through how many degrees will the pointer turn to weigh 1 kg?

(b) Through how many degrees will the pointer turn if I weigh 500 g of tomatoes?

(c) In weighing some apples, I see the pointer turn through 72°. How heavy are the apples?

(d) If some potatoes weigh 3.5 kg, through how many degrees will the pointer turn in weighing them?

(e) Through how many degrees will the pointer turn in weighing 150 g of sweets?

5. Draw the dial of some kitchen weighing scales that will weigh up to 3 kg with one revolution of the pointer (the pointer turns clockwise). Label the dial with 200 g markings (i.e. show 200 g, 400 g, 600 g, 800 g, 1 kg, 1.2 kg, 1.4 kg, and so on, up to 3 kg).

6. Draw the dial of some kitchen scales that will weigh up to 5 kg (in intervals of 250 g) with one revolution of the pointer which turns clockwise.

7. If ten revolutions of the handle on a vice closes (or opens) the vice by 36 mm:
(a) By how many millimetres do five turns of the handle open or close the vice?

(b) To open the vice by 2 mm, through how many degrees must the handle turn?

(c) To open the vice by 5 mm, through how many degrees must the handle turn?

8. If the slowest cutting speed on a milling machine is 40 rev/min (revolutions per minute):
(a) How many seconds would it take to make ten revolutions?

(b) How many seconds would it take to make eight revolutions?

(c) How many seconds would it take to make one revolution?

(d) Through how many degrees would the cutter turn in 1 s?

9. If the cutting speed on a milling machine was 330 rev/min, how many revolutions would it make in 4 s?

10. If 45 revolutions of a dividing head handle turn the workpiece once (through 360°):
(a) How many revolutions are needed to turn the workpiece through 72°?

(b) Through how many degrees do five revolutions turn the workpiece?

(c) Through how many degrees do 12 revolutions turn the workpiece?

(d) How many revolutions are needed to turn the workpiece through 320°?

Exercise 22

What part of a turn is:

1. 45°?	**7.** 144°?	**13.** 280°?	**19.** 540°?
2. 40°?	**8.** 225°?	**14.** 234°?	**20.** 480°?
3. 150°?	**9.** 18°?	**15.** 96°?	**21.** 600°?
4. 108°?	**10.** 320°?	**16.** 275°?	**22.** 990°?
5. 160°?	**11.** 330°?	**17.** 72°?	**23.** 648°?
6. 70°?	**12.** 252°?	**18.** 168°?	**24.** 153°?

Exercise 23

1. How much time has passed when the hour hand of a clock turns through:

(a) 90°?   (b) 60°?   (c) 150°?   (d) 240°?   (e) 330°?

2. How much time has passed when the minute hand of a clock turns through:

(a) 90°?   (b) 30°?   (c) 210°?   (d) 36°?   (e) 108°?

3. Through how many degrees does the minute hand turn between

(a) 12.00 and 12.40?   (b) 10.25 and 11.20?

4. Through how many degrees does the hour hand turn between

(a) 09.00 and 10.00?   (c) 06.00 and 08.30?

(b) 15.00 and 20.00?   (d) 08.15 and 15.45?

5. How many degrees are there between the hour and the minute hands of a clock at (give the smaller angle):

(a) 8 o'clock?   (f) ten-past four?

(b) half-past two?   (g) 05.12?

(c) half-past six?   (h) twenty to twelve?

(d) half-past ten?   (i) 15.50?

(e) twenty-past eight?

The major points of the compass are shown.

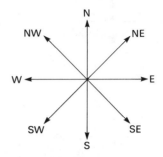

Copy and complete the following table:

	I start facing	I then turn	Degrees turned	Fraction of turn	I am now facing
e.g.	S	clockwise	270°	$\frac{3}{4}$	E
1.	N	clockwise	90°	?	?
2.	N	anticlockwise	?	$\frac{1}{2}$	?
3.	W	?	?	$\frac{1}{4}$	N
4.	?	anticlockwise	270°	?	S
5.	NW	clockwise	45°	?	?
6.	SE	anticlockwise	90°	?	?
7.	SW	clockwise	?	$\frac{3}{8}$	?
8.	S	?	?	$\frac{7}{8}$	SE
9.	?	clockwise	?	$\frac{3}{4}$	NW
10.	NE	anticlockwise	?	?	E
11.	?	clockwise	?	$\frac{3}{8}$	NE
12.	E	anticlockwise	?	?	SW
13.	SE	clockwise	45°	?	?
14.	?	anticlockwise	225°	?	N
15.	NW	anticlockwise	?	$\frac{1}{4}$	?

10 Triangles and Constructions

Exercise 1

Cut out any triangle from a piece of paper.

Tear off all three corners.

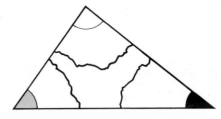

Now place all three corners together as shown below.

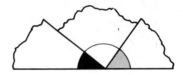

What can you say about the sum of the angles of a triangle?

Exercise 2

Measure and write the size of each of the following angles:

1.

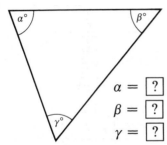

$\alpha = \boxed{?}$

$\beta = \boxed{?}$

$\gamma = \boxed{?}$

2. $x = \boxed{?}$

$y = \boxed{?}$

$z = \boxed{?}$

179

3. $\angle A =$?
$\angle B =$?
$\angle C =$?

A

B

C

6. $\widehat{S} =$?
$\widehat{T} =$?
$\widehat{U} =$?

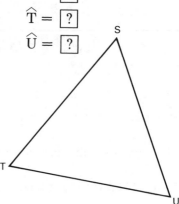

S

T

U

4.

P Q

R

$\angle PQR =$?
$\angle QRP =$?
$\angle QPR =$?

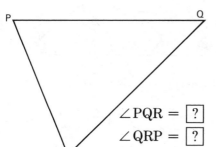

7.

$d =$?
$e =$?
$f =$?

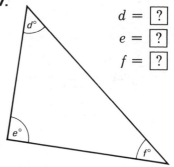

$d°$

$e°$

$f°$

5.

J

K

M

L

$\widehat{KLM} =$?
$\widehat{LMK} =$?
$\widehat{MKL} =$?
$\widehat{JKM} =$?

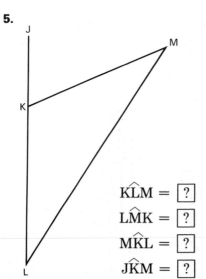

8.

$\alpha° $

$\gamma° $

$\delta° $

$\beta° $

$\alpha =$?
$\beta =$?
$\gamma =$?
$\delta =$?

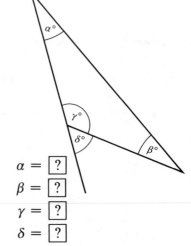

9.

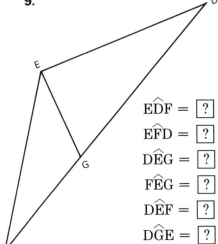

$$\widehat{EDF} = \boxed{?}$$
$$\widehat{EFD} = \boxed{?}$$
$$\widehat{DEG} = \boxed{?}$$
$$\widehat{FEG} = \boxed{?}$$
$$\widehat{DEF} = \boxed{?}$$
$$\widehat{DGE} = \boxed{?}$$
$$\widehat{FGE} = \boxed{?}$$

10.

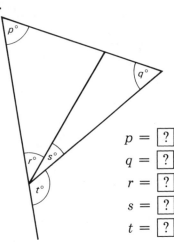

$$p = \boxed{?}$$
$$q = \boxed{?}$$
$$r = \boxed{?}$$
$$s = \boxed{?}$$
$$t = \boxed{?}$$

Exercise 3 M

Calculate the labelled angles:

1.

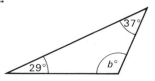

4.

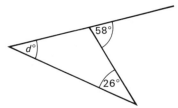

2.

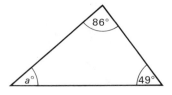

5.

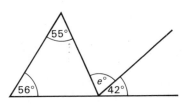

3.

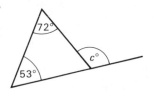

6.

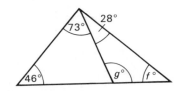

7.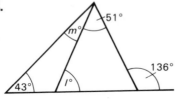

12.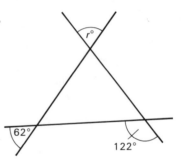

8.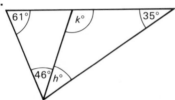

13.

9.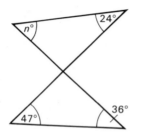

10.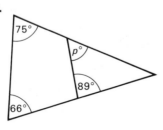

14.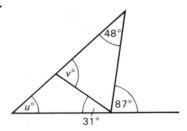

11.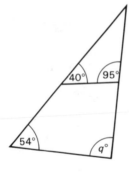

15.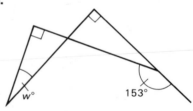

Copy these triangles. Measure each angle and each side.

Also, copy and complete each sentence with the word 'different' or 'equal'.

1.

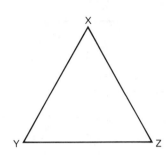

Equilateral triangle

XY = ⬚ mm, YZ = ⬚ mm,
XZ = ⬚ mm
All sides are ⬚ .

∠XYZ = ⬚ , ∠XZY = ⬚ ,
∠YXZ = ⬚
All angles are ⬚ .

2. *Isosceles triangle*

PQ = ⬚ mm, PR = ⬚ mm,
QR = ⬚ mm,
PQ = ⬚ (Which side?)
Two sides are ⬚ .

∠PQR = ⬚ , ∠PRQ = ⬚ ,
∠QPR = ⬚ ,
∠PQR = ∠ ⬚
Two angles are ⬚ .
Equal angles are opposite ⬚ sides.

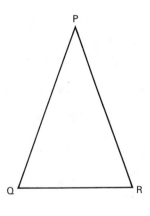

3.

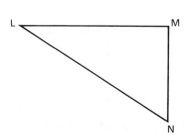

Right-angled triangle

∠LMN = ⬚
Right-angled triangles have one right-angle.

183

4. *Scalene triangle*

AB = $\boxed{?}$ mm, BC = $\boxed{?}$ mm,
AC = $\boxed{?}$ mm
All sides are $\boxed{?}$.

∠ABC = $\boxed{?}$, ∠ACB = $\boxed{?}$,
∠BAC = $\boxed{?}$

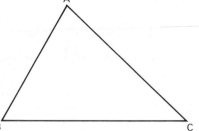

All angles are $\boxed{?}$.
The largest angle is opposite the longest side.
The smallest angle is opposite the smallest side.

Exercise 5 ▬▬▬▬▬▬▬▬▬▬▬▬ **M**

You need to use 9-pin Geoboard (3×3 pinboard) and/or some 3×3 dotty paper.

It is easier to do this work using Geoboard.

Show your answers on the dotty paper.

These two triangles are the same:

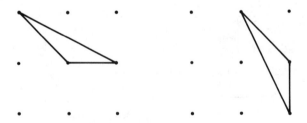

Two triangles are the same if, when cut out, one fits exactly on top of the other.

Check that the two triangles above are the same.

1. Make as many different triangles as you can.

2. How many of your triangles are right-angled triangles?

3. How many of your triangles are isosceles triangles?

4. Are there any equilateral triangles?

5. Are there any scalene triangles?

Exercise 6 ━━━━━━━━━━━━━━━━━━━━━━━━━ M

Calculate the labelled angles:

1.

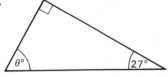

2.

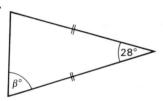

3.

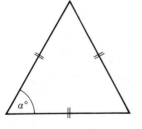

4.

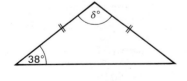

5.

6.

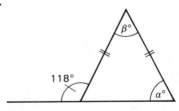

7.

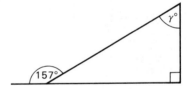

8.

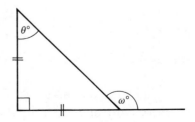

185

9.

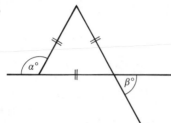

10.

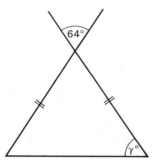

11.

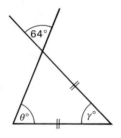

12.

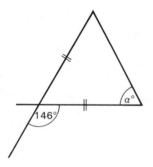

13.

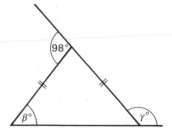

14.

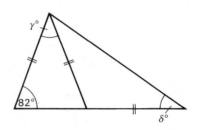

15.

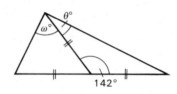

16.

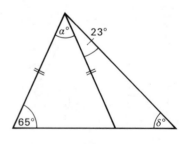

Exercise 7

1. A ladder makes an angle of 26° with a wall. What angle does it make with the ground?

2. A plank makes an angle of 12° with the horizontal. What angle does it make with the vertical?

3. One angle of a triangle measures 22°. If the other two angles are equal, find them.

4. One angle of an isosceles triangle is 92°. What size can the other angles be?

5. One angle of an isosceles triangle is 76°. What size can the other angles be?

6. Two angles of a triangle are 30° and 75°. Could two sides be equal?

7. If the sum of two angles of a triangle is less than the third angle, must the triangle be an obtuse-angled triangle?

8. In △XYZ, ∠XYZ = ∠XZY. Which two sides are equal?

9. In △ABC, AB is longer than AC but is shorter than BC. Which angle could measure 98°?

10. Where possible, draw sketches of:
(*a*) a triangle having three acute, interior angles,
(*b*) a triangle with two right-angles,
(*c*) a triangle with exactly one obtuse interior angle,
(*d*) a triangle with exactly two obtuse interior angles,
(*e*) a triangle with exactly one obtuse exterior* angle,
(*f*) a triangle with exactly two obtuse exterior angles.

Exercise 8

Each of the following questions refers to an isosceles triangle. In each case, one angle of the isosceles triangle is given. Write all the possible values of the other angles.

1. 40°	**6.** 10°	**11.** 140°	**16.** 32°	**21.** 48°
2. 70°	**7.** 100°	**12.** 20°	**17.** 74°	**22.** 66°
3. 120°	**8.** 96°	**13.** 80°	**18.** 98°	**23.** 57°
4. 90°	**9.** 38°	**14.** 50°	**19.** 12°	**24.** 141°
5. 60°	**10.** 46°	**15.** 116°	**20.** 84°	**25.** 79°

*See the glossary, p. 433.

Constructions

Exercise 9

Use a pencil, ruler, protractor, set square and a pair of compasses to carry out these constructions. A quick sketch before you start a construction could be helpful.

1. Construct $\triangle ABC$ where $BC = 80\,mm$, $B\widehat{C}A = 28°$ and $AC = 65\,mm$.
   Write the length of AB.

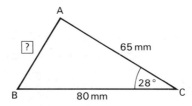

2. Construct isosceles triangle PQR where $QR = 42\,mm$, $PQ = PR$ and the equal angles each measure $73°$.
   Write the length of PQ.

3. Construct isosceles triangle XYZ where $XY = XZ = 64\,mm$, and where the equal angles each measure $76°$.
   Measure YZ.

4. Construct $\triangle UVW$ where $VW = 58\,mm$, $\angle UVW = 62°$ and $\angle VUW = 69°$.
   Measure UV.

5. Construct a right-angled triangle JKL where $J\widehat{K}L = 90°$, $KL = 78\,mm$ and $JL = 83\,mm$. Using a pair of compasses, bisect angle J and let the bisector meet KL at M.
   Measure $J\widehat{L}M$, JM and LM.

6. Construct $\triangle DEF$ where $EF = 70\,mm$, angle E is $39°$ and angle F is $65°$. Using a pair of compasses, bisect side DE and let the perpendicular bisector of DE meet EF at G.
   Measure EG.

7. Construct $\triangle ABC$ where AB = 105 mm, BC = 120 mm and CA = 60 mm. Using a pair of compasses, bisect side BC and also angle ABC. Let the bisector of angle ABC and the perpendicular bisector of side BC meet at P. Measure AP.

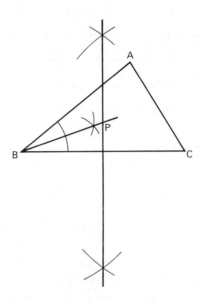

8. PQR is an isosceles triangle where PQ = PR. $\angle$PQR = 72° and QR = 46 mm.
Construct this triangle. Bisect angles Q and R.
If these bisectors meet at X write down the length of PX.

9. Construct $\triangle FGH$ where GH = 112 mm, FH = 74 mm and $G\hat{H}F$ = 41°. Bisect $F\hat{G}H$ and $G\hat{F}H$ using a pair of compasses. Label the point of intersection of these bisectors P. Measure GP.

10. Construct triangle JGM where GM = 54 mm, JM = 62 mm and angle JMG = 85°. Using a pair of compasses, bisect angle JMG and let this bisector meet JG at R. With set square and ruler draw a line RL parallel to side GM, where L lies on side JM. Measure LM.

11. Draw any triangle. Draw the bisectors of all three angles. Write what you notice.

12. Draw any triangle. Draw the perpendicular bisectors of all three sides. Write what you notice.

189

Exercise 10

Use Geo-strips (geometric strips), or make your own from flat, ice-lolly sticks or from card. (If you make your own, make several each of 3 cm, 4 cm, 5 cm, 6 cm, 7 cm, 8 cm, 9 cm, and 10 cm sizes.)

You will also need some paper fasteners.

1. Use three strips all the same size:
   (a) How many different triangles can you make using this one size of strip?
   (b) What sort of triangle can you make?

2. Make a pile of strips of two different sizes. Using any three strips from the pile, make a triangle.
   (a) How many different triangles can you make?
   (b) How many different equilateral triangles can you make?
   (c) How many different isosceles triangles can you make?
   (d) How many different scalene triangles can you make?
   (e) Is it always possible to make a triangle whatever three strips you use from the pile?

3. Make a pile of strips of three different sizes. Using any three strips from the pile, try to make a triangle.
   (a) Is it always possible to make a triangle whatever three sizes of strips you use? (Try a 3 cm, 5 cm, and 9 cm.)
   Now make a pile of strips of three different sizes, where any three will make a triangle.
   (b) How many different triangles can you make?
   (c) How many different equilateral triangles can you make?
   (d) How many different isosceles triangles can you make?
   (e) How many different scalene triangles can you make?

4. If you make a pile of strips of four different sizes, where any three will make a triangle, how many different triangles can you make?

190

11 Calculations with Fractions and Decimals

Addition of Vulgar Fractions

Exercise 1

Carry out the following additions.
Simplify your answers where possible.

A 1. $\dfrac{3}{5}+\dfrac{1}{5}$ 7. $\dfrac{1}{2}+\dfrac{3}{8}$ 13. $\dfrac{1}{2}+\dfrac{2}{5}$ 19. $\dfrac{3}{5}+\dfrac{5}{16}$

2. $\dfrac{5}{8}+\dfrac{2}{8}$ 8. $\dfrac{3}{10}+\dfrac{2}{5}$ 14. $\dfrac{3}{5}+\dfrac{1}{4}$ 20. $\dfrac{1}{2}+\dfrac{1}{4}+\dfrac{1}{8}$

3. $\dfrac{4}{20}+\dfrac{13}{20}$ 9. $\dfrac{1}{4}+\dfrac{5}{16}$ 15. $\dfrac{1}{3}+\dfrac{5}{8}$ 21. $\dfrac{3}{8}+\dfrac{5}{16}+\dfrac{1}{4}$

4. $\dfrac{2}{10}+\dfrac{3}{10}$ 10. $\dfrac{1}{4}+\dfrac{5}{8}$ 16. $\dfrac{1}{4}+\dfrac{13}{20}$ 22. $\dfrac{1}{3}+\dfrac{1}{6}+\dfrac{5}{12}$

5. $\dfrac{7}{16}+\dfrac{5}{16}$ 11. $\dfrac{3}{8}+\dfrac{7}{16}$ 17. $\dfrac{3}{10}+\dfrac{1}{3}$ 23. $\dfrac{2}{5}+\dfrac{1}{4}+\dfrac{3}{10}$

6. $\dfrac{7}{12}+\dfrac{1}{12}$ 12. $\dfrac{3}{5}+\dfrac{3}{20}$ 18. $\dfrac{5}{12}+\dfrac{2}{9}$ 24. $\dfrac{1}{2}+\dfrac{1}{6}+\dfrac{1}{5}$

B 1. $\dfrac{4}{5}+\dfrac{3}{5}$ 4. $\dfrac{5}{8}+\dfrac{7}{8}$ 7. $\dfrac{1}{2}+\dfrac{3}{4}$ 10. $\dfrac{4}{5}+\dfrac{9}{10}$

2. $\dfrac{7}{10}+\dfrac{3}{10}$ 5. $\dfrac{11}{16}+\dfrac{9}{16}$ 8. $\dfrac{5}{8}+\dfrac{1}{2}$ 11. $\dfrac{3}{4}+\dfrac{5}{12}$

3. $\dfrac{7}{10}+\dfrac{9}{10}$ 6. $\dfrac{17}{20}+\dfrac{9}{20}$ 9. $\dfrac{5}{6}+\dfrac{7}{12}$ 12. $\dfrac{2}{3}+\dfrac{7}{9}$

13. $\dfrac{2}{3} + \dfrac{3}{4}$ **16.** $\dfrac{7}{8} + \dfrac{5}{12}$ **19.** $\dfrac{13}{15} + \dfrac{17}{20}$ **22.** $\dfrac{1}{2} + \dfrac{2}{3} + \dfrac{1}{4}$

14. $\dfrac{1}{2} + \dfrac{2}{3}$ **17.** $\dfrac{13}{16} + \dfrac{11}{12}$ **20.** $\dfrac{2}{5} + \dfrac{7}{10} + \dfrac{13}{20}$ **23.** $\dfrac{2}{3} + \dfrac{5}{8} + \dfrac{4}{5}$

15. $\dfrac{3}{4} + \dfrac{7}{10}$ **18.** $\dfrac{2}{5} + \dfrac{5}{6}$ **21.** $\dfrac{5}{6} + \dfrac{3}{4} + \dfrac{11}{12}$ **24.** $\dfrac{3}{10} + \dfrac{3}{4} + \dfrac{3}{5}$

Exercise 2

Copy the following but fill in the missing numbers to make the calculations correct. Note that the fractions in each question and in each final answer are all in their simplest form.

1. $\dfrac{1}{\boxed{?}} + \dfrac{2}{3} = \dfrac{5}{6}$

2. $\dfrac{3}{5} + \dfrac{1}{\boxed{?}} = \dfrac{\boxed{?}}{10} = 1\dfrac{1}{10}$

3. $\dfrac{5}{8} + \dfrac{3}{\boxed{?}} = \dfrac{\boxed{?}}{8} = 1\dfrac{3}{8}$

4. $\dfrac{4}{5} + \dfrac{2}{\boxed{?}} = \dfrac{\boxed{?}}{15} = 1\dfrac{\boxed{?}}{15}$

5. (a) $\dfrac{5}{\boxed{?}} + \dfrac{3}{4} = \dfrac{\boxed{?}}{36} = 1\dfrac{11}{\boxed{?}}$

    (b) $\dfrac{5}{\boxed{?}} + \dfrac{3}{4} = \dfrac{\boxed{?}}{36} = \dfrac{\boxed{?}}{9}$

    (c) $\dfrac{5}{\boxed{?}} + \dfrac{3}{4} = \dfrac{\boxed{?}}{36} = 1\dfrac{1}{\boxed{?}}$

6. $\dfrac{7}{\boxed{?}} + \dfrac{1}{2} = \dfrac{12}{\boxed{?}} = 1\dfrac{2}{\boxed{?}} = 1\dfrac{1}{\boxed{?}}$

7. $\dfrac{5}{\boxed{?}} + \dfrac{3}{5} = \dfrac{43}{\boxed{?}} = 1\dfrac{13}{\boxed{?}}$

10. $\dfrac{3}{\boxed{?}} + \dfrac{2}{5} = \dfrac{31}{\boxed{?}}$

8. $\dfrac{2}{3} + \dfrac{7}{\boxed{?}} = \dfrac{37}{\boxed{?}} = 1\dfrac{13}{\boxed{?}}$

11. $\dfrac{7}{12} + \dfrac{3}{\boxed{?}} = \dfrac{37}{\boxed{?}}$

9. $\dfrac{1}{6} + \dfrac{4}{\boxed{?}} = \dfrac{29}{\boxed{?}}$

12. $\dfrac{3}{\boxed{?}} + \dfrac{1}{6} = \dfrac{11}{\boxed{?}}$

Exercise 3   Addition of Mixed Numbers

Carry out the following additions.
Simplify your answers where possible.

1. $1\frac{1}{8} + 2\frac{3}{4}$

2. $3\frac{2}{9} + 1\frac{1}{3}$

3. $2\frac{3}{5} + 1\frac{1}{10}$

4. $2\frac{1}{3} + 3\frac{1}{6}$

5. $4\frac{5}{12} + 2\frac{1}{4}$

6. $2\frac{7}{8} + 3\frac{1}{2}$

7. $3\frac{2}{3} + 1\frac{5}{6}$

8. $6\frac{11}{12} + 2\frac{1}{4}$

9. $3\frac{1}{5} + 2\frac{2}{3}$

10. $5\frac{1}{3} + 3\frac{1}{4}$

11. $1\frac{7}{10} + 2\frac{1}{3}$

12. $4\frac{7}{12} + 5\frac{3}{8}$

13. $2\frac{3}{10} + 4\frac{5}{6}$

14. $\frac{8}{15} + 3\frac{1}{10}$

15. $5\frac{1}{2} + 2\frac{11}{12}$

16. $2\frac{5}{9} + 9\frac{7}{12}$

17. $1\frac{5}{6} + 7\frac{1}{4}$

18. $3\frac{3}{4} + 4\frac{9}{10}$

19. $8\frac{7}{8} + \frac{5}{6}$

20. $1\frac{11}{16} + 2\frac{7}{10}$

21. $2\frac{5}{6} + 1\frac{1}{3} + 3\frac{7}{12}$

22. $2\frac{4}{5} + 3\frac{8}{15} + 2\frac{2}{3}$

23. $7\frac{1}{6} + 3\frac{1}{5} + 2\frac{3}{10}$

24. $5\frac{7}{8} + 2\frac{1}{4} + 3\frac{2}{3}$

Subtraction of Vulgar Fractions

Exercise 4

Carry out the following subtractions.
Simplify your answers where possible.

1. $\dfrac{9}{10} - \dfrac{6}{10}$

4. $\dfrac{7}{8} - \dfrac{3}{8}$

7. $\dfrac{4}{5} - \dfrac{7}{10}$

10. $\dfrac{1}{2} - \dfrac{1}{3}$

2. $\dfrac{4}{5} - \dfrac{1}{5}$

5. $\dfrac{7}{8} - \dfrac{1}{4}$

8. $\dfrac{3}{4} - \dfrac{5}{12}$

11. $\dfrac{3}{4} - \dfrac{2}{3}$

3. $\dfrac{5}{6} - \dfrac{1}{6}$

6. $\dfrac{2}{3} - \dfrac{1}{6}$

9. $\dfrac{9}{10} - \dfrac{2}{5}$

12. $\dfrac{7}{8} - \dfrac{2}{5}$

13. $\dfrac{3}{4} - \dfrac{1}{6}$ **15.** $\dfrac{11}{12} - \dfrac{1}{8}$ **17.** $\dfrac{13}{16} - \dfrac{7}{12}$ **19.** $\dfrac{15}{16} - \dfrac{1}{4} - \dfrac{3}{8}$

14. $\dfrac{9}{10} - \dfrac{3}{8}$ **16.** $\dfrac{5}{6} - \dfrac{3}{10}$ **18.** $\dfrac{9}{10} - \dfrac{1}{5} - \dfrac{1}{2}$ **20.** $\dfrac{7}{8} - \dfrac{1}{2} - \dfrac{1}{3}$

Exercise 5 Subtraction of Mixed Numbers

Carry out the following subtractions.
Simplify your answers where possible.

1. $1 - \dfrac{3}{8}$

2. $6 - \dfrac{7}{16}$

3. $4\dfrac{7}{10} - \dfrac{4}{10}$

4. $8\dfrac{4}{5} - \dfrac{2}{5}$

5. $4\dfrac{5}{8} - 2\dfrac{3}{8}$

6. $9\dfrac{11}{12} - 1\dfrac{5}{12}$

7. $5\dfrac{3}{4} - 2\dfrac{1}{2}$

8. $4\dfrac{1}{2} - 1\dfrac{1}{6}$

9. $2\dfrac{3}{4} - \dfrac{5}{8}$

10. $5\dfrac{3}{4} - 1\dfrac{5}{16}$

11. $8\dfrac{13}{16} - 6\dfrac{3}{8}$

12. $4\dfrac{11}{15} - 3\dfrac{2}{5}$

13. $3\dfrac{2}{3} - 1\dfrac{3}{5}$

14. $6\dfrac{7}{8} - 6\dfrac{1}{3}$

15. $6\dfrac{3}{4} - 4\dfrac{7}{10}$

16. $3\dfrac{5}{6} - 2\dfrac{2}{9}$

17. $5\dfrac{4}{5} - 1\dfrac{1}{2}$

18. $6\dfrac{3}{5} - 2\dfrac{1}{6}$

19. $9\dfrac{5}{6} - 2\dfrac{3}{8}$

20. $7\dfrac{3}{5} - 4\dfrac{5}{12}$

21. $4\dfrac{9}{10} - 2\dfrac{5}{12}$

22. $8\dfrac{3}{4} - 2\dfrac{1}{2} - 3\dfrac{1}{8}$

23. $10\dfrac{3}{4} - 6\dfrac{1}{3} - 1\dfrac{2}{5}$

24. $8\dfrac{9}{10} - 4\dfrac{2}{5} - 3\dfrac{1}{8}$

Exercise 6

A Copy the following and fill in the missing numbers to make each statement correct:

1. $2\dfrac{8}{5} = 3\dfrac{?}{5}$

2. $6\dfrac{1}{4} = 5\dfrac{?}{4}$

3. $9\dfrac{2}{3} = 8\dfrac{?}{3}$

4. $7\dfrac{17}{10} = 8\dfrac{?}{10}$

5. $3\dfrac{11}{6} = 4\dfrac{?}{6}$

6. $4\dfrac{15}{8} = \boxed{?}\dfrac{7}{8}$

7. $5\dfrac{1}{2} = \boxed{?}\dfrac{3}{2}$

8. $3\dfrac{17}{12} = 4\dfrac{?}{12}$

9. $5\dfrac{11}{20} = 4\dfrac{?}{20}$

10. $3\dfrac{15}{16} = 2\dfrac{?}{16}$

11. $5\dfrac{23}{16} = 6\dfrac{?}{16}$

12. $1\dfrac{26}{15} = 2\dfrac{?}{15}$

13. $3\dfrac{11}{4} = 5\dfrac{?}{4}$

14. $4\dfrac{23}{10} = \boxed{?}\dfrac{3}{10}$

15. $7\dfrac{5}{8} = 4\dfrac{?}{8}$

B Carry out the following subtractions.
Simplify your answers where possible.

1. (a) $\frac{7}{5} - \frac{4}{5}$

   (b) $1\frac{2}{5} - \frac{4}{5}$

2. (a) $2\frac{5}{4} - \frac{3}{4}$

   (b) $3\frac{1}{4} - \frac{3}{4}$

3. (a) $5\frac{13}{10} - \frac{7}{10}$

   (b) $6\frac{3}{10} - \frac{7}{10}$

4. (a) $3\frac{17}{16} - \frac{11}{16}$

   (b) $4\frac{1}{16} - \frac{11}{16}$

5. $4\frac{1}{5} - 2\frac{3}{5}$

6. $6\frac{1}{3} - 1\frac{2}{3}$

7. $3\frac{3}{8} - 2\frac{7}{8}$

8. $8\frac{1}{12} - 6\frac{11}{12}$

9. $5\frac{1}{2} - 2\frac{3}{4}$

10. $7\frac{1}{8} - 3\frac{1}{4}$

11. $9\frac{3}{10} - 4\frac{3}{5}$

12. $8\frac{2}{3} - 1\frac{5}{6}$

13. $4\frac{1}{4} - 2\frac{11}{12}$

14. $3\frac{1}{6} - \frac{7}{12}$

15. $6\frac{7}{16} - 1\frac{5}{8}$

16. $9\frac{21}{32} - 5\frac{13}{16}$

17. $3\frac{3}{4} - 1\frac{5}{6}$

18. $5\frac{1}{2} - 2\frac{2}{3}$

19. $7\frac{2}{5} - 3\frac{1}{2}$

20. $9\frac{7}{10} - 5\frac{3}{4}$

21. $7\frac{1}{8} - 2\frac{5}{6}$

22. $6\frac{1}{2} - 4\frac{3}{5}$

23. $6\frac{5}{8} - 5\frac{11}{12}$

24. $4\frac{3}{10} - 3\frac{5}{8}$

25. $4\frac{5}{9} - 2\frac{5}{6}$

26. $5\frac{9}{20} - 1\frac{2}{3}$

27. $4\frac{3}{10} - 1\frac{7}{10} - 1\frac{1}{10}$

28. $9\frac{5}{8} - 2\frac{3}{8} - 3\frac{7}{8}$

29. $6\frac{1}{2} - 2\frac{3}{8} - 1\frac{3}{4}$

30. $7\frac{1}{4} - 2\frac{5}{6} - 3\frac{1}{3}$

31. $12\frac{1}{4} - 8\frac{3}{5} - 1\frac{9}{10}$

32. $9\frac{5}{8} - 2\frac{1}{3} - 3\frac{5}{6}$

Addition and Subtraction of Vulgar Fractions

Exercise 7

Answer the following. Simplify answers where possible.

1. $6\frac{1}{2} + 2\frac{3}{4} - 3\frac{5}{8}$

2. $5\frac{1}{6} - 1\frac{1}{2} + 2\frac{2}{3}$

3. $9\frac{2}{5} - 4\frac{9}{10} + 2\frac{1}{2}$

4. $4\frac{1}{4} + 3\frac{5}{6} - 2\frac{1}{3}$

5. $6\frac{7}{8} - 3\frac{2}{3} + 5\frac{1}{4}$

6. $7\frac{2}{3} - 4\frac{4}{5} + 1\frac{1}{6}$

7. $3\frac{3}{10} + 4\frac{7}{12} - 5\frac{3}{4}$

8. $5\frac{1}{2} - 2\frac{4}{5} + 3\frac{1}{2}$

9. $15\frac{3}{5} - 9\frac{17}{20} + 5\frac{1}{8}$

10. $8\frac{5}{12} + \frac{1}{5} - 4\frac{7}{8}$

Problems on Addition and Subtraction of Vulgar Fractions

Exercise 8

1. If $\frac{5}{8}$ of my garden is lawn and the rest contains shrubs, what fraction is used for shrubs?

2. A piece of wood is $6\frac{1}{4}$ ft long. What length remains after $2\frac{1}{2}$ ft is cut off?

3. What is the total area of two fields if one measures $1\frac{3}{4}$ acres and the other $1\frac{4}{5}$ acres?

4. A baker used $2\frac{3}{5}$ kg of currants and had $1\frac{7}{10}$ kg left. How many kilograms did she start with?

5. Alec started with $3\frac{1}{2}$ lb of sultanas and used 1 lb 13 oz ($1\frac{13}{16}$ lb). How many pounds did he have left?

6. Finn needed a piece of rope $7\frac{3}{4}$ m long. He had a piece that was 11.3 m ($11\frac{3}{10}$ m) long. How much did he need to cut off?

7. Ravinder Kaur used $2\frac{3}{4}$ m then a further $1\frac{1}{3}$ m of material. What was the total length used?

8. A swimming pool is 6'4'' ($6\frac{1}{3}$ ft) deep at one end and 3'6'' ($3\frac{1}{2}$ ft) deep at the other. How much deeper is it at one end than the other?

9. If $\frac{3}{4}$ of my garden is lawn, while $\frac{1}{10}$ is used for roses:
   (a) What fraction is used for lawn and roses?
   (b) What fraction is left?

10. I used $\frac{2}{5}$ of a pint of milk out of a jug containing $1\frac{3}{8}$ pt. How much milk was left in the jug?

Exercise 9

1. Is it possible to cut off two pieces of wood, one $19\frac{3}{4}$ in long and the other $12\frac{5}{16}$ in long from a piece that is $33\frac{1}{4}$ in in length?

2. A farmer sold three small fields. Their areas measured $\frac{3}{4}$ of an acre, $\frac{2}{3}$ of an acre and $1\frac{2}{5}$ acres. Find the total area.

3. Nigel needs $9\frac{1}{2}$ m of wire netting to make a chicken run. He already has two lengths, one measuring $3\frac{3}{4}$ m and the other $1\frac{4}{5}$ m. What further length does he need to buy, assuming the lengths can be joined without waste?

4. I need three lengths of string, one $3\frac{7}{8}$ ft long, another $2\frac{2}{3}$ ft long and the third, $4\frac{3}{4}$ ft long. What is the total length needed?

5. The diagram shows the plan of a garden:

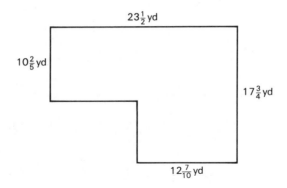

$23\frac{1}{2}$ yd

$10\frac{2}{5}$ yd

$17\frac{3}{4}$ yd

$12\frac{7}{10}$ yd

What length of fencing would be needed to surround the whole garden?

Exercise 10   Comparing Vulgar Fractions

A Consider the fractions $\frac{4}{5}$ and $\frac{2}{3}$.

Adding both numerators and adding both denominators gives

$$\frac{4+2}{5+3} = \frac{6}{8} = \frac{3}{4}$$

and $\frac{3}{4}$ lies between $\frac{4}{5}$ and $\frac{2}{3}$.

By adding numerators and adding denominators of any two fractions, do you *always* obtain a fraction that lies between (but not necessarily half-way between) the two original fractions?

B In part A, $\frac{3}{4}$ was stated to lie between $\frac{4}{5}$ and $\frac{2}{3}$. It was in fact closer in value to $\frac{4}{5}$ rather than $\frac{2}{3}$.

Investigate other pairs of fractions in the same way. For each pair of fractions, create a new fraction by adding numerators and by adding denominators. Try to discover how to tell which of the two original fractions is closer in value to the newly created fraction. A hint, if needed, is at the bottom of this page.

Hint: Examine the denominators of the two original fractions.

Multiplication of Vulgar Fractions

Exercise 11

Work out the following and simplify your answers:

1. $3 \times \dfrac{2}{5}$ **7.** $\dfrac{5}{6} \times 7$ **13.** $9 \times \dfrac{5}{6}$ **19.** $8 \times \dfrac{9}{10}$

2. $4 \times \dfrac{1}{3}$ **8.** $\dfrac{7}{10} \times 4$ **14.** $10 \times \dfrac{2}{5}$ **20.** $8 \times \dfrac{11}{12}$

3. $5 \times \dfrac{3}{4}$ **9.** $\dfrac{5}{12} \times 5$ **15.** $5 \times \dfrac{7}{10}$ **21.** $\dfrac{9}{20} \times 15$

4. $9 \times \dfrac{3}{10}$ **10.** $8 \times \dfrac{1}{4}$ **16.** $\dfrac{5}{8} \times 4$ **22.** $\dfrac{13}{16} \times 12$

5. $15 \times \dfrac{7}{8}$ **11.** $9 \times \dfrac{2}{3}$ **17.** $\dfrac{3}{8} \times 16$ **23.** $10 \times \dfrac{7}{16}$

6. $24 \times \dfrac{4}{5}$ **12.** $6 \times \dfrac{3}{4}$ **18.** $\dfrac{1}{8} \times 28$ **24.** $20 \times \dfrac{21}{32}$

Exercise 12

1. Add $\frac{5}{8}$ of 148 to $\frac{3}{8}$ of 148.

2. Kate gave half of her sweets to Len and one-sixth to Mary. She had 18 sweets left. How many did she start with?

3. Robert ate $\frac{1}{2}$ of his cake. He then gave away $\frac{3}{4}$ of what he had left. What fraction remained?

4. Tim travelled 192 km. If $\frac{5}{8}$ of his journey was by bus, $\frac{3}{4}$ of the remainder by train, and if the final part was by car:
   (*a*) What fraction of his journey was by car?
   (*b*) Find the distance travelled on the train.

5. Ruth spent $\frac{1}{2}$ of her money in one shop and $\frac{1}{4}$ in another. She had £3 left. How much did she start with?

6. Sue spent $\frac{1}{2}$ of her money in one shop and $\frac{1}{4}$ of the remainder in another. She had £3 left. How much did she start with?

7. Alan gave $\frac{1}{3}$ of his marbles to his friend, and $\frac{3}{5}$ of the remainder to his sister. If he started with 45 marbles, how many has he left?

8. Vicky gave $\frac{5}{8}$ of her marbles to Robert and $\frac{3}{4}$ of the remainder to her sister. If she had 9 marbles left, how many did she have to begin with?

9. Three people share a cake. Jack takes $\frac{3}{5}$ of the cake. Ken eats $\frac{3}{4}$ of what was left. Lisa eats the rest. What fraction of the cake does Lisa eat?

10. In a class, $\frac{3}{5}$ of the pupils were girls and there were 12 boys. Another class, having a total of 29 pupils in it, had $\frac{5}{6}$ of the number of girls that were in the first class. How many boys were in the second class?

Exercise 13

Work these out. Where possible, give the answers in their simplest form:

1. $\dfrac{1}{3} \times \dfrac{1}{5}$ **7.** $\dfrac{1}{3} \times \dfrac{7}{8}$ **13.** $\dfrac{3}{5} \times \dfrac{5}{6}$ **19.** $\dfrac{8}{25} \times \dfrac{15}{16}$

2. $\dfrac{1}{4} \times \dfrac{1}{6}$ **8.** $\dfrac{1}{4} \times \dfrac{5}{12}$ **14.** $\dfrac{3}{10} \times \dfrac{5}{9}$ **20.** $\dfrac{5}{16} \times \dfrac{12}{25}$

3. $\dfrac{1}{2} \times \dfrac{1}{8}$ **9.** $\dfrac{3}{5} \times \dfrac{9}{10}$ **15.** $\dfrac{3}{4} \times \dfrac{2}{3}$ **21.** $\dfrac{25}{32} \times \dfrac{16}{25}$

4. $\dfrac{1}{2} \times \dfrac{3}{8}$ **10.** $\dfrac{11}{15} \times \dfrac{2}{3}$ **16.** $\dfrac{7}{12} \times \dfrac{4}{5}$ **22.** $\dfrac{8}{15} \times \dfrac{35}{48}$

5. $\dfrac{7}{10} \times \dfrac{1}{4}$ **11.** $\dfrac{1}{2} \times \dfrac{2}{3}$ **17.** $\dfrac{5}{12} \times \dfrac{9}{20}$ **23.** $\dfrac{63}{100} \times \dfrac{5}{9}$

6. $\dfrac{7}{10} \times \dfrac{3}{4}$ **12.** $\dfrac{3}{4} \times \dfrac{5}{9}$ **18.** $\dfrac{14}{15} \times \dfrac{6}{7}$ **24.** $\dfrac{39}{50} \times \dfrac{35}{52}$

Exercise 14

Work these out. Simplify answers where possible.

1. (a) $\frac{1}{2} \times \frac{8}{5}$

   (b) $\frac{1}{2} \times 1\frac{3}{5}$

2. (a) $\frac{15}{4} \times \frac{1}{3}$

   (b) $3\frac{3}{4} \times \frac{1}{3}$

3. $\frac{1}{8} \times 3\frac{1}{5}$

4. $\frac{5}{6} \times 2\frac{1}{5}$

5. $1\frac{2}{7} \times \frac{7}{8}$

6. $\frac{7}{10} \times 3\frac{1}{3}$

7. $\frac{3}{8} \times 2\frac{2}{5}$

8. $1\frac{1}{5} \times \frac{3}{4}$

9. $\frac{5}{6} \times 1\frac{7}{8}$

10. $\frac{7}{8} \times 2\frac{6}{7}$

11. $1\frac{2}{3} \times \frac{9}{10}$

12. $\frac{3}{5} \times 2\frac{11}{12}$

13. $4\frac{1}{2} \times 1\frac{5}{6}$

14. $1\frac{3}{5} \times 3\frac{3}{4}$

15. $2\frac{1}{10} \times 2\frac{1}{7}$

16. $5\frac{1}{3} \times \frac{5}{12}$

17. $4\frac{1}{6} \times 2\frac{1}{20}$

18. $1\frac{5}{7} \times 2\frac{3}{16}$

19. $\frac{3}{10} \times 3\frac{3}{4}$

20. $5\frac{5}{8} \times 2\frac{2}{9}$

21. $4\frac{2}{7} \times \frac{14}{15}$

22. $1\frac{11}{16} \times 13\frac{1}{3}$

23. $\frac{9}{20} \times 1\frac{13}{15}$

24. $2\frac{1}{12} \times 1\frac{7}{9}$

25. $4\frac{5}{18} \times 3\frac{3}{7}$

Exercise 15

A Work these out:

1. $\frac{1}{3} \times \frac{3}{1}$

2. $\frac{8}{1} \times \frac{1}{8}$

3. $\frac{4}{5} \times \frac{5}{4}$

4. $\frac{7}{8} \times \frac{8}{7}$

5. $\frac{9}{10} \times \frac{10}{9}$

6. $\frac{16}{11} \times \frac{11}{16}$

7. $\frac{3}{4} \times \frac{4}{3} \times \frac{5}{8}$

8. $\frac{8}{15} \times \frac{2}{7} \times \frac{7}{2}$

9. $\frac{3}{10} \times \frac{7}{9} \times \frac{10}{3}$

10. $\frac{9}{16} \times \frac{16}{9} \times \frac{17}{25}$

11. $5\frac{1}{3} \times \frac{3}{16} \times 2\frac{3}{4}$

12. $\frac{4}{15} \times 3\frac{3}{8} \times 3\frac{3}{4}$

B Find the missing fractions:

1. $\frac{1}{5} \times \boxed{?} = 1$

2. $\frac{6}{1} \times \boxed{?} = 1$

3. $\frac{8}{3} \times \boxed{?} = 1$

4. $\frac{5}{12} \times \boxed{?} = 1$

5. (a) $\frac{11}{3} \times \boxed{?} = 1$

   (b) $3\frac{2}{3} \times \boxed{?} = 1$

6. (a) $\boxed{?} \times \frac{15}{4} = 1$

   (b) $\boxed{?} \times 3\frac{3}{4} = 1$

7. $2\frac{2}{5} \times \boxed{?} = 1$

8. $\boxed{?} \times 6\frac{2}{3} = 1$

9. $1\frac{7}{8} \times \boxed{?} = 1$

10. $10\frac{5}{12} \times \boxed{?} = 1$

Division of Vulgar Fractions

Exercise 16

Each one of the parts A to C shows one approach to dividing fractions. Only *one* of the parts needs to be answered.

A Answer these:

1. (*a*) How many fours are there in 20?

(*b*) $20 \div 4 = \boxed{?}$

(*c*) $\dfrac{20}{1} \div \dfrac{4}{1} = \boxed{?}$

(*d*) $\dfrac{20}{1} \times \dfrac{1}{4} = \boxed{?}$

2. (*a*) How many halves are there in 3?

(*b*) $3 \div \dfrac{1}{2} = \boxed{?}$

(*c*) $\dfrac{3}{1} \div \dfrac{1}{2} = \boxed{?}$

(*d*) $\dfrac{3}{1} \times \dfrac{2}{1} = \boxed{?}$

3. (*a*) How many thirds are there in 4?

(*b*) How many $\frac{2}{3}$ are there in 4?

(*c*) $\dfrac{4}{1} \div \dfrac{2}{3} = \boxed{?}$

(*d*) $\dfrac{4}{1} \times \dfrac{3}{2} = \boxed{?}$

4. (*a*) How many $\frac{3}{4}$ are there in $2\frac{1}{4}$?
(i.e. How many $\frac{3}{4}$ are there in $\frac{9}{4}$?)

(*b*) $\dfrac{9}{4} \div \dfrac{3}{4} = \boxed{?}$

(*c*) $\dfrac{9}{4} \times \dfrac{4}{3} = \boxed{?}$

5. (*a*) How many $\frac{3}{5}$ are there in $4\frac{1}{5}$?

(*b*) $\dfrac{21}{5} \times \dfrac{5}{3} = \boxed{?}$

B Copy and complete:

1. $20 \div 4 = \dfrac{20}{4} = \boxed{?}$

2. $3 \div \frac{1}{2} = \dfrac{3}{\frac{1}{2}} = \dfrac{3 \times \boxed{?}}{\frac{1}{2} \times 2} = \dfrac{6}{1} = \boxed{?}$

3. $4 \div \frac{2}{3} = \dfrac{4}{\frac{2}{3}} = \dfrac{4 \times \boxed{?}}{\frac{2}{3} \times 3} = \dfrac{\boxed{?}}{2} = \boxed{?}$

4. $2\frac{1}{4} \div \frac{3}{4} = \dfrac{2\frac{1}{4}}{\frac{3}{4}} = \dfrac{\frac{9}{4}}{\frac{3}{4}} = \dfrac{\frac{9}{4} \times \boxed{?}}{\frac{3}{4} \times 4} = \dfrac{\boxed{?}}{3} = \boxed{?}$

5. $4\frac{1}{5} \div \frac{3}{5} = \dfrac{4\frac{1}{5}}{\boxed{?}} = \dfrac{\boxed{?}}{\frac{3}{5}} = \dfrac{\frac{21}{5} \times \boxed{?}}{\frac{3}{5} \times 5} = \dfrac{\boxed{?}}{3} = \boxed{?}$

6. $\dfrac{3}{5} \div \dfrac{2}{3} = \dfrac{\frac{3}{5}}{\frac{2}{3}} = \dfrac{\frac{3}{5} \times \boxed{?}}{\frac{2}{3} \times 15} = \dfrac{9}{\boxed{?}}$

15 is the LCM of 5 and 3.

C Copy and complete:

1. (a) $20 \div 4 = \dfrac{20}{4} = \boxed{?}$

  (b) $20 \div 4 = \dfrac{20}{\frac{4}{1}} = \dfrac{20 \times \frac{1}{4}}{\frac{4}{1} \times \frac{1}{4}} = \dfrac{20 \times \frac{1}{4}}{1} = 20 \times \frac{1}{4} = \boxed{?}$

2. $3 \div \frac{1}{2} = \dfrac{3}{\frac{1}{2}} = \dfrac{3 \times \boxed{?}}{\frac{1}{2} \times 2} = \dfrac{6}{1} = \boxed{?}$

3. $4 \div \frac{2}{3} = \dfrac{4}{\frac{2}{3}} = \dfrac{4 \times \boxed{?}}{\frac{2}{3} \times \frac{3}{2}} = \dfrac{4 \times \frac{3}{2}}{1} = 4 \times \frac{3}{2} = \boxed{?}$

4. $2\frac{1}{4} \div \frac{3}{4} = \dfrac{2\frac{1}{4}}{\frac{3}{4}} = \dfrac{\frac{9}{4}}{\frac{3}{4}} = \dfrac{\frac{9}{4} \times \boxed{?}}{\frac{3}{4} \times \frac{4}{3}} = \frac{9}{4} \times \frac{4}{3} = \boxed{?}$

5. $4\frac{1}{5} \div \frac{3}{5} = \dfrac{4\frac{1}{5}}{\frac{3}{5}} = \dfrac{\frac{21}{5}}{\frac{3}{5}} = \dfrac{\frac{21}{5} \times \boxed{?}}{\frac{3}{5} \times \frac{5}{3}} = \dfrac{\frac{21}{5} \times \frac{5}{3}}{1} = \frac{21}{5} \times \frac{5}{3} = \boxed{?}$

6. $\frac{4}{5} \div \frac{2}{3} = \dfrac{\frac{4}{5}}{\frac{2}{3}} = \dfrac{\frac{4}{5} \times \boxed{?}}{\frac{2}{3} \times \frac{3}{2}} = \dfrac{\frac{4}{5} \times \frac{3}{2}}{1} = \frac{4}{5} \times \frac{3}{2} = \boxed{?}$

Compare these two stages

(that is, for each question, compare the question with the stage immediately before the answer).

Exercise 17

Work these out. Simplify your answers where possible.

1. $3 \div \frac{1}{4}$

2. $3 \div \frac{3}{4}$

3. $\frac{6}{7} \div 3$

4. $\frac{2}{5} \div 4$

5. $\frac{7}{8} \div \frac{1}{8}$

6. $\frac{7}{8} \div \frac{3}{4}$

7. $\frac{5}{12} \div \frac{5}{9}$

8. $\frac{5}{6} \div \frac{1}{2}$

9. $\frac{8}{9} \div \frac{2}{3}$

10. $\frac{3}{10} \div \frac{6}{25}$

11. $12\frac{1}{2} \div 5$

12. $4\frac{3}{5} \div 2$

13. $5\frac{5}{12} \div 5$

14. $2\frac{4}{5} \div \frac{2}{5}$

15. $2\frac{11}{12} \div \frac{5}{6}$

16. $5\frac{1}{3} \div 1\frac{1}{3}$

17. $1\frac{3}{4} \div 1\frac{1}{4}$

18. $4\frac{2}{7} \div 1\frac{3}{7}$

19. $3\frac{3}{4} \div 2\frac{1}{2}$

20. $2\frac{7}{10} \div 3\frac{3}{5}$

21. $2\frac{2}{3} \div 2\frac{2}{15}$

22. $4\frac{1}{6} \div 4\frac{4}{9}$

23. $4\frac{7}{12} \div 1\frac{3}{8}$

24. $9\frac{1}{3} \div 5\frac{5}{6}$

25. $1\frac{23}{25} \div 4\frac{4}{5}$

26. $1\frac{19}{20} \div 1\frac{5}{8}$

27. $5\frac{5}{8} \div 6\frac{1}{4}$

28. $1\frac{13}{15} \div 4\frac{9}{10}$

Exercise 18   Problems on Multiplication and Division of Vulgar Fractions

1. Jenny walks $1\frac{7}{8}$ km, each way, to and from school each day. How far does she walk in five days?

2. Mr Banerjee works for $7\frac{3}{4}$ h each day.
Find the total hours worked in 5 days.

3. Mrs Marsh works $19\frac{1}{6}$ h in 5 days. If she works the same number of hours each day, find the daily number of hours worked.

4. A litre of a liquid has a mass of $1\frac{1}{8}$ kg. Find the mass of:
(a) $\frac{2}{3}$ ℓ   (b) $5\frac{1}{3}$ ℓ   (c) $2\frac{2}{5}$ ℓ

5. If $3\frac{1}{3}$ ℓ of a liquid has a mass of $4\frac{2}{3}$ kg, find the mass of 1 ℓ of the liquid.

6. A pile of seven pieces of wood of the same thickness is $8\frac{5}{16}$ in high. How thick is each piece?

7. There was $\frac{2}{3}$ of a cake left and then Julie ate $\frac{3}{8}$ of it. What fraction of the cake did Julie eat?

8. A piece of string is $9\frac{9}{10}$ ft long. It is cut into equal-sized pieces, each measuring $1\frac{1}{5}$ ft.
(*a*) How many equal-sized pieces is it cut into?
(*b*) What length, in feet, is left over?

Decimal Fractions

Exercise 19   Rounding

A Write these decimals correct to the nearest whole number:

1. 7.4	**8.** 69.8	**15.** 84.52
2. 3.8	**9.** 99.6	**16.** 91.417
3. 4.9	**10.** 70.1	**17.** 3.862
4. 12.2	**11.** 8.29	**18.** 75.501
5. 25.6	**12.** 71.68	**19.** 48.499
6. 46.5	**13.** 33.37	**20.** 899.712
7. 38.7	**14.** 2.71	

B Write these decimals correct to one significant figure:

e.g. 1 $45.23 = \underline{50}$ (correct to 1 s.f.)

e.g. 2 $0.781 = \underline{0.8}$ (correct to 1 s.f.)

e.g. 3 $0.0062 = \underline{0.006}$ (correct to 1 s.f.)

e.g. 4 $0.965 = \underline{1}$ (correct to 1 s.f.)

1. 67.5	**8.** 0.079	**15.** 0.0572
2. 4.26	**9.** 0.958	**16.** 0.000 23
3. 8.91	**10.** 0.096	**17.** 0.000 18
4. 284	**11.** 2.935	**18.** 79 630
5. 39	**12.** 7.099	**19.** 0.0045
6. 0.471	**13.** 40.97	**20.** 950
7. 0.806	**14.** 0.0081	

Exercise 20   Estimating

Estimate the answers to the following. Work with one significant figure.

e.g. 1 $7.6 + 5.2 \approx 8 + 5 = \underline{\underline{13}}$

e.g. 2 $37.8 - 16.4 \approx 40 - 20 = \underline{\underline{20}}$

1. $48.6 + 21.3$	**9.** $85.7 + 64$	**17.** $43.18 + 76.72$
2. $29.8 + 52.5$	**10.** $31.8 + 75$	**18.** $54.12 - 12$
3. $68.1 - 19.6$	**11.** $9.53 - 2.74$	**19.** $813.2 - 484.8$
4. $74.03 + 56.6$	**12.** $56.2 - 27.3$	**20.** $0.747 + 0.876$
5. $80.7 - 31.4$	**13.** $0.64 + 0.87$	**21.** $0.045 - 0.0182$
6. $9.4 - 1.2$	**14.** $0.912 - 0.325$	**22.** $99.7 - 37.9$
7. $2.91 + 5.83$	**15.** $0.073 - 0.014$	**23.** $4.835 + 9.099$
8. $78.9 - 25.6$	**16.** $0.087 + 0.092$	**24.** $0.0029 + 0.0093$

Exercise 21   Adding and Subtracting Decimal Fractions

Carry out the following calculations:

1. 4.72 $+ 1.89$	**6.** 19.03 $- \;\; 0.65$	
2. 82.4 $- 19.6$	**7.** 2.109 $+ 0.982$	
3. 702.8 $- 256.1$	**8.** 5.4 $- 0.32$	
4. 96.87 $+ 29.3$	**9.** 49.007 $- \;\; 9.718$	
5. 26.8 $+ 46.03$	**10.** 63.02 $- 36.753$	

11. $68.17 + 22.87$

12. $3.91 - 1.69$

13. $40.22 - 29.34$

14. $3.516 + 0.724$

15. $9.63 + 1.48 + 2.78$

16. $26.4 - 9.7$

17. $43.1 - 28.25$

18. $0.462 + 0.819$

19. $0.931 - 0.675$

20. $0.14 + 2.73 + 0.9$

21. $4 - 0.392$

22. $87 - 42.77$

23. $4.09 + 19.3 + 0.971$

24. $10.003 - 4.068$

25. $3.104 - 0.8275$

Multiplying and Dividing Decimal Fractions

Exercise 22

Estimate the answers to the following. Work with one significant figure.

e.g. 1 $\quad 9 \times 3.82 \approx 9 \times 4 = \underline{36}$

e.g. 2 $\quad 63.27 \div 3 \approx 60 \div 3 = \underline{20}$

1. 7.8×5

2. $8.2 \div 4$

3. 6.19×7

4. 3×83.7

5. $76.2 \div 2$

6. $8.813 \div 9$

7. 8×27.49

8. 395.1×6

9. $56.72 \div 3$

10. $412.9 \div 8$

11. 0.714×4

12. 9×16.107

13. 79.84×7

14. $0.2971 \div 6$

15. $1.8406 \div 5$

Exercise 23

Answer the following:

1. 2.9×6

2. 7.4×9

3. $8.4 \div 3$

4. 4×6.7

5. $9.28 \div 4$

6. 8×29.2

7. $31.45 \div 5$

8. $7.308 \div 9$

9. 0.457×3

10. $0.6134 \div 2$

11. 5×0.9307

12. $2.964 \div 6$

13. 3.009×7

14. $6.736 \div 8$

15. $2.002 \div 7$

Exercise 24

A **1.** Key in the number 8.1437 on a calculator.

2. Multiply it by 10.

3. Multiply the answer by 10.

4. Multiply this answer by 10.

5. Write a sentence to explain what happens to a decimal each time it is multiplied by 10.

B **1.** Key in the number 457.2 on a calculator.

2. Divide it by 10.

3. Divide the answer by 10.

4. Divide this answer by 10.

5. Write a sentence to explain what happens to a decimal each time it is divided by 10.

C Write a sentence to explain what happens to a decimal when it is multiplied by:

1. 100   **2.** 1000

D Write a sentence to explain what happens to a decimal when it is divided by:

1. 100   **2.** 1000

E Answer the following:

1. 10×7.64	**9.** 3.192×100	**17.** $1859 \div 1000$
2. 82.95×10	**10.** $820.3 \div 100$	**18.** $2793.5 \div 1000$
3. $741.2 \div 10$	**11.** 1000×1.6172	**19.** 0.0071×100
4. $93.61 \div 10$	**12.** 2.381×1000	**20.** $0.824 \div 10$
5. 0.847×100	**13.** $572.8 \div 100$	**21.** $0.00963 \div 100$
6. 0.025×100	**14.** 48.16×1000	**22.** $45 \div 1000$
7. $443.2 \div 100$	**15.** 7.9×1000	**23.** 2.17×10000
8. $5186 \div 100$	**16.** $7.9 \div 1000$	**24.** $0.0606 \div 1000$

Exercise 25

A Answer these using a calculator:

1. (*a*) 4.392×4
(*b*) 4.392×40
(*c*) 4.392×400
(*d*) 4.392×4000

2. (*a*) 7.163×6
(*b*) 7.163×60
(*c*) 7.163×600
(*d*) 7.163×6000

3. (*a*) 0.027×5
(*b*) 0.027×50
(*c*) 0.027×500
(*d*) 0.027×5000

4. (*a*) $4165.5 \div 3$
(*b*) $4165.5 \div 30$
(*c*) $4165.5 \div 300$
(*d*) $4165.5 \div 3000$

5. (*a*) $2184.5 \div 5$
(*b*) $2184.5 \div 50$
(*c*) $2184.5 \div 500$
(*d*) $2184.5 \div 5000$

6. (*a*) $6719.2 \div 8$
(*b*) $6719.2 \div 80$
(*c*) $6719.2 \div 800$
(*d*) $6719.2 \div 8000$

B Answer these *without using a calculator:*

1. 3.186×200
2. 1.967×30
3. $18.102 \div 20$
4. 400×2.647
5. $493.45 \div 500$
6. 5.0731×6000

7. $5167.2 \div 3000$
8. 0.5627×800
9. $684 \div 9000$
10. $1253.6 \div 400$
11. 0.0197×7000
12. 7.9×900

13. $23.66 \div 700$
14. 96.8×5000
15. $4.716 \div 60$
16. $92.56 \div 800$
17. 0.0091×4000
18. $0.465 \div 300$

Exercise 26

A Answer these using a calculator:

1. (*a*) 4×6
(*b*) 0.4×0.6
(*c*) 0.04×0.6

2. (*a*) 7×5
(*b*) 0.7×5
(*c*) 0.7×0.5

3. (*a*) 9×2
(*b*) 0.9×0.02
(*c*) 0.09×0.02

4. (*a*) 34×3
(*b*) 3.4×3
(*c*) 3.4×0.3

5. (*a*) 56×8
(*b*) 5.6×0.8
(*c*) 0.56×0.8

6. (*a*) 703×4
(*b*) 7.03×0.4
(*c*) 0.703×0.004

Explain how to find the position of the decimal point when two decimals are multiplied.

B Answer these *without using a calculator:*

1. 0.3×0.6
2. 0.7×0.04
3. 0.08×0.02
4. 0.5×0.37
5. 0.61×0.09
6. 8.4×0.03
7. 0.6×5.2
8. 0.05×5.7

9. 0.29×0.4
10. 82.3×0.2
11. 9.75×0.9
12. 0.188×0.7
13. 0.8×0.024
14. 6.97×0.03
15. 0.049×0.8

Exercise 27

A Answer these using a calculator:

1. (a) $0.48 \div 0.6$
   (b) $4.8 \div 6$

2. (a) $0.725 \div 0.5$
   (b) $7.25 \div 5$

3. (a) $5.79 \div 0.3$
   (b) $57.9 \div 3$

4. (a) $0.0412 \div 0.4$
   (b) $0.412 \div 4$

5. (a) $0.696 \div 0.08$
   (b) $69.6 \div 8$

6. (a) $0.0315 \div 0.07$
   (b) $3.15 \div 7$

7. (a) $0.0938 \div 0.02$
   (b) $9.38 \div 2$

8. (a) $0.0468 \div 0.009$
   (b) $46.8 \div 9$

9. (a) $0.492 \div 0.004$
   (b) $492 \div 4$

10. (a) $0.0396 \div 0.003$
    (b) $39.6 \div 3$

11. (a) $0.005\,67 \div 0.009$
    (b) $5.67 \div 9$

12. (a) $8.393 \div 0.07$
    (b) $839.3 \div 7$

B Answer these *without using a calculator:*

1. $0.84 \div 0.3$
2. $0.428 \div 0.4$
3. $9.75 \div 0.5$
4. $0.0162 \div 0.6$
5. $0.758 \div 0.02$
6. $0.0236 \div 0.08$
7. $0.0612 \div 0.09$
8. $0.0455 \div 0.007$

9. $0.147 \div 0.003$
10. $0.0924 \div 0.004$
11. $0.009\,35 \div 0.005$
12. $4.977 \div 0.09$
13. $38.36 \div 0.7$
14. $0.8124 \div 0.06$
15. $0.004\,512 \div 0.08$

Exercise 28

Estimate the answers. Work with one significant figure.

e.g. 1 $329.8 \times 57.6 \approx 300 \times 60 = \underline{18\,000}$

e.g. 2 $0.871 \div 0.029 \approx 0.9 \div 0.03 = 90 \div 3 = \underline{30}$

1. 48.7×29.3	**7.** 647.8×6.8	**13.** $86.24 \div 0.57$
2. 76.5×218.4	**8.** $436.7 \div 19.2$	**14.** 19.7×0.053
3. $127.3 \div 3.8$	**9.** 0.39×7.9	**15.** $0.32 \div 0.39$
4. $89.81 \div 2.9$	**10.** $26.7 \div 0.46$	**16.** $0.693 \div 0.24$
5. 70.7×2.65	**11.** $0.079 \div 8.3$	**17.** 316×0.062
6. $583.7 \div 8.1$	**12.** 0.094×36.1	**18.** 0.57×0.085

Exercise 29

A Answer these using a calculator:

1. (*a*) 276×34	**3.** (*a*) 71×93	**5.** (*a*) 76×27
(*b*) 2.76×3.4	(*b*) 7.1×9.3	(*b*) 0.76×0.27
(*c*) 27.6×3.4	(*c*) 0.71×9.3	(*c*) 0.76×0.027
2. (*a*) 19×45	**4.** (*a*) 46×604	**6.** (*a*) 82×563
(*b*) 1.9×4.5	(*b*) 0.46×60.4	(*b*) 8.2×0.563
(*c*) 1.9×0.45	(*c*) 4.6×0.604	(*c*) 0.82×0.563

B Answer these. As a check, estimate each answer.

1. 6.6×3.4	**6.** 0.31×6.9	**11.** 0.74×0.32
2. 25.7×1.8	**7.** 5.14×0.17	**12.** 0.436×0.88
3. 42.1×2.4	**8.** 2.83×0.025	**13.** 0.016×0.58
4. 8.73×5.6	**9.** 0.98×41.2	**14.** 0.63×0.092
5. 7.02×9.1	**10.** 0.83×1.21	**15.** 0.035×0.057

Exercise 30

A Answer these using a calculator:

1. (*a*) $20.8 \div 1.3$	**3.** (*a*) $252.3 \div 2.9$
(*b*) $208 \div 13$	(*b*) $2523 \div 29$
2. (*a*) $16.92 \div 4.7$	**4.** (*a*) $23.45 \div 0.35$
(*b*) $169.2 \div 47$	(*b*) $2345 \div 35$

5. (*a*) $0.952 \div 0.68$
   (*b*) $95.2 \div 68$

6. (*a*) $0.8439 \div 0.87$
   (*b*) $84.39 \div 87$

7. (*a*) $94.8 \div 0.79$
   (*b*) $9480 \div 79$

8. (*a*) $532 \div 9.5$
   (*b*) $5320 \div 95$

9. (*a*) $0.3111 \div 0.051$
   (*b*) $311.1 \div 51$

10. (*a*) $0.0884 \div 0.026$
   (*b*) $88.4 \div 26$

11. (*a*) $3640 \div 0.056$
   (*b*) $3\,640\,000 \div 56$

12. (*a*) $0.2701 \div 7.3$
   (*b*) $2.701 \div 73$

Compare both answers to each question.
Write what you notice.

B Answer these. Check each answer by estimating.

1. $3.08 \div 1.4$
2. $34.58 \div 3.8$
3. $3.172 \div 6.1$
4. $1.512 \div 0.24$
5. $0.544 \div 0.85$
6. $4.8 \div 0.75$
7. $1344 \div 0.42$
8. $0.1274 \div 0.091$

9. $5292 \div 5.4$
10. $4.356 \div 6.6$
11. $0.129 \div 1.5$
12. $62.9 \div 3.7$
13. $0.0162 \div 0.045$
14. $0.8652 \div 0.84$
15. $1245 \div 8.3$

Exercise 31

In each of the following, the decimal point has not been given in the
answer. Find the correct answer.

1. $0.8 \times 0.6 = 48$
2. $0.9 \times 0.03 = 27$
3. $4.2 \div 0.3 = 14$
4. $6.1 \times 0.4 = 244$
5. $6.78 \div 0.2 = 339$
6. $4.6 \times 1.9 = 874$
7. $0.29 \times 8.4 = 2436$
8. $7.2 \div 9.6 = 75$
9. $5.58 \div 3.1 = 18$
10. $0.56 \times 41 = 2296$

11. $6.308 \div 0.76 = 83$
12. $9.9 \times 88 = 8712$
13. $0.78 \times 0.26 = 2028$
14. $0.9193 \div 0.29 = 317$
15. $57.15 \div 0.15 = 381$
16. $21.3 \times 32.8 = 69864$
17. $6.068 \div 0.37 = 164$
18. $146.88 \div 48 = 306$
19. $19.2 \times 8.1 = 15552$
20. $222.18 \div 16.1 = 138$

Decimal Fractions: Four Rules

Exercise 32

Without using calculating aids and without working these out, find which answers are *definitely wrong:*

1. $5.6 \times 2.9 = 162.4$
2. $4.6 \times 97 = 446.3$
3. $8.63 + 4.78 = 13.42$
4. $37.5 + 23.2 = 60.7$
5. $8.64 \div 2.4 = 36$
6. $41.2 \times 6.3 = 259.56$
7. $76.24 - 23.86 = 53.62$
8. $53.6 + 32.51 = 378.7$
9. $147.23 \div 5.4 = 27.3$
10. $197 \times 3.2 = 630.4$
11. $5.2 \times 7.8 = 40.58$
12. $6.08 + 27.4 = 33.12$
13. $546.2 - 37.1 = 509.1$
14. $13.63 \div 4.7 = 2.7$
15. $38 \times 74.3 = 282.34$
16. $209.44 \div 5.6 = 3.74$
17. $14.77 + 8.069 = 22.839$
18. $880.6 \div 1.4 = 62.9$
19. $12.46 \times 0.41 = 51.6$
20. $13.72 \div 0.49 = 28$

Exercise 33

Here is a test. Check the answers. If an answer is wrong, copy the question and find the correct answer.

1.
$$\begin{array}{r} 64.8 \\ + 13.6 \\ \hline 77.14 \\ \hline \end{array}$$

2.
$$\begin{array}{r} 58.38 \\ - 19.19 \\ \hline 39.19 \\ \hline \end{array}$$

3.
$$\begin{array}{r} 4.176 \\ \times \quad 6 \\ \hline 25.056 \\ \hline \end{array}$$

4.
$$\begin{array}{r} 9.273 \\ - 3.845 \\ \hline 5.328 \\ \hline \end{array}$$

5.
$$4\overline{)19.52} \quad 48.8$$

6.
$$\begin{array}{r} 28.76 \\ + 93.87 \\ \hline 122.63 \\ \hline \end{array}$$

7.
$$\begin{array}{r} 81.45 \\ - 26.59 \\ \hline 54.86 \\ \hline \end{array}$$

8.
$$9\overline{)46.71} \quad 5.19$$

9.
$$\begin{array}{r} 3.078 \\ \times \quad 8 \\ \hline 24.624 \\ \hline \end{array}$$

10.
$$7\overline{)89.11} \quad 1.273$$

11.
$$8\overline{)3.256} \quad 0.47$$

12.
$$\begin{array}{r} 52.9 \\ + \quad 3.76 \\ \hline 90.5 \\ \hline \end{array}$$

13.
$$\begin{array}{r} 7.286 \\ - 2.993 \\ \hline 5.713 \\ \hline \end{array}$$

14.
$$\begin{array}{r} 4.92 \\ 23.7 \\ 0.689 \\ + \quad 7.5 \\ \hline 36.809 \\ \hline \end{array}$$

15.
$$\begin{array}{r} 36.73 \\ \times \quad 5 \\ \hline 18.365 \\ \hline \end{array}$$

16.
$$\begin{array}{r} 94.8 \\ 3.76 \\ + 45.2 \\ \hline 177.6 \\ \hline \end{array}$$

17.	16.7	18.	30.6	19.	6.7	20.	2.9
	× 2.8		× 7.4		23)154.1		42)87.78
	1336		1224		138		84
	+ 3340		2142		161		378
	46.76		336.6		161		378
					0		0

Exercise 34 **M**

e.g. 480 pages of a certain make of paper are 50 mm thick:
(a) Find the thickness of 36 sheets.
(b) How many pages have a total thickness of 45 mm?

Look carefully at this method:

No. of pages	Thickness	Notes
480	50 mm	
240	25 mm	$480 \div 2 = 240$
48	5 mm	$480 \div 10 = 48$
24	2.5 mm	$48 \div 2 = 24$
12	1.25 mm	$24 \div 2 = 12$
36	3.75 mm	$24 + 12 = 36$

(a) So 36 sheets are <u>3.75 mm thick</u>

(b) 45 mm = 50 mm − 5 mm
     and   480 pages − 48 pages = 432 pages

     hence, <u>432 pages</u> have a total thickness of 45 mm.

1. Copy the table then add further rows to help you to answer the following questions:
   (a) Find the thickness of 18 sheets.
   (b) Find the thickness of 30 sheets.
   (c) Find the thickness of 126 sheets.
   (d) How many sheets have a total thickness of 15 mm?
   (e) How many sheets have a total thickness of 22.5 mm?

2. For £100 I can buy 360 kg of a certain type of seed. Make a table as on the previous page, then use it to answer these questions.

(a) Find the cost of 4.5 kg of seed.

(b) What is the cost of 13.5 kg?

(c) How much does 31.5 kg cost?

(d) How many kilograms can you buy for £1?

(e) How many kilograms can you buy for £30.25?

Exercise 35

A *calorie* is the unit that is used to tell us how much energy is produced by certain types of food.

We use energy every day even when we are sleeping.

An everage adult uses:

running	19.4 calories per minute
swimming	11.2 calories per minute
cycling	8.2 calories per minute
walking	5.2 calories per minute
sleeping	1.2 calories per minute

Work out the number of calories used by the following people:

1. Mr Race who runs for 9 min.

2. Mrs Trotter who runs for 35 min.

3. Mr Webb who enjoys a 45 min swim.

4. Mr Walker who has a $1\frac{1}{4}$ h walk every evening.

5. Mrs Tyrer whose cycle ride took 53 min.

6. Mrs Long who has a short run that lasts 7 min, then walks for 18 min and then swims for 20 min.

7. Mr Short whose long bike ride takes $2\frac{1}{2}$ h, after which he walks for 12 min and then sleeps for 1 h 20 min.

8. Mrs Allday who walks for 5 h, runs for 25 min, swims for 55 min, cycles for 3 h and then sleeps for 2 h.

Exercise 36

1. A rectangle measures 9.6 cm by 3.8 cm. Find its perimeter.

2. Calculate the perimeter of the regular pentagon shown here.

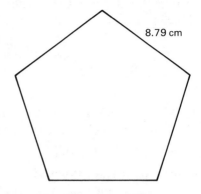

8.79 cm

3. From a piece of wire 32.4 m in length, pieces measuring 7.6 m, 3.9 m and 8.9 m are cut off. What length is left?

4. Which gives the bigger answer:
   (a) 18 × 6 or 18 ÷ 6?
   (b) 18 × 0.6 or 18 ÷ 0.6?
   (c) 1.8 × 0.6 or 1.8 ÷ 0.6?

5. The product of two numbers is 6.02. One of the two numbers is 0.7. Find the other number.

6. I bought two 4 m lengths of copper tubing. I cut 3.4 m off one length and 2.83 m off the other. The rest was waste. Calculate the total length of the waste.

7. A parallelogram has a perimeter of 46.8 cm. Two of its sides each measure 12.8 cm. Find its other two sides.

8. A car travels 13.9 km on one litre of petrol. How far will it travel on 16 ℓ?

9. How many pieces of string, each measuring 1.4 m, can be cut from a 32.2 m length?

10. On 1 ℓ of petrol, a car can travel 14.3 km. Which calculation, 14.3 × 0.85 or 14.3 ÷ 0.85 gives the distance the car will travel on 0.85 ℓ of petrol?

11. The given kite has a perimeter of 29.24 m. If one of its sides measures 4.78 m, find the lengths of the other sides.

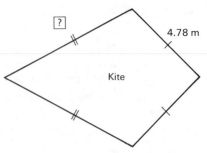

12. When travelling by air, my luggage allowance is 20 kg. If my two cases have masses of 12.47 kg and 6.38 kg, how many kilograms of my allowance is not used?

13. The perimeter of a triangle is 32.1 cm. Two of its sides measure 14.6 cm and 9.7 cm. Find the third side.

14. A chess board is 29.6 cm square. If the 29.6 cm includes a 1.2 cm border, how big is each of the 64 small squares?

15. A container full of sand has a mass of 0.448 kg. If the container has a volume of 250 cm³ and if it has a mass of 98 g when empty, find the mass, in grams, of 1 cm³ of sand.

Exercise 37   Remainders

A Give the answers to these in three different ways:
(a) with a remainder, (b) as a vulgar fraction, (c) as a decimal.

(a) $\dfrac{2 \text{ rem. } 3}{8 \overline{)19}}$

(b) $\dfrac{19}{8} = \underline{\underline{2\frac{3}{8}}}$

(c) $\dfrac{2.\,3\,7\,5}{8 \overline{)19.^{3}0^{6}0^{4}0}}$

1. $17 \div 2$	**4.** $79 \div 8$	**7.** $218 \div 25$	**10.** $213 \div 8$
2. $35 \div 4$	**5.** $63 \div 10$	**8.** $77 \div 16$	**11.** $309 \div 20$
3. $27 \div 5$	**6.** $31 \div 20$	**9.** $89 \div 32$	**12.** $281 \div 16$

B Give sensible answers to these problems (a decimal or vulgar fraction or a number with a remainder):

1. (a) Share 21 bars of chocolate equally amongst six people.
(b) Share 21 marbles equally amongst six people.

2. (*a*) 138 m of rope is cut into 8 m lengths.
How many pieces are obtained?
(*b*) 138 m of rope is cut into eight equal lengths.
How long is each piece?

3. How many pupils can be given five books each out of a pile of 98 books?

4. If 54 cakes are shared equally amongst 16 people, work out what each person receives.

5. How many people can share 157 sweets if they each receive 12 sweets?

Exercise 38   Rounding: Decimal Places

A The number 41.302 is written to three decimal places. How many decimal places are there in each of these numbers?

1. 5.73	**6.** 6.870	**11.** 0.550 00	**16.** 5.9008
2. 8.095	**7.** 29.030	**12.** 30.070	**17.** 0.6002
3. 216.4	**8.** 0.974	**13.** 981.6	**18.** 0.073 00
4. 30.705	**9.** 0.005	**14.** 12.409	**19.** 0.010 10
5. 4.50	**10.** 0.804 00	**15.** 306.0	**20.** 0.009 00

B *e.g. 1*   14.87 = <u>14.9</u> correct to 1 d.p. (decimal place)

e.g. 2   46.24 = <u>46.2</u> correct to 1 d.p.

e.g. 3   6.35 = <u>6.4</u> correct to 1 d.p.

(*Note*   6.35 lies half-way between 6.3 and 6.4. Anything that is *half-way* should be *rounded upwards*.)

e.g. 4   9.839 = <u>9.84</u> correct to 2 d.p.

e.g. 5   17.6818 = <u>17.68</u> correct to 2 d.p.

e.g. 6   2.8065 = <u>2.807</u> correct to 3 d.p.

e.g. 7   4.6998 = <u>4.700</u> correct to 3 d.p.

e.g. 8   4.6998 = <u>4.70</u> correct to 2 d.p.

e.g. 9   4.6998 = <u>4.7</u> correct to 1 d.p.

e.g. 10   13.2499 = <u>13.2</u> correct to 1 d.p.

1. Round the following decimals to one decimal place:
   (a) 41.28   (d) 79.64   (g)   4.801   (j)   13.419
   (b)   9.36   (e) 44.53   (h) 38.252   (k)   4.974
   (c) 12.72   (f) 22.19   (i) 53.062   (l) 349.95

2. Round these to two decimal places:
   (a)   1.472   (d) 50.631   (g) 56.365   (j) 14.749
   (b) 13.237   (e)   9.264   (h)   4.5138   (k) 16.399
   (c) 36.586   (f)   1.348   (i) 80.2762   (l)   9.997

3. Round these decimals to the number of decimal places stated:
   (a) 45.46 to 1 d.p.   (n)   0.516 to 2 d.p.
   (b)   7.63 to 1 d.p.   (o) 38.7185 to 3 d.p.
   (c)   9.328 to 2 d.p.   (p)   0.324 to 1 d.p.
   (d) 74.145 to 2 d.p.   (q)   6.309 to 2 d.p.
   (e)   2.8693 to 3 d.p.   (r) 87.3929 to 1 d.p.
   (f)   9.470 to 2 d.p.   (s) 27.3418 to 3 d.p.
   (g) 11.0356 to 3 d.p.   (t) 99.9999 to 3 d.p.
   (h) 54.214 to 2 d.p.   (u)   2.6749 to 1 d.p.
   (i) 63.5837 to 3 d.p.   (v)   0.007 to 2 d.p.
   (j) 63.5837 to 2 d.p.   (w)   5.0924 to 3 d.p.
   (k) 62.5837 to 1 d.p.   (x)   0.7532 to 1 d.p.
   (l) 29.742 to 2 d.p.   (y)   0.6071 to 3 d.p.
   (m) 16.047 to 1 d.p.   (z)   3.9954 to 2 d.p.

Exercise 39

Work out the following giving each answer correct to two decimal places:

1. $187 \div 16$ 9. $137 \div 4.8$ 17. $6.15 \div 1.3$
2. $429 \div 125$ 10. $23 \div 3$ 18. $13 \div 4.2$
3. $77 \div 32$ 11. $48 \div 9$ 19. $6.785 \div 3.2$
4. $28.6 \div 75$ 12. $2 \div 7$ 20. $0.46 \div 0.31$
5. $21.4 \div 3.4$ 13. $3.7 \div 1.2$ 21. $70.17 \div 6.4$
6. $750 \div 80$ 14. $53 \div 0.97$ 22. $581 \div 62.5$
7. $853 \div 65$ 15. $2.7 \div 1.4$ 23. $9.631 \div 8.9$
8. $218 \div 325$ 16. $5.6 \div 17$ 24. $84.33 \div 1.7$

12 Plane and Solid Shapes

The Elements of Euclid

Polygons

Exercise 1

For each of the given polygons:
(*a*) Write its name.
(*b*) Write whether it is a regular or irregular polygon.
(*c*) Write whether it is a convex or a re-entrant polygon.

1.

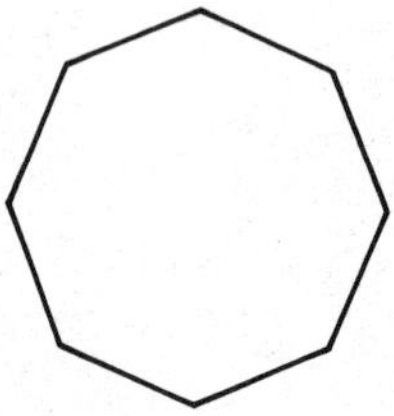

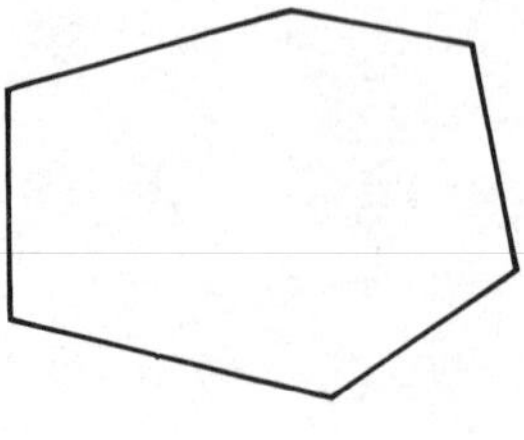

5.

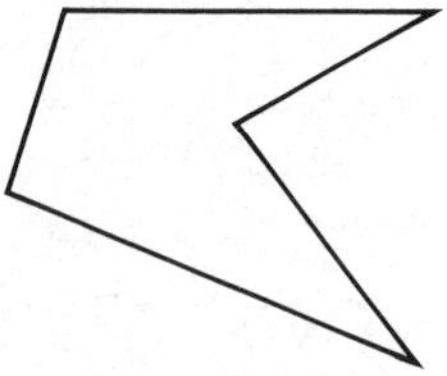

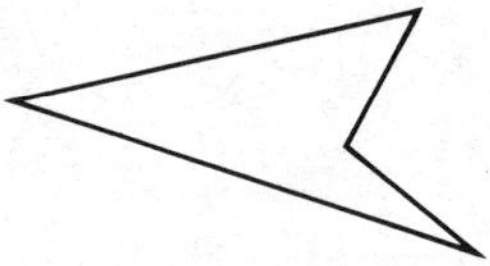

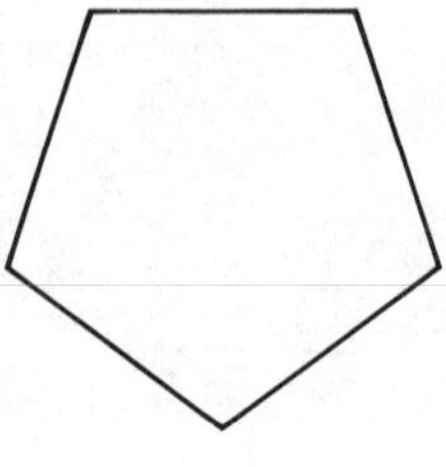

9.

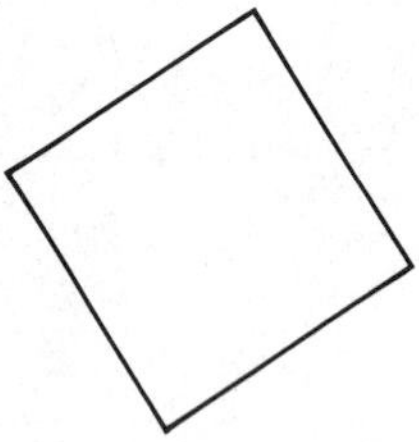

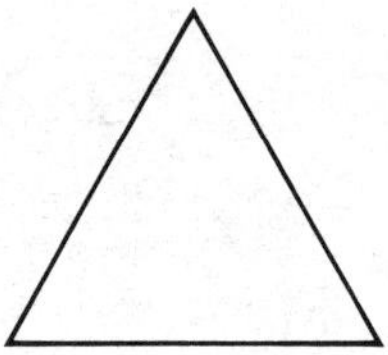

2.

6.

10.

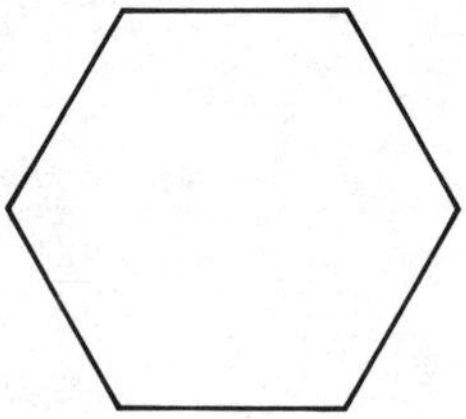

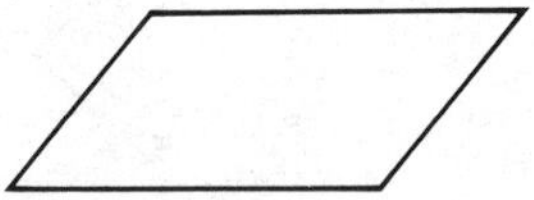

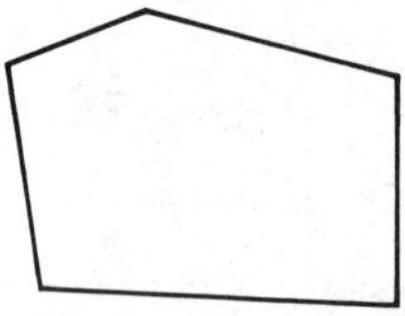

3.

7.

11.

4.

8.

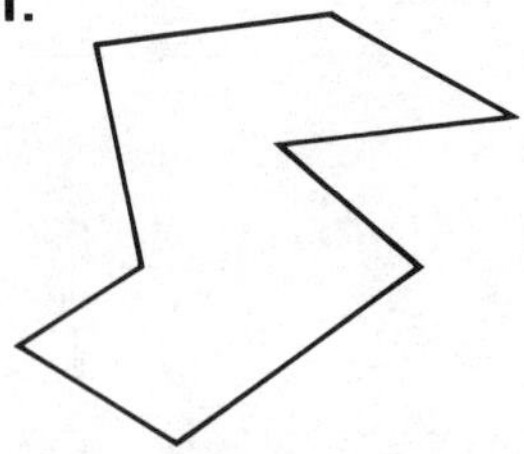

12.

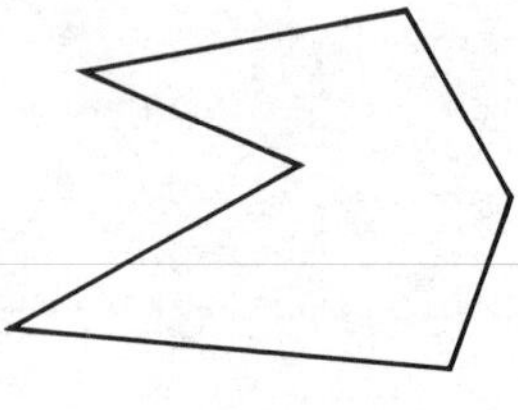

Quadrilaterals

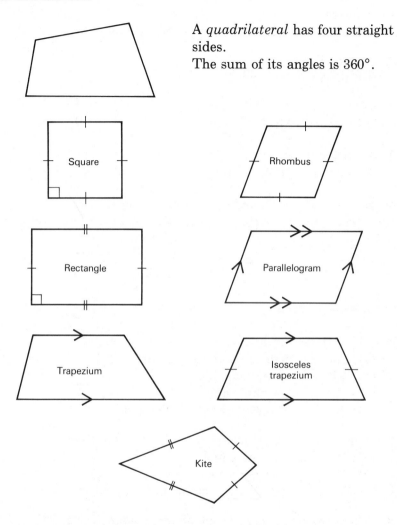

A *quadrilateral* has four straight sides.
The sum of its angles is 360°.

Exercise 2

Use Geo-strips (geometric strips), or make your own from flat ice-lolly sticks or from card. (If you make your own, make a few of several different sizes.)

You will also need paper fasteners and some pieces of fine elastic.

Make:

1. a square.
Is it always a square, or could it be a rhombus?

2. a rectangle.
Is it always a rectangle?

3. a kite.
Is it always a kite?

4. a trapezium.
Is it always a trapezium?

Make diagonals for each quadrilateral out of elastic.
Note what happens to the diagonals as each quadrilateral changes shape.

Exercise 3

A **1.** Which statement is always true for a rectangle?
   (*a*) The diagonals cross at right-angles.
   (*b*) All the sides are equal.
   (*c*) The diagonals are equal.
   (*d*) Only one of the diagonals is bisected.

2. Which statement is always true for a rhombus?
   (*a*) The diagonals are equal.
   (*b*) The angles are all right-angles.
   (*c*) The diagonals are perpendicular to each other.

3. Which statement is always true for a parallelogram?
   (*a*) The diagonals are equal.
   (*b*) Opposite angles are equal.
   (*c*) All the angles are equal.

B The properties of various quadrilaterals are given. List, for each question, all possible quadrilaterals that have the given properties.

   1. There are four equal sides.
   2. There are four right-angles.

3. Diagonals are of equal length.
4. Diagonals are perpendicular to each other.
5. There is exactly one pair of parallel sides.
6. There are two pairs of parallel sides.
7. Opposite angles are equal.
8. Opposite angles are equal but are not right-angles.
9. Opposite sides are equal.
10. Diagonals bisect each other.
11. Diagonals bisect each other at right-angles.
12. Exactly one pair of opposite angles are equal.
13. There are two pairs of equal sides (all four sides are not equal).
14. Only one diagonal is bisected by the other.

Exercise 4

1. Construct parallelogram ABCD where AB = 58 mm, AD = 35 mm and B$\hat{A}$D = 64°. Draw and measure diagonal BD.

2. Construct parallelogram WXYZ where WX = 68 mm, XY = 40 mm and <WZY = 112°.
   Draw and measure diagonal WY.

3. Construct a parallelogram where the diagonals measure 72 mm and 90 mm and an angle between the diagonals is 130°.
   Give the lengths of the sides.

4. Construct parallelogram JKLM where JK = 70 mm, diagonal JL = 86 mm and diagonal KM = 64 mm:
   Measure: (a) side KL, (b) <JKL.

5. Construct a rectangle with sides measuring 65 mm and 37 mm.
   Measure its diagonals.

6. Construct a rectangle with diagonals measuring 88 mm, if an angle between the diagonals is 64°.
   Measure its sides.

7. Construct a rectangle with diagonals measuring 82 mm, if one pair of opposite sides are 44 mm in length.
How long are the other sides?

8. Construct a square with sides measuring 49 mm. (You must not use a protractor.) Write the length of the diagonals.

9. Construct a square where the diagonals measure 56 mm. How long are its sides?

10. Construct a rhombus with sides measuring 45 mm, where one of its angles is 107°. Write the lengths of both diagonals.

11. Construct a kite with sides of 73 mm and 36 mm, where the angle between those sides is 98°:
(a) Write the lengths of both diagonals.
(b) Write the sizes of the other two angles.

12. Construct a kite in which the angle between the two short sides is 95°; the two short sides each measure 33 mm and the long diagonal is 77 mm in length:
(a) Find the length of each long side of the kite.
(b) Find the angle between a long and short side.

Exercise 5

Use a large sheet of paper.
It can be any shape.
Make sure that its edges are *not* straight.

1. By folding the paper (nothing else is allowed) make a rectangle.
2. Use another piece of paper to fold a square.
3. Use another piece to fold a rhombus.
4. Use another piece to fold a kite.

Rule lines on your correct folds.

Exercise 6

A 1. Draw a rectangle that is not a square.

2. A rhombus has at least one angle that is a right-angle. What is its special name?

3. A rectangle has diagonals that are perpendicular to each other. What sort of rectangle is it?

4. The diagonals of a quadrilateral bisect each other, but not at right-angles. What sort of quadrilateral could it be?

5. A quadrilateral has diagonals of different lengths. If the diagonals bisect each other at right-angles, what sort of quadrilateral could it be?

B Copy these sentences. Complete each one by filling in the missing name of the quadrilateral.

1. A parallelogram containing right-angles is a ? .

2. A parallelogram with equal diagonals is a ? .

3. A rhombus containing right-angles is a ? .

C Copy these sentences. Complete each one by filling in a special property in place of the question mark.

1. A rhombus is a parallelogram with ? .

2. A square is a rectangle with ? .

D 1. Are the properties of a parallelogram also true for a rectangle?

2. Are the properties of a rectangle also true for a parallelogram?

3. Are the properties of a rectangle also true for a square?

4. Are the properties of a square also true for a rectangle?

5. Are the properties of a kite also true for a square?

Exercise 7

A 1. (*a*) Draw a convex quadrilateral and label it ABCD.
  (*b*) Mark the mid-points of the sides of the quadrilateral. Label them P, Q, R, S where P is the mid-point of AB, Q the mid-point of BC, R the mid-point of CD and S the mid-point of DA.
  (*c*) Join P to Q to R to S to P.

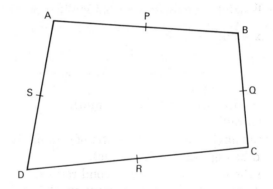

2. Repeat question 1 for other convex quadrilaterals, and write what you notice about quadrilateral PQRS.

B Repeat part A for a re-entrant* quadrilateral.

C Investigate the following special quadrilaterals in the same way as in part A:

1. a parallelogram, **4.** a rectangle,
2. a square, **5.** a rhombus,
3. a kite, **6.** an isosceles trapezium.

*See Exercise 1, p. 220.

More Polygons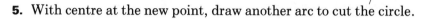

Exercise 8   To Construct a Regular Hexagon

1. Set your pair of compasses to the same radius as the side of the required hexagon.

2. Draw a circle.

3. Mark a point on its circumference.

4. With centre at that point, draw an arc to cut the circle. (Keep the same radius throughout.)

5. With centre at the new point, draw another arc to cut the circle.

6. Repeat until you reach your starting point (five arcs).

7. Join all six points in order.

Exercise 9

1. (a) Draw a circle (radius about 30 mm).
   Draw a radius.
   Draw an angle of 45° at the centre of your circle (your radius should be one arm of this angle).
   Make the other arm into a second radius.
   Now from this new radius, draw another angle of 45° at the centre of your circle.
   Continue doing this until you reach the first radius again.
   (b) How many 45° angles have you drawn?
   (c) Why did you obtain that number of angles?
   (d) Join, in order, the points at which these radii meet the circumference.
   (e) What sort of polygon have you drawn?

2. (a) Draw another circle with the same radius as before.
   (b) What angle do you need to draw at the centre to make a hexagon?
   (c) Draw a hexagon using this method.

3. (*a*) Draw another circle.

    (*b*) What is the name of the polygon you would obtain if you were to draw angles of 72° at the centre?

    (*c*) Draw this polygon.

4. What angle would you use to make a regular decagon?

5. State whether or not you would obtain a regular polygon if you were to draw these angles at the centre of a circle:

(*a*) 30°	(*d*) 40°	(*g*) 15°	(*j*) 18°
(*b*) 90°	(*e*) 50°	(*h*) 24°	(*k*) 22½°
(*c*) 70°	(*f*) 20°	(*i*) 65°	(*l*) 37½°

Exercise 10   M

1. Draw these polygons (they need not be regular):

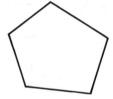

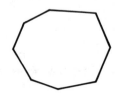

2. Draw in all the diagonals for each polygon (the diagonals of the heptagon have been drawn).

3. Copy and complete the table:

Name of polygon	Number of sides, n	Number of diagonals	$n - 3$	$n(n - 3)$
triangle	3	0	0	0
square	4	2	1	4
pentagon	?	?	?	?
hexagon	?	?	?	?
heptagon	7	?	4	28
octagon	?	?	?	?
nonagon	9	?	?	?
decagon	10	?	?	?

4. Compare the number of diagonals with the numbers in the $n(n - 3)$ column.

5. How many diagonals has a 20-sided polygon?

Exercise 11 ▬▬▬▬▬▬▬▬▬▬▬▬▬▬▬▬ **M**

Make, out of paper or card, four quadrilaterals the same as this:

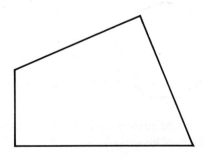

Put all four together to make:

1. a square,

2. a trapezium,

3. a parallelogram,

4. a pentagon,

5. an octagon,

6. two squares (one inside the other),

7. two rectangles (one inside the other).

Exercise 12   Polygons and Rigidity ━━━━━

Use Geo-strips (geometric strips). You will also need paper fasteners.

1. Make a triangle. Is a triangle a *rigid* shape?

2. Make a quadrilateral.
Its shape changes, so it cannot be rigid.
Use another piece of Geo-strip to make your quadrilateral rigid.

3. Make a pentagon. Is it rigid?
By using some more pieces of Geo-strip, make your pentagon rigid.

4. Make a hexagon. Is it rigid?
By using some more pieces of Geo-strip, make your hexagon rigid.

5. Make any other polygon. Make it rigid using more Geo-strips.

6. Write down what you noticed about how to make any polygon rigid.

Exercise 13 ━━━━━━━━━━━

Collect pictures and drawings from magazines to show how a triangle is used to make a structure rigid.

For example, pictures of bridges, pylons, cranes, and some furniture show the importance of the triangle.

Tessellations

Exercise 14

Carefully copy these polygons.

Make at least six of each out of thin card or paper.

The radius of the circumscribed circle, *r*, is given.

Each side should measure 12.5 mm.

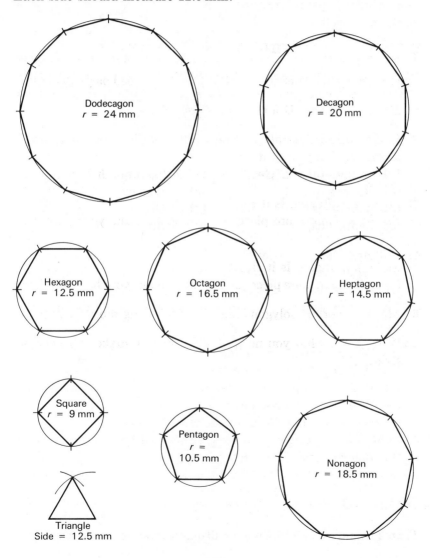

Dodecagon
r = 24 mm

Decagon
r = 20 mm

Hexagon
r = 12.5 mm

Octagon
r = 16.5 mm

Heptagon
r = 14.5 mm

Square
r = 9 mm

Pentagon
r =
10.5 mm

Nonagon
r = 18.5 mm

Triangle
Side = 12.5 mm

Exercise 15

Here is a *tiling* (or *tessellation*) used by bees. Bees form hexagons in making their honeycombs.

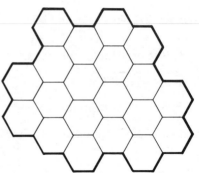

We say that shapes *tessellate* if we can fit a lot of them together without any overlap, and without gaps. So, regular hexagons tessellate.

To help you with these questions you need a set of polygons made of card or plastic (sometimes called 'discovery shapes' or 'geometric shapes'). You can make your own by tracing or copying those on p. 231.

1. Which other regular polygons will tessellate on their own? Test:
   (*a*) equilateral triangles,   (*e*) octagons,
   (*b*) squares,   (*f*) nonagons,
   (*c*) pentagons,   (*g*) decagons,
   (*d*) heptagons,   (*h*) dodecagons.

2. Will any triangle tessellate?
   Test your answer by making 20 to 30 identical triangles and trying to make them tessellate.
   Either stick your triangles in your book or make a drawing of the tiling pattern.

3. (*a*) Will a rectangle tessellate?
   (*b*) Will any parallelogram tessellate?
   (*c*) Will any trapezium tessellate?
   (*d*) Will any kite tessellate?
   (*e*) Will any quadrilateral tessellate?
   Show your answers in your book, either by drawing or by sticking the quadrilaterals in your book.

Exercise 16

Try to explain why all triangles or all quadrilaterals should tessellate.

Shapes such as these tessellate:

Such shapes can be found printed on fabrics and wallpapers:

1. Copy one of these shapes and use dotty paper (or squared paper) to show how it tessellates. (You may find it easier to cut out your shapes before trying to see if they tessellate.)

2. Make a tessellating pattern of your own.
   You will need to invent a shape (such as these) that will tessellate.

Exercise 18

Tessellations can be formed by offsetting shapes:

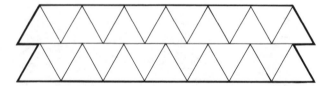

1. Try to make a pattern of your own where the shapes are offset.

2. Try to make such a pattern using squares.

3. Try to make such a pattern using hexagons.

Exercise 19

Bricks are laid to form a tessellating pattern.
Here are some different ways of laying bricks:

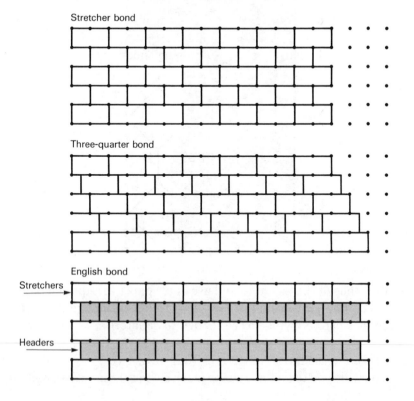

Stretcher bond

Three-quarter bond

English bond

Stretchers

Headers

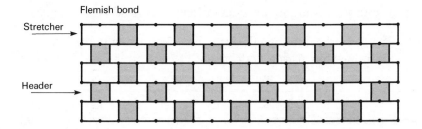

Flemish bond

Stretcher →

Header →

Lengthwise bricks are called *stretchers*. Bricks laid across the thickness of a wall are called *headers*.

1. Copy these into your graph book or on to dotty paper.

2. Which of the bonds uses the least number of bricks?

3. Which of the bonds uses the most headers?

Exercise 20

1. Try to make a tessellation using octagons.
   It does not work. There are gaps.
   However, the gaps can be filled using squares:

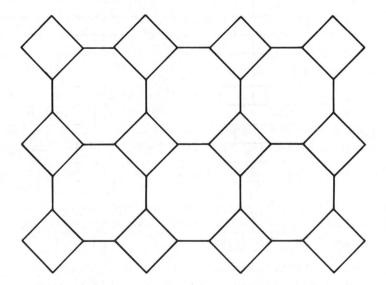

Copy this tessellation.

2. Try to find some more tessellations that need two polygons.

3. Try to find some tessellations that need three polygons. Find one that uses a dodecagon.

The Pyramids

The Egyptian pyramids were built as burial places for their pharaohs. They were built from about 2680 BC onwards.

The Great Pyramid at Giza, near Cairo, is one of the Seven Wonders of the World. It is about 140 m high and has a square base where each side is 230 m long (made to an accuracy of 3 cm). Its base area would hold about 7 or 8 football pitches.

It was built with simple hand tools. A Greek, Herodotus, wrote in the fifth century BC that it probably took 100 000 workers about 20 years to build it. Over two million blocks of stone were used. Most had masses between 2–3 t, although some were considerably larger.

The pyramids were built so that their four faces pointed north, south, east and west. The shafts (shown on the diagram opposite) were probably used for ventilation, but one interesting theory states that they were designed so that rays from the stars could shine into the burial chamber.

Because the pharaohs were buried together with their most valuable treasures, the entrances were blocked up and false passages and rooms were built.

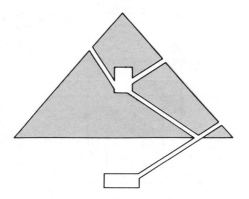

Solids

Exercise 21 ◼ M

Here are some drawings of solids. (It would be useful to see some models of these.)

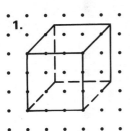

1.

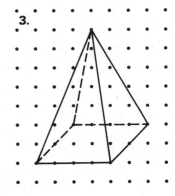

3.

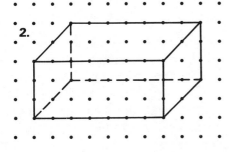

2.

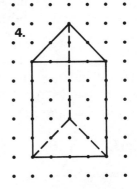

4.

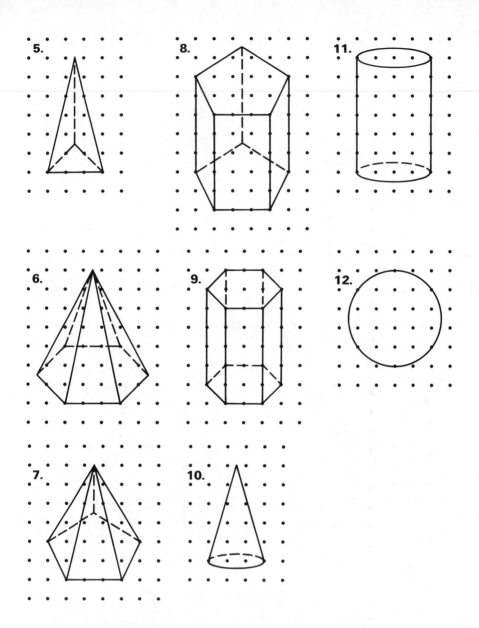

Copy and name the solids (use dotty paper).
Choose the names from this set:
{cube, cuboid, triangular prism,* pentagonal prism, hexagonal prism, cylinder, triangular pyramid, square pyramid, pentagonal pyramid, hexagonal pyramid, cone, sphere}

*See the glossary, p. 435.

238

It is quite easy to draw cuboids on dotty paper.
(The dots should form triangles and should be used the right way up.)

This is right: This is wrong:

Parts of cuboids have been drawn.
Copy them on dotty paper.
Complete the cuboids.

1.

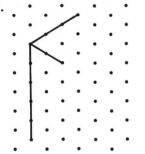

3.

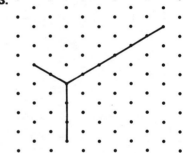

2.

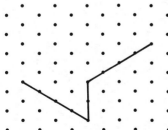

4.

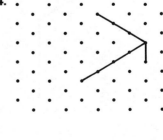

5.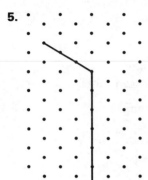

8.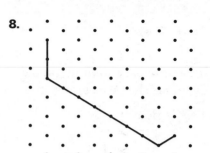

6.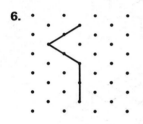

9.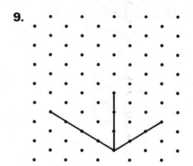

7.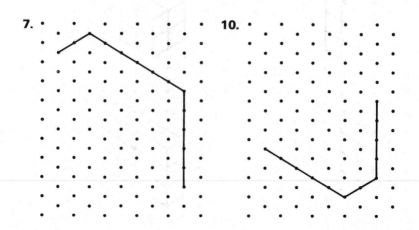

10.

240

Exercise 23

In each of the following, some cubes may be hidden. For each solid, find both the minimum and the maximum number of cubes there could be.

1.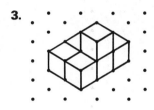

6.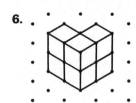

2.

7.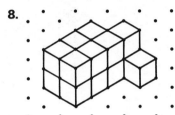

3.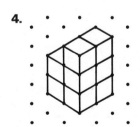

8.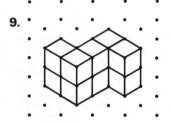

4.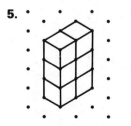

9.

5.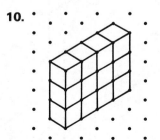

10.

241

11. 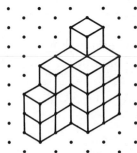   **12.**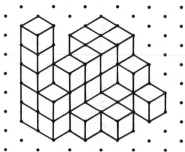

Exercise 24

Build each of these with cubes.
Add an extra cube where the shading is.
Draw some of the final shapes on dotty paper.

e.g.

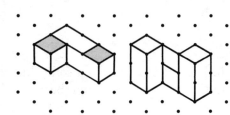

1. 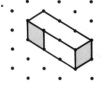   **3.** 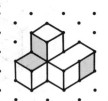   **5.**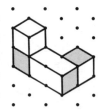

2. 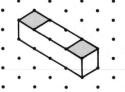   **4.** 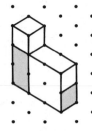   **6.**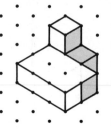

7.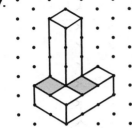

9.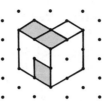

8.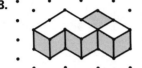

10.

Exercise 25   M

A *polyhedron* (plural — 'polyhedra') is a solid that has *plane* (i.e. flat) faces. A cylinder is not a polyhedron, because it has a curved face.

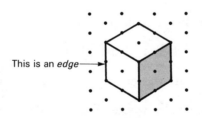

This is an *edge*

A cube is shown.
One *face* is shaded.

The corners are called *vertices.*
Each corner is called a *vertex.*

A Leonhard Euler (1707–83), a Swiss mathematician, discovered a formula relating the number of faces, edges, and vertices of any polyhedron.

Copy and complete this table, then try to find the formula:

Polyhedron	Number of faces, F	Number of vertices, V	Number of edges, E	$F + V$
cuboid	?	?	12	14
square pyramid	?	?	?	?
triangular prism	?	?	?	?
triangular pyramid	?	4	?	?
pentagonal prism	?	?	?	?
pentagonal pyramid	?	?	?	?
hexagonal prism	8	?	?	?
hexagonal pyramid	?	?	?	?

B **1.** Find out if these formulae are true for all polyhedra:
   (a) $E = 2F$ (c) $3F < 2E$ (e) $F < E - 2$
   (b) $3V = 2E$ (d) $F < E$ (f) $E \geqslant V + 2$

2. For which polyhedra does $F = V$?

3. Name some polyhedra where $3V = 2E$.

4. Name a polyhedron where $E = 2F - 1$.

5. Name two polyhedra where $F + E = V + 8$.

Exercise 26

1. Name four sports where a spherical ball is used.

2. Name a sport where a ball that is not shaped like a sphere is used.

3. Make a drawing to show how a cone is used in everyday life.

4. Show how cylinders are used in everyday life.

5. Make a drawing to show how a triangular prism is used in everyday life.

6. Give two examples where a cuboid is used in everyday life.

Nets of Solids

A shape that can be folded to make a solid is called a *net*.

Here is a net of a cube:

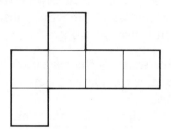

Here is the same net of a cube. It now has tabs on half of its edges to enable the cube to be made.

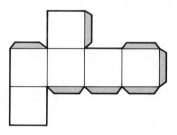

Exercise 27

1. Which of these shapes are nets of a cube:

A.
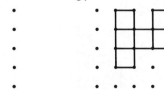

C.
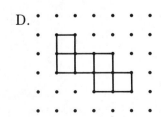

B.
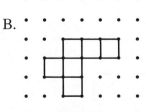

D.

2. Try to find *all* possible nets of a cube.

3. Which nets of a cube can be drawn in pencil without taking the pencil off the paper, and without going over any line twice? For example, the net shown can be drawn in this way by starting at S, following the arrowed and numbered journey and finishing at F.

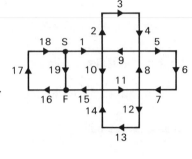

4. This shape is the net of an open box made with square faces.
Find all possible nets of an open box.

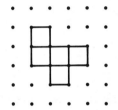

5. Repeat question 3 for nets of an open box.

Exercise 28   To Plait a Cube

Make this pattern out of squared paper. Fold the edges of each square downwards. Now start to plait a cube.

On this diagram 1o folds over the top of 1u (o means 'over' and u means 'under'). 2u folds down, then 2o folds over the top.

Continue doing this until you reach the flap. The flap simply tucks in.

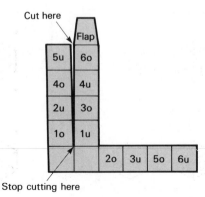

246

1. Here are four views of the same cube:

Work out which letter is opposite which.

2. Here are three views of another cube:

Which letter is opposite which?

In questions 3 to 5, sketch the given cubes. On your sketches, fill in the letters missing from the blank faces. The letters must be shown in the way they would be marked on the cubes. (Use dotty paper for your sketches.)

3.

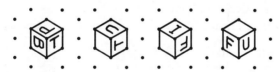

4.

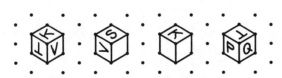

5.

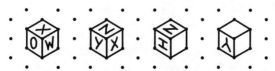

Exercise 30

Collect as many different-shaped cardboard containers as you can.

Cut along some of the edges so that they unfold to make a net.

Draw the nets in your exercise book.

Do not forget to give the names of the solids (e.g. 'net of a triangular prism').

Exercise 31

1. A rectangular box (a cuboid) is 10 cm long, 6 cm wide and 4 cm high. Here is one possible net of this box drawn to one-quarter of its true size.

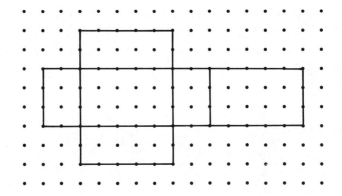

Draw two other different nets of this box (both should be one-quarter of the true size).

2. On squared dotty paper, draw a half-size net of a box (a cuboid) that measures 6 cm by 4 cm by 3 cm.

3. On squared dotty paper, draw a cuboid-shaped box to one-third of its full size, if its true size is 9 cm by 7.5 cm by 6 cm.

Exercise 32

1. Here is a net of a triangular
   prism. Copy this net, but
   make your copy larger.
   (Make each rectangular face
   7 cm long and 3 cm wide.)
   Make your copy on paper (or
   thin card).
   Put flaps on it. Cut out the
   net.
   Fold it to make a triangular
   prism.

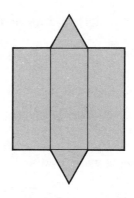

2. Draw a net of a square pyramid. (Make it any size you wish.)
   Use paper (or thin card). Put flaps on it.
   Cut it out. Fold it to make a square pyramid.

Exercise 33

Draw the net of a cone without its circular base (i.e. an open cone).

Exercise 34

Make a model of a building
such as a church.

If you make a church, you will
probably need to make cuboids,
a triangular prism and a
pyramid.

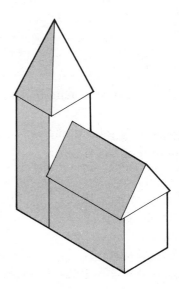

1. Is it possible to draw a straight line on:
   (a) a cube?
   (b) the curved face of a cylinder?
   (c) a sphere?
   (d) the curved face of a cone?
   (e) a square pyramid?

2. The drawings show two solids that were made from straws (pipe cleaners were used at the vertices to join the straws together):

   (a)

   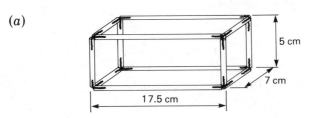

   (b)

   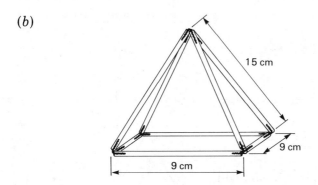

   What is the total length of the straws used for each solid?

3. Name any solid that has:
   (a) six plane faces,
   (b) no edges, no vertices,
   (c) five plane faces,
   (d) two plane faces, one curved face, two curved edges, no vertices,
   (e) six edges,
   (f) one vertex,
   (g) three more edges than faces.

Here are two different views of a
square pyramid:

The first view shows what a
square pyramid looks like from
the front. It is called a *front
elevation*.

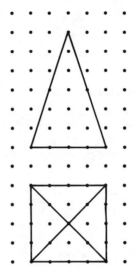

The second view shows what the
square pyramid looks like from
above. A view of something
from above is called a *plan*.

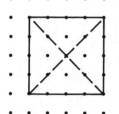

This drawing shows what a square pyramid
looks like from below.

The lines shown by dashes stand for the
edges of the pyramid that cannot be seen
(they are 'hidden' edges).

Check them by looking at a square pyramid from different
directions.

Draw a front elevation and a plan for each of these solids:

1. triangular prism

2. cylinder

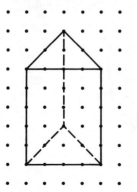

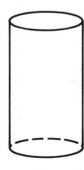

13 Area

Estimating Areas by Counting Squares

Exercise 1   **M**

By counting squares, estimate the area of the beech, silver birch and ash tree leaves:

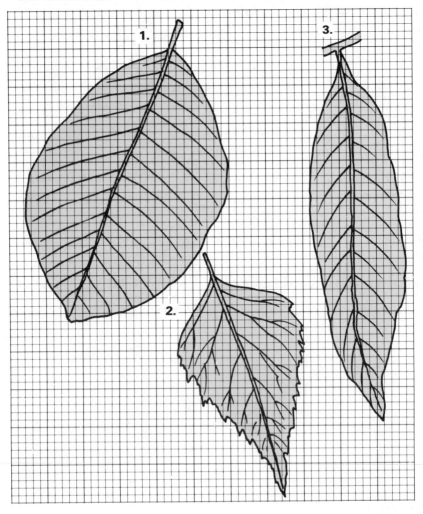

1. A grid of squares has been drawn over a map of the Isle of Man:
   (a) By counting squares, estimate the area of the Isle of Man, including the Calf of Man, giving the answer in terms of the drawn squares.
   (b) If each square covers an area of 2.5 square miles, estimate the area of the Isle of Man giving the answer in square miles.

Isle of Man

2. The map shows several English counties as they were in 1086 according to the Domesday Survey:

(a) By counting squares, estimate, in terms of the given squares, the total area outlined by the thick line.

(b) Calculate the outlined area if each square covers an area of 32 square miles.

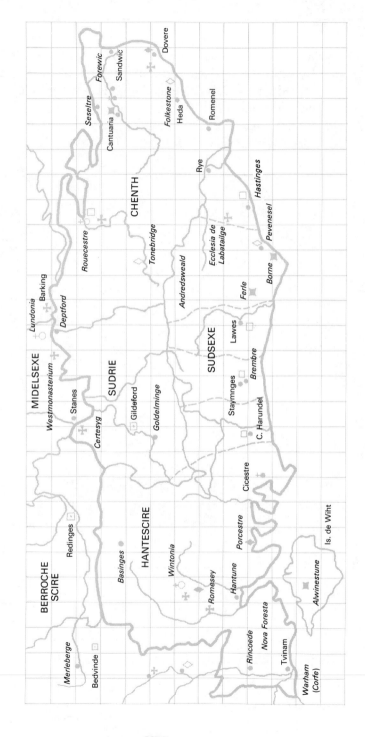

Copy and complete:

1.

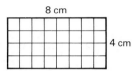

8 cm

4 cm

Number of squares that will fit in the length = 8

Number of rows of squares = $\boxed{?}$

Area of rectangle = 8 × $\boxed{?}$ cm^2 = $\boxed{?}$ cm^2

2.

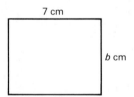

7 cm

3 cm

Number of squares that will fit in the length = $\boxed{?}$

Number of rows of squares = $\boxed{?}$

Area of rectangle = $\boxed{?}$ × $\boxed{?}$ cm^2 = $\boxed{?}$ cm^2

3.

7 cm

b cm

Number of squares that will fit in the length = $\boxed{?}$

Number of rows of squares = $\boxed{?}$

Area of rectangle = $\boxed{?}$ × b cm^2 = $\boxed{?}$ cm^2

4.

l cm

b cm

Number of squares that will fit in the length = l

Number of rows of squares = $\boxed{?}$

Area of rectangle = $\boxed{?}$ × $\boxed{?}$ = lb

Area of a Rectangle

Area of a rectangle, $A = l \times b$
or $A = lb$

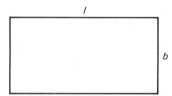

Exercise 4

A **1.** Find the area of the following rectangles:

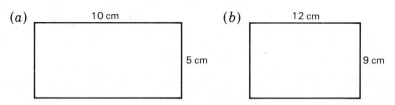

(a) 10 cm   5 cm

(b) 12 cm   9 cm

2. Find the area of the rectangle in the middle:

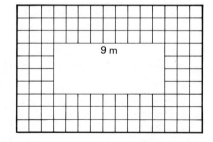

9 m

3. Find the area of a rectangle of length 8 cm and breadth 6 cm.

4. A rectangle is 8.5 m long and 4 m wide. Find its area.

5. A rectangle is 45 mm long. If its breadth is 20 mm, find its area.

6. Find the area of a square with sides measuring 9 cm.

7. A rectangle measures 6.2 cm by 1.7 cm. Find its area.

8. A rectangle measures $3\frac{3}{4}$ cm by $2\frac{2}{3}$ cm. Find its area.

B Find the area of each of these rectangles:

	Length	Breadth			Length	Breadth
1.	13 cm	6 cm		**7.**	42 m	40 m
2.	21 m	7 m		**8.**	7.6 cm	1.3 cm
3.	19 cm	12 cm		**9.**	24 cm	9.1 cm
4.	5.8 m	3 m		**10.**	8.7 m	3.2 m
5.	9 cm	7.3 cm		**11.**	$8\frac{3}{4}$ cm	$3\frac{1}{5}$ cm
6.	50 mm	30 mm		**12.**	$4\frac{1}{2}$ m	$1\frac{1}{3}$ m

Exercise 5

1. Calculate the area of a rectangular room of length 5 m and breadth 4.3 m.

2. Room 1 is 4 m square while Room 2 measures 5 m by 3 m:
   (a) Which of the above rooms is bigger?
   (b) How much bigger is the larger room?

3. A room is 3.9 m square. Another room which is rectangular measures 5.1 m by 2.95 m.
   (a) Find both areas.
   (b) Which room is larger and by how much?

4. Find the area of a rectangular lawn that is 23 m long and 11 m wide.

5. An Association football pitch measures 100 m by 72 m. Calculate its area.

6. A rectangular piece of card is 30 cm long and 23 cm wide. Calculate its area.

7. A rectangle is 15 cm long. If its perimeter is 46 cm, calculate its area.

8. A square has a perimeter of 18 cm. Calculate its area.

9. An area that is 4 m square is to be paved with 500 mm square paving stones. How many are needed?

10. Part of a bathroom wall, an area measuring 2.4 m by 1.5 m, is tiled using 15 cm square wall tiles. If no tiles were wasted, how many were used?

11. A floor measuring 3 m by 1.5 m is to be tiled using special floor tiles that are 30 cm by 20 cm. If the tiles can be stuck to the floor in any direction, calculate the minimum number of whole tiles needed to completely cover this floor.

12. I have 45 paving stones that are 600 mm square. If I use them to pave an area measuring 6 m by 4.8 m, how many more of the 600 mm square paving stones will I need to finish the job?

13. A piece of card measures 1 m by 800 mm. If it is cut into 2 cm squares to make counters, how many counters should there be?

14. A rectangular garden measuring 30 m by 24 m is to be seeded using a grass seed, where 80 g of seed covers 1 m^2:
    (a) How many grams of seed are needed?
    (b) If each box of grass seed holds 5 kg, how many boxes are needed?

15. How much paint do I need to buy to paint one side of a garage door measuring 6 m by 2.8 m and both sides of 8 doors measuring 1.9 m by 0.7 m, if 3 ℓ of paint will cover 32 m^2? (*Note* $\frac{1}{2}\ell$ tins of paint can be bought.)

Exercise 6

Find the area of each of the following shapes:

1.

2.

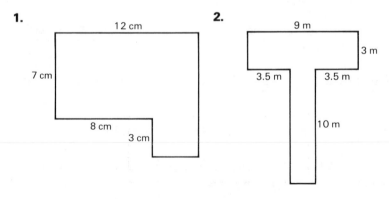

3.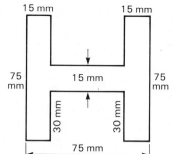

5.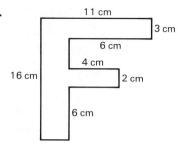

4.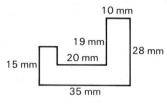

6.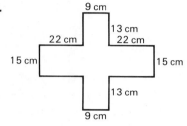

Exercise 7

Calculate the shaded areas:

1.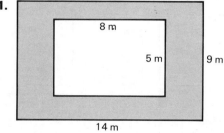

2.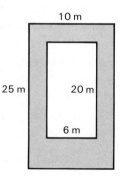

3. The border is 2 cm wide:

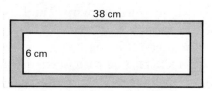

4.

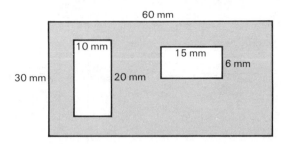

5.

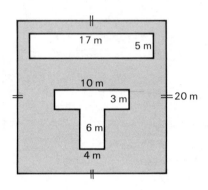

Exercise 8

1. Calculate the area of carpet needed to cover the floor of the given room:

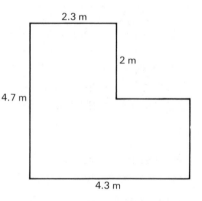

2. A rectangular lawn measures 30 m by 17 m. It is surrounded by a path that is 1.5 m wide.
   (*a*) Calculate the area of the path.
   (*b*) If the path is to be treated with weedkiller and if one packet of weedkiller covers 34 m², how many packets are needed?

3. Calculate the area of the shrubbery (the shaded area).

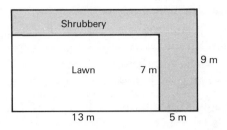

Exercise 9

1. Two gardens each measure 8 m by 7 m:

(a) *Around* the first garden is a path 2 m wide. Find the area of the path.

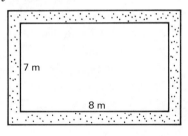

(b) *Inside* the second garden is a path 2 m wide. Find the area of this path.

(c) Find the difference in the areas of the two paths.

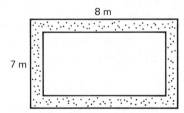

2. Repeat question 1 for other gardens having paths around them and inside them, the paths being 2 m wide.

Write what you notice.

3. Try other gardens. For each garden you try, find the difference in area between a path around the garden and a path inside the garden having the same width. Use paths that are not 2 m wide.

Write what you notice.

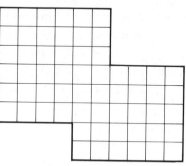
A 1. Cut out any size of rectangle from a piece of squared paper. Make sure it measures a whole number of centimetres along each side.

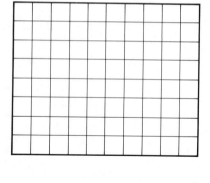

This rectangle is 10 squares by 8 squares (it is not full-size).
(*a*) What is the area of your rectangle?
(*b*) What is its perimeter?

2. Cut a corner off your rectangle (as shown). The cut off piece need not be 4 squares by 3 squares (choose your own size).
(*a*) What is the area of the remaining shape?
(*b*) What is its perimeter?

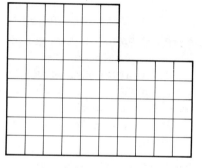

3. Now cut off another corner:
(*a*) What is the area of the remaining shape?
(*b*) What is its perimeter?

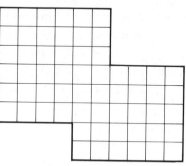

4. Cut off another corner and find the area and perimeter of the remaining shape.

5. Cut off the last corner and find the area and perimeter of the remaining shape.

B Make a table as shown opposite. (Two answers have been filled in for the given rectangle. Your answers may be different.)

Write what you notice.

	Area of shape	Perimeter of shape
1.	$80\,\text{cm}^2$	$36\,\text{cm}$
2.	?	?
3.	?	?
4.	?	?
5.	?	?

Exercise 11   **M**

Copy and complete the given table showing the possible number of rectangles that can be drawn having the given perimeter.

Each edge of the rectangles must measure a whole number of centimetres.

For example:
There are 3 rectangles that have a perimeter of 12 cm
(5 cm by 1 cm, 4 cm by 2 cm and 3 cm by 3 cm).

Perimeter	Number of rectangles
4 cm	?
6 cm	?
8 cm	?
10 cm	?
12 cm	3
14 cm	?
16 cm	?
18 cm	?

1. The length of a rectangle is given by $l = (x + 4)$ cm while the breadth is $b = (x + 3)$ cm:

(a) Copy and complete this table (one value has been filled in for you).

(b) By examining the values in the table, try to work out the area when $x = 7$.

x	Area, A
0	?
1	?
2	30
3	?
4	?
5	?
6	?

(c) Now plot a graph of A against x. Use a scale of 1 cm to $\frac{1}{2}$ cm on the x-axis (i.e. 2 cm represents 1 cm).
On the A-axis, let 1 cm represent 5 cm².

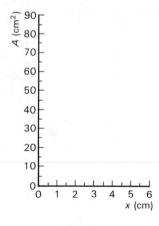

(*d*) Make out another table.
This time, the table should show x and l.

Complete it.

x	$l = x + 4$
0	?
1	?
2	6
3	?
4	?
5	?
6	?

(*e*) Plot a graph of l against x. Use a scale of 1 cm to $\frac{1}{2}$ cm on both axes (i.e. 2 cm to 1 cm).

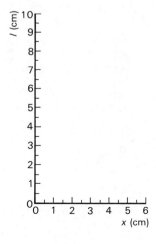

2. Repeat question 1, parts (*a*), (*b*) and (*c*), where the length of the rectangle, $l = (x + 5)$ cm and the breadth, $b = (x + 2)$ cm.

(*d*) Make out a table showing x and b and complete it:

x	$b = x + 2$
0	?
1	?
2	?
3	?
4	6
5	?
6	?

(*e*) Plot a graph of b against x. Use a scale of 2 cm to 1 cm on both axes.

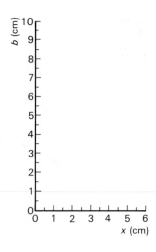

Exercise 13 To Find a Side Given the Area

A Find the missing length in each of these rectangles:

1.

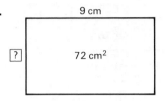

9 cm

? | 72 cm²

5.

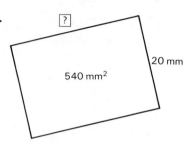

?

540 mm²

20 mm

2.

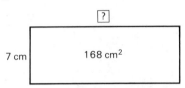

?

7 cm | 168 cm²

6.

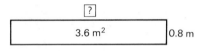

?

3.6 m²

0.8 m

3.

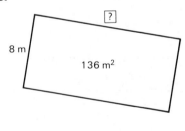

?

8 m

136 m²

7.

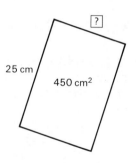

?

25 cm

450 cm²

4.

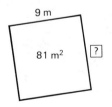

9 m

81 m²

?

8.

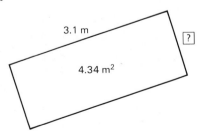

3.1 m

4.34 m²

?

B Copy and complete the table for the given rectangles:

	Length	Breadth	Area
1.	14 cm	7 cm	?
2.	8 m	?	56 m^2
3.	?	5 cm	90 cm^2
4.	?	11 m	154 m^2
5.	24 mm	?	384 mm^2
6.	?	0.9 m	3.33 m^2
7.	26 m	15 m	?
8.	6.8 cm	?	23.12 cm^2
9.	?	3.5 cm	37.1 cm^2
10.	?	$2\frac{1}{2}$ m	$10\frac{1}{2}$ m^2

Surface Area of a Cuboid

Exercise 14

1. Draw the nets of these cuboids, then calculate their surface areas:

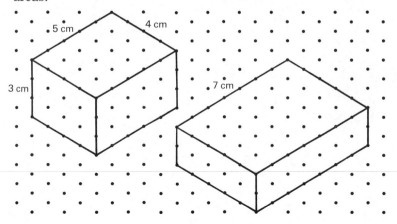

268

2. A box without a lid is 9 cm long, 7 cm wide and has a height of 3 cm:
  (*a*) Sketch a net of the box.
  (*b*) Calculate the total surface area of the box.

3. Each edge of a cube measures 4 cm. Calculate its total surface area.

4. Each edge of a cube measures 2.8 cm. Calculate its total surface area.

5. A cuboid measures 12 cm by 8 cm by 5 cm. Sketch a net, then calculate the total surface area of the cuboid.

Exercise 15

Calculate the total surface area of each of these cuboids:

	Length	Breadth	Height		Length	Breadth	Height
1.	6 m	4 m	2 m	**6.**	18 cm	10 cm	6 cm
2.	8 cm	3 cm	5 cm	**7.**	24 mm	16 mm	10 mm
3.	10 cm	7 cm	4 cm	**8.**	3 m	2.2 m	2 m
4.	9 cm	8 cm	3 cm	**9.**	8.5 cm	6 cm	2.5 cm
5.	0.5 m	0.3 m	0.2 m	**10.**	4.2 cm	3.6 cm	1.9 cm

Exercise 16

1. A room is 5 m long, 4 m wide and 2.4 m high:
  (*a*) Find the area of the floor.
  (*b*) Find the area of one of the big walls. (Ignore doors and windows.)
  (*c*) Find the total area of all four walls. (Ignore doors and windows.)

2. A room is 4 m long, 3.5 m wide and 2.4 m high. Ignoring doors and windows, find the total area of all four walls.

3. A biscuit tin is 24 cm long, 22 cm wide and 10 cm high. Calculate the total surface area of the outside of the tin, ignoring the lid.

Perpendicular Heights of Parallelograms and Triangles

Each diagram shows either a parallelogram or a triangle with a base and perpendicular height marked and labelled:

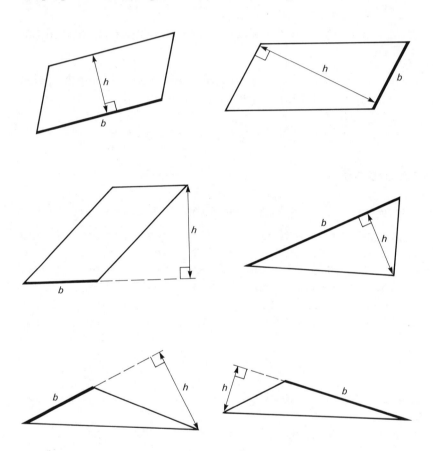

Exercise 17 M

Copy each of the following shapes. The sizes need not be exact. If a side is marked or labelled, draw, in a different colour, the height that is perpendicular to that side. If, however, a perpendicular height is given, then draw a side to which it is perpendicular, in a different colour.

1.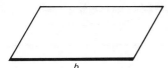

2.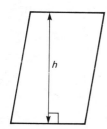

3.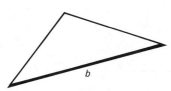

4.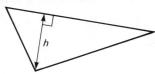

5.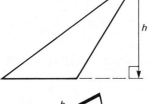

6.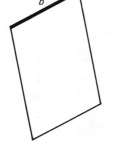

7.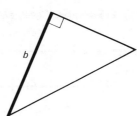

8.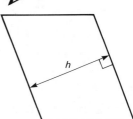

9.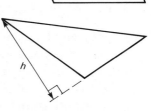

10.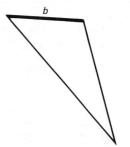

11.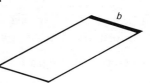

12.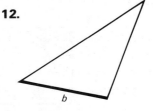

Areas of Parallelograms and Triangles

Exercise 18

1. Draw a parallelogram on a piece of paper. Cut it out.

Using one straight cut, cut your parallelogram into two pieces so that the two pieces can be moved to form a rectangle.

2. (*a*) Draw any triangle on a piece of paper and cut it out.

(*b*) Cut out another triangle that is identical to the first.

(*c*) Place both triangles together to form a parallelogram.

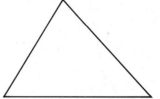

(*d*) Compare the bases and perpendicular heights of a triangle and the parallelogram formed.

Write what you notice.

Exercise 19

Using the ideas in Exercise 18 and the diagrams in this exercise, try to find formulae for the area of these shapes:

1. Area of parallelogram = $\boxed{?}$

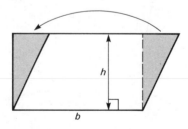

2. Area of a triangle = ⬚?

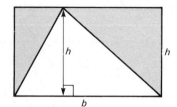
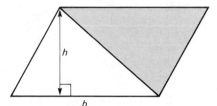

Exercise 20

Find the area of each of these shapes:

1.

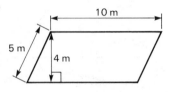

10 m
5 m
4 m

4.

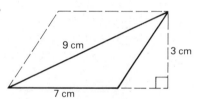

9 cm
3 cm
7 cm

2.

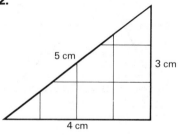

5 cm
3 cm
4 cm

5.

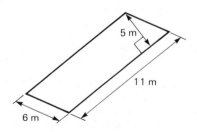

5 m
11 m
6 m

3.

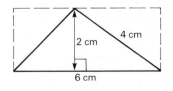

4 cm
2 cm
6 cm

6.

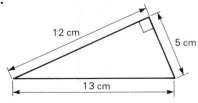

12 cm
5 cm
13 cm

273

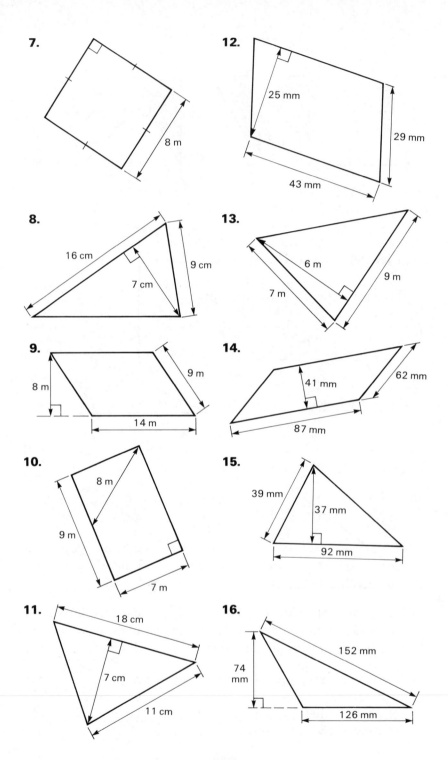

7.

8.

16 cm

7 cm

9 cm

9.

8 m

9 m

14 m

10.

8 m

9 m

7 m

11.

18 cm

7 cm

11 cm

12.

25 mm

29 mm

43 mm

13.

6 m

9 m

7 m

14.

41 mm

62 mm

87 mm

15.

39 mm

37 mm

92 mm

16.

152 mm

74 mm

126 mm

Miscellaneous Questions on Area

Exercise 21

1. A rectangle has an area of 153 cm². If it is 9 cm wide, calculate its length.

2. A rectangle is 8.4 cm long. It has an area of 31.08 cm². Find its width.

3. In the given diagram, calculate the shaded area.

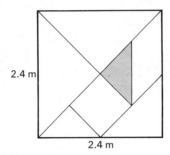

4. A parallelogram has a base of 8.9 m and a perpendicular height of 3.3 m. Find its area.

5. A right-angled triangle has sides measuring 3.5 cm, 8.4 cm and 9.1 cm. Calculate its area.

6. A rectangle of length 96 mm has the same area as a square with side 72 mm. Calculate the breadth of the rectangle.

7. A square has sides of length 10 cm. A rectangle, having an area equal to three times that of the square, is 25 cm long. Calculate the breadth of this rectangle.

8. A rectangle of length 7 cm has an area of 35 cm². A right-angled triangle has the same perimeter as this rectangle. If two sides of the triangle are 8 cm and 10 cm, calculate its area.

9. A parallelogram and rectangle have the same area. Both have a base that measures 9.7 cm and the perpendicular height of the parallelogram is 6.28 cm. Find the breadth of the rectangle, giving reasons for your answer.

10. A parallelogram and triangle have the same sized area and the same sized base (the base of each measures 6.8 cm). The perpendicular height of the triangle is 4.7 cm. Find the perpendicular height of the parallelogram giving reasons for your answer.

11. Calculate the shaded area:

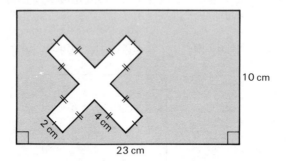

10 cm

2 cm

4 cm

23 cm

12. Calculate the shaded area:

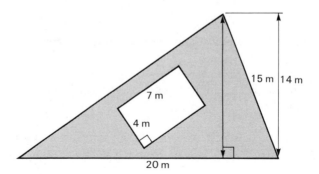

7 m

4 m

15 m 14 m

20 m

Exercise 22

1. Calculate the area of a rectangular garden that measures 18 m by 13 m.

2. A rectangular carpet measuring 3.4 m by 2.5 m is placed in a room 4.1 m long and 3.8 m wide. Calculate the area of floor not covered by the carpet.

3. The drive of a house is in the shape of a parallelogram as shown.
Calculate the area of the drive.

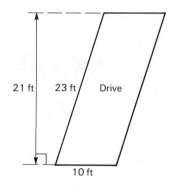

21 ft   23 ft   Drive

10 ft

4. A rectangular garden is divided into two parts, a lawn and a flower bed. The dimensions are shown on the diagram.

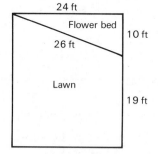

24 ft

Flower bed

26 ft   10 ft

Lawn

19 ft

(a) Calculate the area of the flower bed.
(b) What shape is the lawn?
(c) Calculate the area of the lawn.

5. A rectangular piece of wall has been tiled using 15 cm square tiles. 12 tiles fit in each row. If the tiled area is 21 600 cm², how many rows of tiles must there be?

Exercise 23

1. Draw any parallelogram. Divide it into four triangles by drawing in both diagonals. Find the area of each of the four triangles.

2. Repeat question 1 for a different parallelogram.

3. Investigate the areas of the four triangles formed when any parallelogram has both diagonals drawn in. Write what you discover.

14 **Algebra**

Algebraic Expressions

$4 \times x$ may be written as $4x$,
and $x \times y$ may be written as xy.

Exercise 1

Where letters are used, write the answers in algebraic form:

1. (a) What is the sum of 6 and 9?
  (b) What is the sum of a and b?
  (c) What is the sum of x and 3?

2. (a) What number is 5 more than 7?
  (b) What number is 5 more than n?
  (c) What number is d more than n?

3. (a) Subtract 4 from 12.
  (b) Subtract 4 from k.
  (c) Subtract t from k.

4. (a) What must be added to 14 to give 32?
  (b) What must be added to 14 to give w?
  (c) What must be added to h to give 32?
  (d) What must be added to h to give w?

5. (a) Write down a number that is 9 more than 12.
  (b) Write down a number than is 9 more than f.
  (c) Write down a number that is y more than 12.
  (d) Write down a number that is y more than f.

6. (a) By how many is 37 bigger than 19?
  (b) By how many is p bigger than q?

278

7. (a) What is 43 minus 18?
   (b) What is l minus m?

8. What number is s more than r?

9. What number is u less than g?

10. (a) What number is obtained if y is increased by z?
    (b) What number is obtained if y is decreased by z?

Exercise 2

Write in algebraic form:

1. c added to e,
2. g minus v,
3. 2 times x,
4. d times 5,
5. the sum of h and 4,
6. f plus 9,
7. the product of 3 and k,
8. the product of t and u,

9. r divided by 3,
10. 8 divided by z,
11. w divided by n,
12. b more than y,
13. p less than a,
14. j decreased by 13,
15. 12 decreased by m,
16. l take s.

Exercise 3

Answer these and where letters are used, write the answer in algebraic form:

1. (a) Alun has 12 sweets, while Beverley has 15 sweets. How many have they altogether?
   (b) Amanda has q sweets while Bill has e sweets. How many sweets have they altogether?

2. (a) Carol travelled 4 miles by bus and 23 miles by train. How far was that altogether?
   (b) Darren travelled b miles by bus and 18 miles by train. How far as that altogether?

3. (a) Erica has 29 marbles and Fergus has twice as many. How many marbles has Fergus got?
   (b) Gary has m marbles and Helena has twice as many. How many marbles has Helena got?

4. In a test, Ian got p more marks than Jill. If Jill got 62 marks, how many marks did Ian get?

5. Ken has g books, while Maureen has t books. How many books have they altogether?

6. Lynne has a apples. If she has twice as many as Marcus, how many apples has Marcus got?

7. Norman ran r km and walked w km:
(a) How far did he travel altogether?
(b) How much further did he walk than run?

8. Oliver travelled 59 miles altogether. If he travelled t miles on the train and the rest of the journey by bus, how far did he travel by bus?

9. Patricia will be g years old in 4 years' time. How old is she now?

10. y pencils are shared equally amongst 5 people. How many should each person receive?

11. A rectangular field is p m long and q m wide. What is the area of the field?

12. What is the size of angle x?

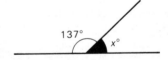

13. It is 8 km from Kirkston village to Hinton, and Hinton is h km from Loxton. How far is it from Kirkston to Loxton if:
(a) Hinton lies between Kirkston and Loxton on the Kirkston to Loxton Road?
(b) Loxton lies on the Kirkston to Hinton road?
(c) Kirkston lies on the Hinton to Loxton road?

14. A hall holds 350 people, and 350 tickets were printed for a play to be held there. Over 200 of the tickets were sold and 67 people paid at the door, since they did not buy a ticket. There were only h spare seats for the performance. How many people watched that performance of the play?

15. I bought a packet of good-quality envelopes and each envelope cost y p. I then bought some cheaper envelopes and there were twice as many envelopes in this new packet. The cost of the packet of cheaper envelopes was exactly half the cost of the packet of good-quality envelopes. What was the cost of each cheap envelope?

Exercise 4

1. How many days are there in:
(*a*) 1 week?　　　(*b*) 3 weeks?　　　(*c*) w weeks?

2. How many pence are there in:
(*a*) £1?　　　(*b*) £7?　　　(*c*) £x?

3. How many pounds are there in:
(*a*) 400 p?　　　(*b*) 900 p?　　　(*c*) d p?

4. How many millilitres are there in:
(*a*) 1 ℓ?　　　(*b*) 6 ℓ?　　　(*c*) p ℓ?

5. How many centimetres are there in:
(*a*) 10 mm?　　　(*b*) 80 mm?　　　(*c*) y mm?

6. How many centimetres are there in u m?

7. How many minutes are there in t h?

8. How many minutes are there in T s?

9. How many grams are there in W kg?

10. Change w g into kilograms.

Exercise 5

Write the following as algebraic expressions (i.e. use letters instead of words):

e.g. Multiply the number by 2, then subtract 7 becomes $2n - 7$.

1. Multiply the number by 6.

2. Take 12 from the number.

3. Divide the number by 3.

4. Halve the number.

5. Multiply the number by 3, then subtract 4.

6. Double the number, then add 12.

7. Subtract 9 from 4 times the number.

8. Find one-quarter of the number, then add 5.

9. Add 5 to the number, then multiply the result by 6.

10. Take 3 from the number, then divide the result by 4.

Exercise 6

Write the following algebraic expressions in words:

e.g. $3n + 8$ becomes 'multiply the number by 3, then add 8'.

1. $n + 8$ **6.** $5g - 3$

2. $x - 7$ **7.** $\frac{w}{2} - 7$

3. $2t$ **8.** $4(p - 5)$

4. $\frac{m}{4}$ **9.** $(a + 6) \div 2$

5. $6k + 1$ **10.** $12 - 3u$

Exercise 7

This diagram illustrates the expression $a + b$:

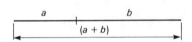

This diagram illustrates the expression $x - y$:

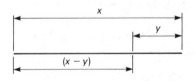

This diagram shows that $2c + 5c = 7c$

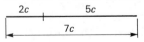

Draw diagrams to show that:

1. $4m + 5m = 9m$

2. $8t - 3t = 5t$

3. $x + y = y + x$

4. $n + n + n = 3n$

Exercise 8   Number of Terms

How many terms are there in each of these expressions?
(Do not simplify any of the expressions.)

e.g.1 $4x + 3y - 2$ has 3 terms,

e.g.2 $24x + 7$ has 2 terms,

e.g.3 $9atx$ has 1 term.

1. $m + 2n$

2. $4y - k + 2h$

3. $4a + 6t$

4. $7pqr$

5. $4gh - 2d + 8dfg$

6. $14 - 2p$

7. $6 + 3t - 7k$

8. $4bcjl$

9. $8wxz - 5$

10. $10 - 3abc$

11. $2x + 3 + 5y + 4x - 2y$

12. $12 + 3 - 4 + 7 + 2 - 9$

13. $a - b + c - d - e + f + g$

14. $abc - def + g$

15. $4t + 7u + 6 - 2u - t$

16. $5 + 6n - 1 + 4l$

Like Terms

Exercise 9

Copy and complete the following to make true statements:

1. $4 + 4 = 2 \times \boxed{?}$

$7 + 7 = \boxed{?} \times 7$

$x + x = \boxed{?} \times x$

2. $4 + 4 + 4 = 3 \times \boxed{?}$

$6 + 6 + 6 = \boxed{?} \times 6$

$n + n + n = 3 \times \boxed{?}$

3. $2 + 2 + 2 + 2 + 2 = \boxed{?} \times 2$

$k + k + k + k + k = \boxed{?} \times k$

4. $3 + 3 + 3 + 3 + 3 + 3 = \boxed{?} \times 3$

$d + d + d + d + d + d = \boxed{?} \times d$

5. $6 - 6 = \boxed{?}$

$9 - 9 = \boxed{?}$

$a - a = \boxed{?}$

$3y - 3y = \boxed{?}$

6.

$2 + 7 = \boxed{?}$

$2 \text{ apples} + 7 \text{ apples} = \boxed{?} \text{ apples}$

$2a + 7a = \boxed{?} a$

7.

$3 + 9 = \boxed{?}$

$3 \text{ pens} + 9 \text{ pens} = \boxed{?} \text{ pens}$

$3p + 9p = \boxed{?} p$

8.

$8 - 3 = \boxed{?}$

$8 \text{ sweets} - 3 \text{ sweets} = \boxed{?} \text{ sweets}$

$8s - 3s = \boxed{?} s$

Exercise 10

Write the following in a shorter form. If no shorter form is possible, write 'NO SHORTER FORM'.

1. $x + x + x + x$

2. $3a + 2a + 4a$

3. $2d + 5d + d$

4. $3s + 8s - 4s$

5. $5m - m + 3m - 2m$

6. $4k - 2k + 8k + k$

7. $7l - 3l + 3l + l$

8. $6p + 4p - 4p - 6p$

9. $4c - c - c + 3c - 2c$

10. $5y + 3y - 7y + 9y - 2y$

11. $x + x + y + x + y$

12. $a + b + b + b + a + a$

13. $c + 2d + d + 2c + 4d$

14. $4t + 3u + 8t - 2u - 5t$

15. $12q + 8s - 5q - 4s + 6s$

16. $3k + 12l - 5l - 2k + 6l$

17. $16h - 4h + 10f - 5h - 9f$

18. $2d + 4e + f + 7$

19. $3z - z + 5i - 3i - z - i$

20. $4v + 7j - 2v - 4j - 2v$

21. $7e + 5 - 2e + 3$

22. $6m + 8 - 4m - 5$

23. $15g + 6w - 6w + g$

24. $6t + 4h - 2t + 3n$

25. $7z + 3i + 6f + 2$

26. $6j + 5w - 2j - 4w - 3j$

27. $4t + 7$

28. $3k + m - 2k + 4m - k$

29. $9z - z + 8g - 2z - 7g$

30. $4v + w - 3v - w + v$

Exercise 11

Find an expression for the perimeter of each of the following shapes. Simplify your answers where possible.

1.

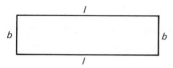

2.

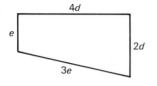

3.

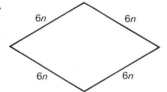

4.

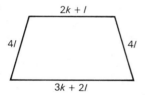

5.

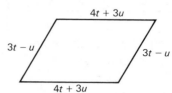

6.

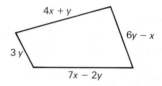

7.

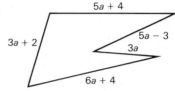

8.

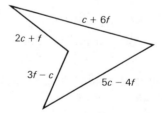

Exercise 12

Write the following in a shorter form and simplify your answers:

1. Andrea had $4k$ pounds. She spent $2k$ pounds, earned $9k$ pounds, was given $5k$ pounds, then she spent a further $6k$ pounds.
   (*a*) How much did Andrea have left?
   (*b*) Find the amount of money left when $k = 7$.

2. Mrs Jameson already had $3t$ tins and $5p$ packets in her trolley. She picked up a further $6t$ tins and p packets. Her son then took $4t$ tins and $3p$ packets from her.

(*a*) What did Mrs Jameson have left?

(*b*) What did Mrs Jameson have left if $t = 4$ and $p = 2$?

3. Colin had m mints and $9c$ chocolates. He ate $3c$ chocolates, bought $5m$ mints and $7c$ chocolates, then ate $3m$ mints and $6c$ chocolates.

(*a*) What did Colin have left?

(*b*) What did Colin have left if $m = 6$ and $c = 4$?

Exercise 13

1. If $x = 6$ and $y = 4$, find the value of:

(*a*) xy (*b*) yx

What do you notice about the two answers?

2. If $m = 13$ and $n = 7$, find the value of:

(*a*) mn (*b*) nm

What do you notice about the two answers?

3. If $k = 4$ and $l = 5$, find the value of:

(*a*) $2kl$ (*b*) $2lk$

What do you notice about the two answers?

4. If $a = 2$ and $b = 6$, find the value of:

(*a*) $3ab$ (*b*) $4ab$ (*c*) $3ab + 4ab$ (*d*) $7ab$

What do you notice about the answers to parts (*c*) and (*d*)?

5. If $p = 7$ and $q = 4$, find the value of:

(*a*) $3pq$ (*b*) $2qp$ (*c*) $3pq + 2qp$ (*d*) $5pq$

What do you notice about the answers to parts (*c*) and (*d*)?

Exercise 14

Write each of the following in a shorter form. If an expression cannot be simplified, write 'NO SHORTER FORM'.

1. $5ac + 3ac + 2ca$
2. $7xy - 2yx + 4yx$
3. $2pm + 3pt + 4mp$
4. $6de + 5fe - de - 2ef$
5. $mt + tm + ms + tm$
6. $4gh + 8 + 3gh - 5$
7. $8sa + 5se + 8as + 3ae$
8. $7 + 4tx - 3 - xt + 2$
9. $4st + 7su + 3ut$
10. $7kl + 4km - 7lk + 3ml$

11. $3fn - 2nf + 7 + 3nf - 5$
12. $5vz + 3wz - zv + 4vw$
13. $kn - nk + 5 + 3k - 2$
14. $4ad - 3 + 2d - da + 3d$
15. $m + 8t + 2mt - m - 2tm$
16. $4y + 3jy + 2j + 5y - yj$
17. $2bp + 3b + 7 + 4pd + 2p$
18. $4tac + 3tca - 5cat$
19. $7net - ten + 3tn - 2ent$
20. $5gas + 2gs - gs - 3sag + 7g$

Note

$$4 + 4 + 4 = 12$$

and

$$3 \times 4 = 12$$

Also that

$$4x + 4x + 4x = 12x$$

and

$$3 \times 4x = 12x$$

also that

$$3 \times 4x = 3 \times 4 \times x$$
$$= 12 \times x$$
$$= 12x$$

Multiplying Terms

Exercise 15

Simplify:

1. $4 \times 2u$
2. $6 \times 4c$
3. $8 \times 3d$
4. $2 \times 7x$
5. $5 \times 9p$
6. $7 \times 6m$
7. $3 \times 3q$
8. $6 \times 5y$

9. $9 \times 8e$
10. $3 \times 7z$
11. $4 \times 6n$
12. $8 \times 7f$
13. $5 \times 3v$
14. $2 \times 6r$
15. $7 \times 8g$
16. $6 \times 3s$

287

17. $7h \times 4$ **21.** $9w \times 8$

18. $7 \times 4k$ **22.** $7 \times 7i$

19. $2l \times 5$ **23.** $12a \times 7$

20. $5t \times 2$ **24.** $6 \times 14b$

Exercise 16

Simplify:

1. $5 \times p \times q$	**11.** $4 \times ad$	**21.** $7r \times 4s$
2. $3 \times 2 \times c$	**12.** $3 \times pqr$	**22.** $9t \times 2u$
3. $4 \times 5 \times d \times e$	**13.** $5 \times 3mp$	**23.** $4w \times 6v$
4. $3 \times 7 \times x \times y$	**14.** $4 \times f \times 6$	**24.** $3xy \times z$
5. $2 \times m \times 3$	**15.** $f \times 6g$	**25.** $3xy \times 4z$
6. $4 \times j \times 3$	**16.** $6 \times fg$	**26.** $3x \times 2y \times 4z$
7. $k \times 7$	**17.** $h \times 2k$	**27.** $6a \times 3bc$
8. $l \times 2 \times 9$	**18.** $2 \times l \times 7$	**28.** $5de \times 3f$
9. $2l \times 9$	**19.** $4 \times m \times 3 \times n$	**29.** $7gh \times 4kl$
10. $9l \times 2$	**20.** $6p \times 3q$	**30.** $8m \times 3np \times 2q$

Dividing Terms

$$2 \times 4 = 8 \quad \text{and} \quad 2 \times 4t = 8t$$

Also $8 \div 2 = 4$ so $8t \div 2 = 4t$

Now $3 \times 7 = 21$ and $3x \times 7 = 21x$

Also $21 \div 7 = 3$ so $21x \div 7 = 3x$

Exercise 17

Simplify:

1. $6a \div 2$	**6.** $9f \div 9$	**11.** $32n \div 8$
2. $12x \div 3$	**7.** $24m \div 8$	**12.** $26k \div 2$
3. $14t \div 7$	**8.** $25c \div 5$	**13.** $40w \div 5$
4. $8y \div 8$	**9.** $10u \div 10$	**14.** $42d \div 7$
5. $18g \div 6$	**10.** $30h \div 6$	**15.** $100z \div 25$

Miscellaneous Questions

Exercise 18

Simplify the following where possible:

1. $3 \times 7c$
2. $3 + 7c$
3. $2x + 6y$
4. $2x \times 6y$
5. $x + y + x + y$
6. $x + y + xy$
7. $4tu + 3ut$
8. $7a - 2a + 4d - a$
9. $2mn + 4m + n$
10. $ak + ka$

11. $5wv \times 3t$
12. $5wv + 3t$
13. $5wv - 2w$
14. $9y - 9$
15. $3z - z$
16. $4l \times 4$
17. $3n \div 3$
18. $4p \times 9$
19. $3u \times 2w$
20. $abc \times 4d$

Exercise 19

For each statement, write whether it is true or false:

1. $4x + 7x = 11x$
2. $9a - 3a = 6$
3. $3m + 4 = 7m$
4. $2 \times 6p = 12p$
5. $2 + 6p = 8p$
6. $5d - d = 5$
7. $4 \times 3y = 4y \times 3$
8. $7k \times 3 = 21k$
9. $2d + 6e = 8de$
10. $8u + u = 9u$

11. $12q \div 4 = 3q$
12. $8n - 8 = n$
13. $3t + 4 = 7t$
14. $13k - 6k = 7k$
15. $18w \div w = 18$
16. $3c + 4d = 3d + 4c$
17. $3c \times 4d = 3d \times 4c$
18. $10z \div 5 = 2$
19. $12l - l = 11l$
20. $2e \times 8f = 16ef$

Exercise 20

1. How many millimetres are there in:
   (a) $1\,\text{cm}$?   (b) $5\,\text{cm}$?   (c) $l\,\text{cm}$?   (d) $4l\,\text{cm}$?

2. $3\,\text{ft} = 1\,\text{yd}$, how many feet are there in:
   (a) $6\,\text{yd}$?   (b) $d\,\text{yd}$?   (c) $5d\,\text{yd}$?   (d) $9d\,\text{yd}$?

3. How many pence are there in:

   (*a*) £6?   (*b*) £*t*?   (*c*) £4*t*?   (*d*) £$\frac{t}{2}$?

4. 12 in $=$ 1 ft, how many inches are there in:

   (*a*) *p* ft?   (*b*) 5*p* ft?   (*c*) $\frac{p}{4}$ ft?   (*d*) $\frac{p}{3}$ ft?

5. How many centimetres are there in:

   (*a*) *g* m?   (*b*) 9*g* m?   (*c*) 4*g* m?   (*d*) $\frac{g}{2}$ m?

Exercise 21

1. I have 3 boxes. Each box contains 6*a* apples.
   (*a*) How mamy apples have I?
   (*b*) If I sell 5*b* apples, how many apples shall I have left?

2. A bus journey costs 3*b* p. What is the cost if 9 people travel on that journey?

3. There are 8*z* buttons in a packet:
   (*a*) How many buttons have I if I have 7 packets?
   (*b*) If I use 19*z* buttons, how many will I have left?

4. Rachel has 6*c* coins. Her friend Susie has twice as many, while Tony has only one-third the number of coins that Rachel has. How many coins do they have altogether?

5. Ursula had read 15*p* pages of a book. Victor had read 9*p* pages more than Ursula, while William had read 4*q* pages less than Victor. How many more pages than Ursula had William read?

Exercise 22   A Secret Code

a	b	c	d	e	f	g	h	i	j	k	l	m
1	2	3	4	5	6	7	8	9	10	11	12	13

n	o	p	q	r	s	t	u	v	w	x	y	z
14	15	16	17	18	19	20	21	22	23	24	25	26

This is how the code works:

e.g. $3k - h$
$= 3 \times 11 - 8$ (since $k = 11$ and $h = 8$)
$= 33 - 8$
$= 25$
$= \underline{y}$ (from the table, $y = 25$)

Answer *all* of these questions. Each answer is a letter. All the letters, written down one after the other, will give a sentence. Find the sentence.

1. $5e$

2. $v - g$

3. $3h - c$

4. $\dfrac{x}{3}$

5. $2e - i$

6. $8b + d + 2$

7. $3j - y$

8. $2f + 7$

9. $l + j - a$

10. $u \div 7$

11. $8c - 7c$

12. $k + n - 20$

13. $2i + 1$

14. $z - m + 6$

15. $o - f - c$

16. $p + 1 + d$

17. $m - 1$

18. $2g - b$

19. $4d + h + a$

20. $x \div f$

21. $w - r$

22. $s + q - z - g$

23. $\frac{3}{4}$ of t

24. $2g - 10$

25. $(3l + n) \div 10$

26. $w - q - b$

27. $2u - v$

28. $(6 + z) \div 4$

29. $(v + 3) \div e$

30. $\dfrac{z}{2}$

31. $(r - 3) \div c$

32. $7s - 5s + 3s - 4s$

33. $2l + b - g$

34. $y - s + k - p$

35. $2c + m - l$

36. $\dfrac{h}{2} + a$

37. $5h - k - f$

38. $2q - y - 4$

39. $2k + t - 30$

40. $2(u - o)$

41. $t \div 5$

42. $3(x - s)$

43. $3w - r - q - t$

44. $\dfrac{o}{3}$

Brackets

The diagram shows that
$4(5 + 2) = 4 \times 5 + 4 \times 2$
$= 20 \;\; + 8$
$= \underline{\underline{28}}$

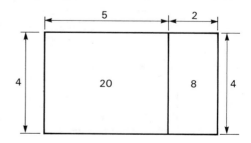

Exercise 23

Copy and complete the following. In each case, write the areas of the small rectangles inside them.

Also, remove the brackets and compare the answers with the areas of the rectangles.

1. (*a*)

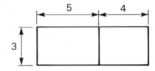

(*b*) $3(5 + 4) = \boxed{?}$

2. (*a*)

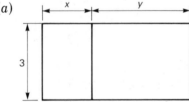

(*b*) $3(x + 4) = \boxed{?}$

3. (*a*)

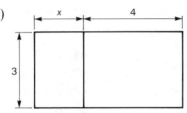

(*b*) $3(x + y) = \boxed{?}$

4. (*a*)

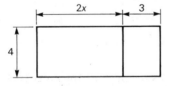

(*b*) $4(2x + 3) = \boxed{?}$

5. (*a*)

(*b*) $2(3 + 7 + 5) = \boxed{?}$

6. (*a*)

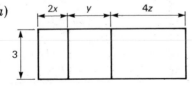

(*b*) $3(2x + y + 4z) = \boxed{?}$

Exercise 24

Multiply out:

1. $4(3 + 5)$
2. $6(8 - 6)$
3. $2(g + 7)$
4. $5(p - 9)$
5. $3(4 + t)$
6. $2(9 - h)$
7. $4(2n + 3)$
8. $7(2k - 4)$
9. $3(5 - 3v)$
10. $8(2 + 3y)$

11. $5(3d - 4a)$
12. $6(7r + u)$
13. $5(q - 9e)$
14. $4(3f + 7s)$
15. $10(8w - 5x)$
16. $3(6z + 7l)$
17. $2(x + y - z)$
18. $6(t - 3u + 2v)$
19. $3(8p - 2q + 5r)$
20. $5(9b - c + d)$

21. $2m(4n + 3)$
22. $4c(6d - 7)$
23. $3h(8 - 3f)$
24. $7w(2 + 8a)$
25. $5e(5l - 6m)$
26. $4k(8i + 4j)$
27. $9s(t - 4y)$
28. $3b(9g + 4h)$
29. $6j(5r - 4n)$
30. $8g(5p - 7b)$

Exercise 25

Remove the brackets and simplify the answers:

1. $6(6f + 9)$
2. $\dfrac{(10c + 8)}{2}$
3. $\frac{1}{2}(4d - 14)$
4. $(5j + 7) \times 4$
5. $\frac{1}{4}(12u + 20q)$
6. $\dfrac{(25w - 35e)}{5}$

7. $\frac{1}{3}(21 - 18k + 6l)$
8. $\dfrac{(12a + 30v - 6x)}{6}$
9. $\frac{1}{8}(40z - 72 + 32s)$
10. $\frac{1}{5}(45m - 5n + 15)$
11. $\frac{1}{4}(8p + 36q - 28r)$
12. $\dfrac{(63x - 14y - 49z)}{7}$

Exercise 26

Simplify each of the following by removing the brackets then by collecting like terms where possible:

1. $(a + 2) + (3a + 5)$
2. $(4u + 7) + (5u + 3)$
3. $(9x + 1) + (2x + 6)$
4. $(8t + 9) + (4 + 7t)$
5. $(10v + 5w) + (2v - 3w)$
6. $(y + 9z) + (2y - z)$
7. $(7b + 4c) + (2b + 10c)$
8. $(5k + 3l) + (7k + 3l)$

9. $(9d + 8e) + (d - 6e)$
10. $(4g + 15h) + (11g + h)$
11. $2(3x + 8) + (2x - 4)$
12. $5(2f + 7) + (7f + 2)$
13. $3(6 + q) + (4q + 13)$
14. $8(4l + 6p) + (3l - 5p)$
15. $4(6t + 4u) + (t + 4u)$
16. $(d + 8h) + 2(6d + 2h)$

17. $(3m + 7n) + 2(7m - 3n)$

18. $(9k + v) + 7(k + 3v)$

19. $(5w + 6b) + 4(8w + 5b)$

20. $(2r + 12s) + 10(7r + 2s)$

21. $3(9a + 6c) + 2(2a - 6c)$

22. $5(7j + 2w) + 3(3j + 7w)$

23. $8(5e + 2y) + 4(7e - 4y)$

24. $3(8u + 2k) + 9(2u + 5k)$

25. $7(3x + 5f) + 6(5x + 9f)$

26. $2(8g + 4c) + 8(8g + 3c)$

27. $4(2e + 9v) + 3(3e - 8v)$

28. $9(z + h) + 7(7z + 10h)$

29. $6(2d + 8a) + 3(7d - 9a)$

30. $7(5m + 6p) + 8(10m + 9p)$

15 Order of Precedence and Formulae

Order of Precedence

Exercise 1

Find the value of:

1. (a) 3 lots of 8
(b) 3×8

2. (a) 8 lots of 6
(b) 8×6

3. (a) 3 lots of $4 + 5$
(b) $3 \times 4 + 5$
(c) $3 \times 7 + 2$
(d) $3 \times 9 - 6$
(e) $7 \times 4 + 9$

4. (a) 4 added to 2 lots of 8
(b) $3 + 2$ lots of 7
(c) $8 + 2 \times 7$
(d) $9 + 3 \times 5$
(e) $12 + 4 \times 8$

5. (a) $15 - 2$ lots of 4
(b) $20 - 2 \times 5$
(c) $18 - 2 \times 9$
(d) $45 - 5 \times 7$
(e) $61 - 7 \times 6$

6. (a) 2 lots of $6 + 5$ lots of 4
(b) $2 \times 6 \; + 5 \times 4$
(c) $2 \times 11 + 6 \times 7$
(d) $4 \times 9 \; - 5 \times 3$
(e) $7 \times 7 \; - 9 \times 3$

7. $9 + 3 \times 6$

8. $18 - 4 \times 2$

9. $7 \times 9 - 25$

10. $4 \times 7 + 31$

11. $9 \times 10 + 46$

12. $62 + 3 \times 12$

13. $100 - 4 \times 20$

14. $4 \times 5 + 5 \times 6$

15. $5 \times 9 + 8 \times 7$

16. $9 \times 6 - 6 \times 8$

17. $10 \times 8 - 9 \times 7$

18. $2 \times 14 + 3 \times 16$

19. $15 \times 5 - 10 \times 6$

20. $12 \times 9 + 11 \times 8$

21. $4 \times 12 + 2 \times 10 + 3 \times 2$

22. $8 \times 4 - 4 \times 6 + 6 \times 9$

23. $9 \times 8 + 37 - 4 \times 13$

24. $120 + 3 \times 5 \times 4$

25. $4 \times 2 \times 7 - 27$

26. $5 \times 9 \times 4 - 9 \times 14$

27. $69 + 2 \times 6 \times 10 + 7 \times 8$

28. $8 + 4 \times 7 \times 2 + 5 \times 10$

29. $8 \times 2 - 7 \times 3 + 9 \times 7 \times 2$

30. $4 \times 19 + 7 \times 12 - 6 \times 15$

Exercise 2

Find the value of:

1. $12 \div 2 + 7$
2. $28 \div 4 - 3$
3. $56 \div 2 - 13$
4. $40 - 20 \div 4$
5. $49 + 18 \div 6$
6. $60 - 30 \div 2$
7. $95 - 40 \div 5$
8. $14 \div 2 + 28 \div 7$

9. $21 \div 3 - 50 \div 10$
10. $60 \div 5 + 64 \div 4$
11. $15 \times 6 - 48 \div 6$
12. $7 \times 12 + 56 \div 8$
13. $90 \div 5 + 8 \times 9$
14. $49 \div 7 + 3 \times 10 - 42 \div 7$
15. $60 \div 12 + 72 \div 6 + 36 \div 2$
16. $96 \div 6 - 84 \div 7 + 5 \times 16$

Order of Calculations on a Calculator

Try this on your calculator:

If your calculator shows the answer 22, then it sorts out the order of calculating for you,

since $\quad 4 + 3 \times 6$

$\quad = 4 + 18$

$\quad = 22$

$4 + 3 \times 6 \neq 42$ so if your calculator gives the answer 42, the answer is wrong.

You then need to work out the answer in a different way.

We can use $\quad 4 + 3 \times 6 = 3 \times 6 + 4$
(since 4 added to 3 lots of 6 = 3 lots of 6 add 4).

So   gives 22 (the correct answer).

Try it on your calculator.

Exercise 3

Answer these using a calculator:

1. $6 \times 5 + 19$
2. $9 + 4 \times 3$
3. $54 - 8 \times 5$
4. $39 + 7 \times 19$
5. $116 - 13 \times 5$
6. $89 + 18 \times 7$

7. $205 - 2 \times 17$	**13.** $300 - 240 \div 12$	**19.** $11 \times 16 + 14 \times 13$
8. $57 + 9 \times 19$	**14.** $417 + 544 \div 17$	**20.** $999 \div 37 + 984 \div 41$
9. $37 + 96 \div 4$	**15.** $923 - 855 \div 19$	**21.** $625 \div 25 - 196 \div 14$
10. $152 - 112 \div 2$	**16.** $640 - 529 \div 23$	**22.** $68 \times 37 - 42 \times 43$
11. $197 + 156 \div 6$	**17.** $39 \div 3 + 7 \times 14$	**23.** $29 \times 56 + 702 \div 39$
12. $192 \div 3 + 206$	**18.** $13 \times 12 - 186 \div 2$	**24.** $935 \div 11 + 16 \times 26$

Exercise 4   Changing the Order of a Calculation

A Find the value of:

1. (a) $3 \times 6 \times 5$
   (b) $3 \times 5 \times 6$

2. (a) $24 \div 4 \div 2$
   (b) $24 \div 2 \div 4$

3. (a) $18 \div 3 \times 2$
   (b) $18 \times 2 \div 3$

4. (a) $3 \times 8 \div 2$
   (b) $3 \div 2 \times 8$

5. (a) $4 \times 12 \div 8$
   (b) $4 \div 8 \times 12$

6. (a) $16 \times 5 \div 40$
   (b) $16 \div 40 \times 5$

7. (a) $12 \times 2 \div 3 \times 4$
   (b) $12 \times 2 \times 4 \div 3$
   (c) $12 \div 3 \times 2 \times 4$

8. (a) $15 \times 2 \div 5 \div 3 \times 6$
   (b) $15 \times 2 \times 6 \div 5 \div 3$
   (c) $15 \div 5 \div 3 \times 2 \times 6$
   (d) $15 \div 5 \times 2 \div 3 \times 6$

9. (a) $50 \div 2 \times 6 \div 5 \div 3$
   (b) $50 \times 6 \div 2 \div 5 \div 3$
   (c) $50 \div 2 \div 5 \div 3 \times 6$

10. (a) $20 \times 6 \div 4 \div 3 \times 8 \div 10$
   (b) $20 \times 6 \times 8 \div 4 \div 3 \div 10$
   (c) $20 \div 4 \div 3 \div 10 \times 6 \times 8$
   (d) $20 \div 10 \times 6 \div 4 \div 3 \times 8$

B Answer these in your head using quick methods. Write the answer only.

1. $90 \times 12 \div 10$	**5.** $12 \times 15 \div 4$	**9.** $14 \times 8 \div 7 \div 4$
2. $56 \times 6 \div 8$	**6.** $10 \div 8 \times 4$	**10.** $2 \div 6 \times 9 \times 8$
3. $3 \div 4 \times 8$	**7.** $16 \times 3 \div 6$	**11.** $18 \times 7 \times 2 \div 9$
4. $7 \div 3 \times 9$	**8.** $9 \div 24 \times 16$	**12.** $72 \div 9 \times 13 \div 4$

C Find the value of:

1. (a) $20 - 6 + 4 - 3$
   (b) $20 - 6 - 3 + 4$
   (c) $20 + 4 - 6 - 3$

2. (a) $45 + 19 - 12 + 16 - 20$
   (b) $45 + 19 + 16 - 12 - 20$
   (c) $45 - 12 - 20 + 19 + 16$
   (d) $45 - 20 - 12 + 19 + 16$

3. (*a*) $53 + 19 + 16 - 12 - 19$
   (*b*) $53 + 19 - 19 + 16 - 12$
   (*c*) $53 - 12 + 16 + 19 - 19$

4. (*a*) $87 - 48 + 31 - 27 + 48$
   (*b*) $87 + 48 - 48 + 31 - 27$
   (*c*) $87 + 48 - 48 - 27 + 31$
   (*d*) $87 + 48 + 31 - 27 - 48$

D Answer these in your head using quick methods.
Write the answers only.

1. $14 + 18 - 12 + 8 - 9$
2. $8 + 19 - 7 + 1 - 6$
3. $21 + 13 - 21 + 9 - 4$
4. $56 + 15 + 17 - 56 - 17$
5. $81 + 47 - 47 - 81 + 16$
6. $74 + 20 - 50 - 20 + 6$

7. $61 - 18 + 19 - 20 - 12$
8. $84 - 19 - 14 + 5 - 20$
9. $93 + 47 - 36 - 53 + 12$
10. $44 - 40 + 66 - 60$
11. $41 + 72 - 31 + 29 - 52$
12. $65 + 48 - 38 - 55 + 12$

Use of Brackets

Exercise 5

Find the value of:

1. $4 \times (3 + 5)$
2. $7 \times (8 - 4)$
3. $9 \times (7 - 2)$
4. $8 \times (5 + 7)$
5. $(9 + 8) \times 2$

6. $48 \div (6 - 2)$
7. $(14 + 14) \div 7$
8. $(39 + 24) \div 9$
9. $(99 - 23) \div 4$
10. $84 \div (5 + 7)$

11. $108 \div (21 - 12)$
12. $42 \times (29 - 22)$
13. $(5 + 23) \times 8$
14. $(46 + 82) \div 8$
15. $(97 - 38) \times 5$

Exercise 6

Use a calculator to help with these. If the calculator has brackets
(parentheses) on it then use them. Compare the answers obtained in
each part of each question. Write which part, if any, gives the same
answer as the answer to part (*a*).

1. (*a*) $2 \times (12 + 3)$
   (*b*) $2 \times 12 + 3$
   (*c*) $2 \times 12 + 2 \times 3$

2. (*a*) $(12 + 3) \times 2$
   (*b*) $12 + 3 \times 2$
   (*c*) $12 \times 2 + 3 \times 2$

3. (*a*) $2 \times (12 - 3)$
   (*b*) $2 \times 12 - 3$
   (*c*) $2 \times 12 - 2 \times 3$

4. (*a*) $(12 - 3) \times 2$
   (*b*) $12 - 3 \times 2$
   (*c*) $12 \times 2 - 3 \times 2$

5. (a) $2 \times (12 \times 3)$
(b) $2 \times 12 \times 3$
(c) $(2 \times 12) \times (2 \times 3)$

6. (a) $(12 \times 3) \times 2$
(b) $12 \times 3 \times 2$
(c) $(12 \times 2) \times (3 \times 2)$

7. (a) $2 \times (12 \div 3)$
(b) $2 \times 12 \div 3$
(c) $(2 \times 12) \div (2 \times 3)$

8. (a) $(12 \div 3) \times 2$
(b) $12 \div 3 \times 2$
(c) $(12 \times 2) \div (3 \times 2)$

9. (a) $2 + (12 + 3)$
(b) $2 + 12 + 3$
(c) $(2 + 12) + (2 + 3)$

10. (a) $(12 + 3) + 2$
(b) $12 + 3 + 2$
(c) $(12 + 2) + (3 + 2)$

11. (a) $2 + (12 - 3)$
(b) $2 + 12 - 3$
(c) $(2 + 12) - (2 + 3)$

12. (a) $(12 - 3) + 2$
(b) $12 - 3 + 2$
(c) $(12 + 2) - (3 + 2)$

13. (a) $2 + (12 \times 3)$
(b) $2 + 12 \times 3$
(c) $(2 + 12) \times (2 + 3)$

14. (a) $(12 \times 3) + 2$
(b) $12 \times 3 + 2$
(c) $(12 + 2) \times (3 + 2)$

15. (a) $2 + (12 \div 3)$
(b) $2 + 12 \div 3$
(c) $(2 + 12) \div (2 + 3)$

16. (a) $(12 \div 3) + 2$
(b) $12 \div 3 + 2$
(c) $(12 + 2) \div (3 + 2)$

Exercise 7

A Write a statement, without brackets, that has the same value as the given statement. (Your answers to Exercise 6 may help.)

e.g. $4 \times (8 + 6) = 4 \times 8 + 4 \times 6$

1. $9 + (8 + 4)$
2. $3 \times (5 + 7)$
3. $4 \times (18 \div 6)$
4. $16 + (5 \times 6)$

5. $20 + (15 - 9)$
6. $(6 + 7) + 5$
7. $(8 - 2) \times 4$
8. $3 \times (14 - 6)$

9. $9 + (36 \div 6)$
10. $4 \times (6 \times 3)$
11. $(4 \times 9) + 3$
12. $(2 \times 8) \times 4$

B For each statement, write whether it is true or false:

1. $(3 + 9) \times 2 = 3 \times 2 + 9 \times 2$
2. $18 \div 6 + 3 = 18 + 3 \div 6$
3. $28 \div 2 + 2 = 28 \div 4$
4. $7 \times (8 - 3) = 7 \times 8 - 7 \times 3$

5. $6 \times 9 + 6 \times 5 = 6 \times (9 + 5)$
6. $5 \times (13 - 6) = 5 \times 13 - 6$
7. $7 + (4 \times 4) = 7 + 4 \times 4$
8. $6 + 3 \times 8 = 9 \times 8$

9. $42 - 12 \div 3 = 42 - 4$

10. $15 - 6 \times 2 = 15 \times 2 - 6$

11. $9 \times 8 \div 4 = 9 \times (8 \div 4)$

12. $10 + (4 + 7) = 10 + 4 + 10 + 7$

13. $10 + (4 \times 7) = 10 + 4 \times 7$

14. $6 + 4 \times 3 = (6 + 4) \times 3$

15. $25 + (14 - 8) = 25 + 14 - 8$

16. $8 \times 9 + 13 = 9 \times 8 + 13$

Substituting Numbers for Letters

Exercise 8

1. If $a = 8$, find the value of:

(a) $4a$ (c) $a - 5$ (e) $3a + 7$ (g) $4 + 2a$ (i) $3a + 2a$

(b) $7a$ (d) $15 - a$ (f) $6a - 11$ (h) $5a$ (j) $8a - 3a$

2. If $l = 6$, find the value of N if:

(a) $N = 7l$ (d) $N = 8l - 15$ (g) $N = 9l + l$

(b) $N = 19 - l$ (e) $N = 12 + 3l$ (h) $N = 19l - 11l$

(c) $N = 4l + 9$ (f) $N = 7l - 4l$

3. If $w = 12$, $x = 4$, $y = 3$ and $z = 2$, find the value of:

(a) $5w$ (f) $4z + 13$ (k) $wz + 7$ (p) $w \div z$

(b) $x + w$ (g) $7y - 2x$ (l) $2wy - 25$ (q) $\dfrac{xy}{2}$

(c) $w + z - y$ (h) wx (m) $5xy + 3x$ (r) $\dfrac{wx}{6}$

(d) $3x + y$ (i) $3xz$ (n) $5xy + 3y$ (s) $\dfrac{wy}{z}$

(e) $14 - 3y$ (j) xyz (o) $8xy$ (t) $\dfrac{w}{x} + yz$

4. If $a = 7, b = 4, c = 0, d = 9, e = 8, f = 3, g = 6$ and $h = 12$, find the value of:

(a) $7d$ (f) $\dfrac{h}{f} + 2a$ (k) $4g + 8f$ (p) $6(d - g)$

(b) eg (g) abc (l) $4(g + 2f)$ (q) $6d - 6g$

(c) $6af$ (h) def (m) $(a + b) \times f$ (r) $4h - (d + e)$

(d) $5h - fg$ (i) $3f + 3b$ (n) $a + bf$ (s) $4h - d + e$

(e) $\dfrac{d}{3} + e$ (j) $3(f + b)$ (o) $af + bf$ (t) $4h - d - e$

5. (a) If $Y = 49$, find the value of X where $X = 180 - Y$.

(b) Use $A = bh$ to find A, when $b = 28$ and $h = 15$.

(c) Find x, if $x = 4y - 3z$ and $y = 9$ when $z = 4$.

(d) Given that $A = \frac{1}{2}(x + y)$, find A when $x = 14$ and $y = 18$.

(e) If $D = \frac{1}{2}(X - Y)$, find D when $X = 43$ and $Y = 27$.

(f) If $A = \dfrac{V}{h}$, calculate A when $V = 574$ and $h = 14$.

(g) Find D when $A = 56$, $d = 7$ and $D = \dfrac{2A}{d}$.

(h) If $l = \dfrac{A}{b}$, calculate l when $b = 19$ and $A = 437$.

Using Formulae

Exercise 9

1. The area of a rhombus can be found by halving the product of its diagonals. Calculate the area of a rhombus with diagonals measuring 24 cm and 8 cm.

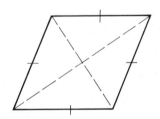

2. The circumference of a circle is approximately three times its diameter. Estimate the circumference of a circle that has a diameter of 9 cm.

3. The average speed travelled on a journey can be found by dividing the total distance travelled by the total time taken. Calculate the average speed for a journey of:

(a) 148 miles in 4 h,

(b) 147 miles in $3\frac{1}{2}$ h.

4. When buying goods in a sale, the sale price is the normal price less the discount. Calculate the sale price if the normal price is £46.99 and there is £8.47 discount.

5. When two angles lie on a straight line, the unknown angle can be found by subtracting the known angle from 180°. Find the unknown angle shown in the diagram.

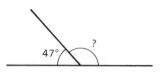

6. The product of the length, breadth and height of a cuboid gives its volume. Find the volume of a cuboid with dimensions 15 cm, 9 cm and 6 cm.

Exercise 10

1. The perimeter of a square is four times the length of a side. This can be written as the formula $P = 4l$.
Use the formula to find the perimeter when the length of each side measures:

(*a*) 9 cm   (*b*) 0.6 m   (*c*) 4.7 m

2. The area of a triangle can be found by dividing the product of its base and perpendicular height by two. This formula can be written as $A = \frac{1}{2}bh$.
Use the formula to find the area of a triangle having a base of length 15 cm and a perpendicular height of 12 cm.

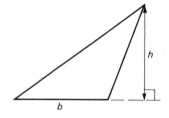

3. The length of a rectangle can be found by dividing its area by its breadth. The formula can be written as

$$l = \frac{A}{b}.$$

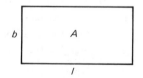

Use the formula to find the breadth when:
(*a*) $A = 112$ and $b = 8$,   (*b*) $A = 360$ and $b = 15$.

4. When two resistors, r_1 and r_2, are connected in series, as shown in the diagram, the total resistance in the circuit, R, is the sum of the two resistances. We can write $R = r_1 + r_2$.

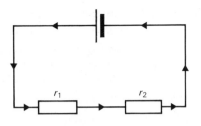

Find the total resistance, R ohms, in a circuit, if $r_1 = 2.6$ and $r_2 = 3.7$.

5. The number of seconds, n, in x min can be obtained by multiplying the number of minutes by 60. The formula is $n = 60x$. Use the formula to find the number of seconds in 8 min.

6. (*a*) On Earth, the weight of a person (in newtons) can be found by multiplying a person's mass (in kilograms) by 10. Find the weight of someone on Earth with a mass of 45 kg.

(*b*) If the person in part (*a*) is on the Moon, that person's weight can be found by multiplying the mass by 1.6. Find that person's weight on the Moon.

Exercise 11

1. $A = lb$ gives the area of a rectangle.

Find A when $l = 12$ and $b = 9$.

2. $A = bh$ gives the area of a parallelogram. Calculate the area when $b = 15$ and $h = 14$, both measurements being in centimetres.

3. (*a*) The formula $a = 180 - (b + c)$ gives the third angle of any triangle, when the other two angles are known.

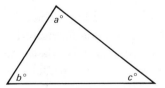

Use the formula to find the third angle when the other two angles are 86° and 58°.

(b) The formula $a = 180 - b - c$ also gives the third angle of any triangle, when the other two angles are known. Use this version of the formula to find the third angle when the other two angles are 109° and 37°.

4. The circumference of a circle can be found using the formula $C = \pi d$. Find the circumference of a circle with diameter, $d = 9\,\text{m}$ if $\pi = 3.142$.

5. $V = \frac{1}{3}Ah$ gives the volume of any pyramid, where the area of the base is A units^2 and the perpendicular height, h units. Use the formula to find the volume of a triangular pyramid, where the area of the base is $22\,\text{cm}^2$ and the perpendicular height is 12 cm.

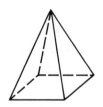

6. In the diagram, distance z is given by the formula:

$$z = x + y$$

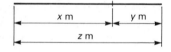

Find z when $x = 7.69$ and $y = 4.92$.

7. $F = \dfrac{9C}{5} + 32$ can be used to change degrees Celsius (°C) into degrees Fahrenheit. Use the formula to change the following temperatures to degrees Fahrenheit (°F)
(a) 20 °C (b) 5 °C (c) 75 °C (d) 35 °C

8. The area of a trapezium can be found using the formula:

$$A = \tfrac{1}{2}(a + b)h$$

where a and b are the lengths of the parallel sides, and h is the perpendicular distance between those parallel sides.

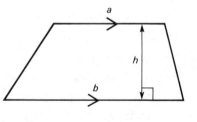

Use the formula to find the area of a trapezium if the parallel sides measure 19 cm and 11 cm, and the perpendicular distance between those sides is 12 cm.

Exercise 12   Some Formulae Used in Science

You will probably use the following formulae in science sometime:

1. Work is the product of a force and the distance moved in the direction of the force:

Work done   =   force   × distance moved
(in joules, J)   (in newtons, N)   (in metres, m)

that is $W = Fs$

Find the work done by a person who lifts a weight of 240 N to a height of 1.5 m.

2. $\text{Power} = \dfrac{\text{work done}}{\text{time}}$

Power is in watts (W), work done is in joules (J) and time is in seconds (s).

(a) Find the power of a machine that does 1440 J of work in $\frac{1}{2}$ min.

(b) Find the power of a light bulb that uses 3600 J in 1 min.

3.   Power   =   voltage   ×   current
(watts, W)   (volts, V)   (amps, A)

that is $P = V \times I$

This can be rewritten as $I = \dfrac{P}{V}$.

Use this final version of the formula to find the current carried by an iron that works at 240 V, if it has a maximum power of 1008 W.

4. Ohm's law gives a formula connecting voltage, V (volts, V), current, I (amps, A), and resistance, R (ohms, Ω). It is $R = \dfrac{V}{I}$.

Use the formula to find the resistance of an electric kettle, if it carries a current of 8.5 A at a voltage of 240 V. (Give the answer correct to one decimal place.)

5. $\text{Density} = \dfrac{\text{mass}}{\text{volume}}$

Use this formula to find the density (in grams per cubic centimetre, or g/cm^3) of brass, if 80 cm^3 of brass has a mass of 672 g.

305

6. $$\text{Pressure} = \frac{\text{force}}{\text{area}}$$

The formula above gives the pressure (in newtons per square metre, N/m^2) due to a force (in newtons, N) acting over an area (in square metres, m^2).

Find the pressure when:
(*a*) a force of 450 N spreads over an area of 6 m^2,
(*b*) a force of 360 N spreads over an area of 1.8 m^2.

7. The formula for potential energy is $\text{PE} = mgh$.

Note PE does *not* mean $\text{P} \times \text{E}$ in this instance. It stands for one number only.)

Find the increase in potential energy (that is, the value of PE) when a body of mass, $m = 53$ kg is lifted a height, h, of 3 m. The acceleration due to gravity, $g = 10$ m/s^2 (m/s^2 is read as metres per second squared, or as metres per second per second).

The unit of potential energy is joules, J.

8. Use the formula $v = u + gt$ to find the final velocity, v (metres per second, m/s) of a body that falls for a time, t, of 8 s if its initial velocity, $u = 25$ m/s and the acceleration due to gravity $g = 10$ m/s^2.

Constructing Formulae

Exercise 13

1. The diameter, d, of a circle is twice its radius, r. Write the formula, then use it to find the diameter of a circle having a radius of 1.87 m.

2. Write a formula to give the perimeter, P cm, of an equilateral triangle with side, l cm.
Use the formula to find the perimeter of an equilateral triangle with side 7.4 cm.

l cm

3. Write down a formula for the perimeter, P cm, of the given isosceles triangle. Use the formula to find the perimeter, when the two equal sides each measure 4.6 cm and the third side measures 3.9 cm.

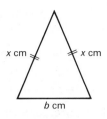

4. The sides of a scalene triangle are d mm, e mm and f mm. Write a formula for its perimeter, P mm.
   (a) Use the formula to find the perimeter, in millimetres, when $d = 57$, $e = 79$ and $f = 62$.
   (b) Write the perimeter of the triangle in centimetres.

5. Write down a formula for the perimeter, P m, of the given rectangle.

Use the formula to calculate the perimeter when $l = 9.6$ and $b = 5.3$.

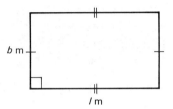

6. Write a formula that gives the length, l cm in terms of x, y and z.

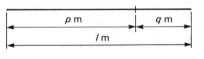

Use the formula to find l when $x = 8.3, y = 12.9$ and $z = 5.8$.

7. Write a formula that gives p in terms of q and l. Use the formula to find p when $l = 15.3$ and $q = 4.8$.

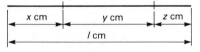

8. If n articles cost £l each, write a formula to find the total cost, £T, giving T in terms of n and l. Use the formula to find the total cost of 7 articles that cost £19 each.

9. An estimate of the diameter, d, of a circle is that it is approximately one-third of the circumference, C. Write a formula giving d in terms of C.

Use the formula to estimate the diameter of a circle having a circumference of 19.5 cm.

10. Write a formula to give the number of days, n, in w weeks. Use the formula to find the number of days in 13 weeks.

Exercise 14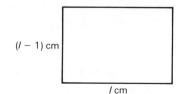

In the given rectangle, the breadth is 1 cm shorter than the length. Since the length $= l$ cm, the breadth $= (l - 1)$ cm.

$(l - 1)$ cm

l cm

1. Write a formula giving the perimeter, P cm, in terms of l. Simplify the right-hand side of the formula (use like terms).

2. (a) Copy the given table.
  (b) Use your formula to help you to complete the table.

Length, l cm	Breadth, $(l - 1)$ cm	Perimeter, P cm
2	1	?
3	2	?
4	?	14
5	?	?
6	5	?
7	?	?
8	?	?
9	?	?
10	?	?
11	?	?
12	?	?

3. (a) Draw a pair of axes as shown. Let 1 cm represent 1 cm on the length axis, and 2 cm represent 5 cm on the perimeter axis.
   (b) Use your table to help you to plot points of perimeter against length.
   (c) Join the points.

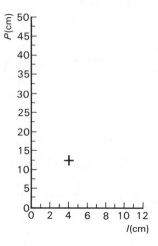

Exercise 15

1. If $x * y$ means $2(x + y)$, find the value of:
   (a) $3 * 5$ (c) $1 * 12$ (e) $(3 * 2) * 4$
   (b) $5 * 3$ (d) $3 * (2 * 4)$

2. If $a * b$ means $\frac{1}{2}(a + b)$, find the value of:
   (a) $2 * 8$ (c) $7 * 5$ (e) $(8 * 4) * 6$
   (b) $8 * 2$ (d) $6 * 3$ (f) $8 * (4 * 6)$

3. If $p * q$ means $4p - q$, find the value of:
   (a) $5 * 6$ (c) $2 * 2$ (e) $(3 * 2) * 4$
   (b) $6 * 5$ (d) $3 * (2 * 4)$

4. If $m * n$ means $3m + 2n$, find the value of:
   (a) $7 * 4$ (c) $10 * 5$ (e) $(2 * 5) * 3$
   (b) $4 * 7$ (d) $2 * (5 * 3)$

5. If $e * f$ means $ef + 3f$, find the value of:
   (a) $4 * 2$ (c) $5 * 1$
   (b) $2 * 4$ (d) $3 * (6 * 2)$

16 Directed Numbers

Exercise 1

1. An aeroplane flying at 3250 m drops to a height of 1400 m. What height has it lost?

2. A man had £39 in his bank account. He then wrote a cheque for £97. By how much was he now overdrawn?

3. Mr Simmons was overdrawn by £46. If he then spent a further £88 from the same account, by how much would he then be overdrawn?

4. Mrs Howe's bank account is overdrawn by £73. How much must she deposit to have a credit of £51?

5. Mrs Cash has £53 in her bank account. She spends £48, deposits £26 in the account and then spends a further £69. By how much is she overdrawn?

6. Mr Copper was overdrawn by £27. He deposited £55 in the account, used a cheque for £86, deposited £18 in the account and then signed another cheque, this time for £63. By how much is he now overdrawn?

7. A submarine dives from a depth of 1463 m to a depth of 2171 m. By how many metres has it just dived?

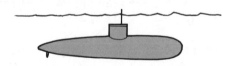

8. A submarine is at a depth of 1898 m. If it then dives a further 365 m, what is its new depth?

9. In the football league, two teams have exactly the same number of points. Team A had scored 39 goals but had 47 scored against them, while team B had scored 32 goals and had 39 goals scored against them. Which of the two teams should be higher in the league? Why?

10. In a competition, Adam gained 68 points and lost 75 points, Beryl gained 51 points and lost 37 points, Camilla gained 46 points and lost 55 points, Dilwyn gained 54 points and lost 62 points, Edward gained 63 points and lost 48 points while Fiona gained 40 points and lost 54 points.

Sort these six people into order on 'point difference', giving the largest first. (For each person, compare points gained with points lost.)

Positive and Negative Numbers

Here is a number line. It shows numbers that are greater than and numbers that are less than zero.

Numbers greater than zero are called 'positive numbers' and numbers less than zero are called 'negative numbers'.

$\left. \begin{array}{l} ^{+}3 \\ (+3) \\ +3 \text{ in some texts} \end{array} \right\}$ are read as 'positive three'.

$\left. \begin{array}{l} ^{-}3 \\ (-3) \\ -3 \text{ in some texts} \end{array} \right\}$ are read as 'negative three'.

A number without a symbol in front of it is a positive number. $^{+}3$ may be written as 3 and read as 'three' rather than as 'positive three'.

Positive and negative numbers (*directed numbers*) and a number line are used when measuring temperature.

Exercise 2

A Write the temperature, in degrees Celsius (°C), shown on each of these thermometers:

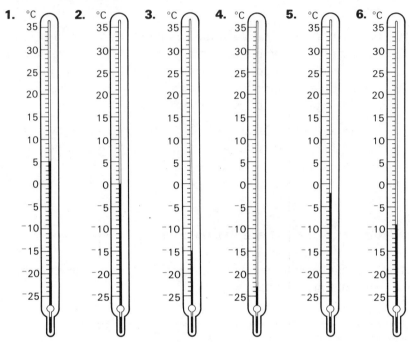

B **1.** Which is warmer, ⁻13 °C or 8 °C?

2. Which is colder, ⁻9 °C or ⁻2 °C?

3. Is ⁻8 °C warmer than 8 °C?

4. Write these temperatures in order, from coldest to hottest:
9 °C, ⁻1 °C, ⁻5 °C, ⁻14 °C, ⁻2 °C, ⁻17 °C, 13 °C, 0 °C

5. Here is a list of temperatures:
⁻3 °C, 6 °C, ⁻6 °C, ⁻15 °C, ⁻4 °C, 7 °C, ⁻9 °C, ⁻14 °C, 21 °C,
0 °C, 14 °C, 17 °C, ⁻21 °C, 10 °C, ⁻12 °C, 19 °C, ⁻16 °C, ⁻31 °C,

Choosing your answers from the above list:
(a) Write the fifth highest temperature.
(b) Write the sixth lowest temperature.
(c) Write the temperature that is slightly higher than ⁻12 °C.
(d) List the temperatures that are colder than ⁻10 °C.

Copy and complete:

	Previous temperature	Temperature change	New temperature
1.	6 °C	$^+4$ °C	? °C
2.	16 °C	$^-9$ °C	? °C
3.	9 °C	? °C	21 °C
4.	? °C	$^+11$ °C	13 °C
5.	31 °C	? °C	18 °C
6.	$^-7$ °C	$^+18$ °C	? °C
7.	$^-3$ °C	? °C	5 °C
8.	$^-5$ °C	$^-4$ °C	? °C
9.	$^-10$ °C	? °C	17 °C
10.	7 °C	$^-8$ °C	? °C
11.	4 °C	$^-11$ °C	? °C
12.	$^-4$ °C	? °C	$^-7$ °C
13.	? °C	$^+11$ °C	5 °C
14.	? °C	$^-9$ °C	9 °C
15.	? °C	$^-14$ °C	$^-5$ °C
16.	? °C	$^-6$ °C	$^-8$ °C
17.	$^-15$ °C	? °C	$^-6$ °C
18.	0 °C	? °C	$^-12$ °C
19.	14 °C	$^-28$ °C	? °C
20.	? °C	$^+17$ °C	0 °C
21.	$^-9$ °C	$^+9$ °C	? °C
22.	$^-13$ °C	? °C	13 °C
23.	? °C	$^-21$ °C	0 °C
24.	11 °C	? °C	$^-11$ °C
25.	$^-14$ °C	? °C	23 °C

Exercise 4   Addition and Subtraction Using a Number Line

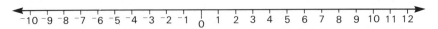

Answer the following questions. The number line above may help you.

1. $7 + 2$

2. $^+3 + 5$

3. $0 + 11$

4. $^-2 + 5$

5. $^-7 + 13$

6. $^+12 - 7$

7. $7 - 5$

8. $5 - 7$

9. $3 - 3$

10. $5 - 12$

11. $^+7 - 13$

12. $8 - 3$

13. $^-8 - 3$

14. $4 + 8$

15. $^-4 - 8$

16. $^-9 - 12$

17. $4 + 9$

18. $^-4 + 9$

19. $^-9 + 4$

20. $9 - 4$

21. $4 - 9$

22. $^-4 - 9$

23. $^-9 - 4$

24. $^-8 - 11$

25. $^-1 - 15$

26. $15 + 1$

27. $19 - 3$

28. $3 - 19$

29. $4 + 11 - 6$

30. $7 - 2 + 4$

31. $12 - 1 - 5$

32. $^-3 + 8 + 5$

33. $5 + 4 - 13$

34. $3 - 9 - 6$

35. $^-4 + 1 + 11$

36. $16 - 12 + 12$

37. $^-7 + 13 + 7 - 1$

38. $^-14 - 7 - 7 + 14$

39. $14 - 3 + 3 - 6$

40. $19 - 4 - 19 + 4$

Addition of Directed Numbers

Exercise 5

It is not necessary to answer all three parts of this exercise:

A **1.** Copy these. By finding a pattern, fill in the missing answers.

(a) $^+3 + ^+3 = ^+6$
$^+3 + ^+2 =$
$^+3 + ^+1 =$
$^+3 + 0 =$
$^+3 + ^-1 =$
$^+3 + ^-2 = ^+1$
$^+3 + ^-3 =$
$^+3 + ^-4 =$
$^+3 + ^-5 =$
$^+3 + ^-6 =$
$^+3 + ^-7 =$
$^+3 + ^-8 =$

(b) $^-3 + ^+7 = ^+4$
$^-3 + ^+6 = ^+3$
$^-3 + ^+5 =$
$^-3 + ^+4 =$
$^-3 + ^+3 = 0$
$^-3 + ^+2 =$
$^-3 + ^+1 =$
$^-3 + 0 = ^-3$
$^-3 + ^-1 =$
$^-3 + ^-2 =$
$^-3 + ^-3 =$
$^-3 + ^-4 =$

314

2. $^+3 + {}^-2 = {}^+1$ which can also be
written as $3 + {}^-2 = 1$
   If $3 + {}^-2 = 3 \boxed{?} 2$
What is the missing operation*?

B In a certain school, the pupils were given merit marks for good work or good behaviour and were given de-merit marks for poor work or bad behaviour.

The pupils were given cards with merit marks or de-merit marks on them.

The cards looked like this:

$\boxed{^+2}$ is worth 2 merit marks and $\boxed{^-3}$ is worth 3 de-merit marks

e.g. 1 If John got $\boxed{^+6}$ and $\boxed{^-2}$ he would have 4 marks altogether, since $\boxed{^+6}$ and $\boxed{^-2}$ is the same as $\boxed{^+4}$.

We would write $\boxed{^+6} + \boxed{^-2} = \boxed{^+4}$.

e.g. 2 $\boxed{^+2} + \boxed{^-5} = \boxed{^-3}$.

1. Work these out:

(a) $\boxed{^+2} + \boxed{^+5}$ (i) $\boxed{^-6} + \boxed{^+1}$

(b) $\boxed{^+5} + \boxed{^-3}$ (j) $\boxed{^-5} + \boxed{^+8} + \boxed{^-2}$

(c) $\boxed{^+4} + \boxed{^-4}$ (k) $\boxed{^-7} + \boxed{^+4} + \boxed{^+1}$

(d) $\boxed{^+6} + \boxed{^-2} + \boxed{^+3}$ (l) $\boxed{^-9} + \boxed{^-3} + \boxed{^+4}$

(e) $\boxed{^+4} + \boxed{^-3} + \boxed{^+1}$ (m) $\boxed{^+8} + \boxed{^-5} + \boxed{^-6}$

(f) $\boxed{^+8} + \boxed{^-3}$ (n) $\boxed{^+6} + \boxed{^-3} + \boxed{^-3}$

(g) $\boxed{^-3} + \boxed{^+8}$ (o) $\boxed{^-4} + \boxed{^+7} + \boxed{^-5}$

(h) $\boxed{^-5} + \boxed{^+9}$ (p) $\boxed{^-3} + \boxed{^-2} + \boxed{^+9}$

2. $\boxed{^+6} + \boxed{^-2} = \boxed{^+4}$ and this can be written as $^+6 + {}^-2 = {}^+4$
and this is the same as $6 + {}^-2 = 4$.

If $6 + {}^-2 = 6 \boxed{?} 2$, what is the missing operation?

*See the glossary, p. 435.

C 4↑ means 'a journey four places up'.

3↓ means 'a journey three places down'.

6↑ + 2↓ can be read as 'a journey six places up *followed by* a journey two places down'.

e.g. 1 6↑ + 2↓ = $^+4$

e.g. 2 5↓ + 3↑ = $^-2$

Answer these:

1. 5↑ + 4↑

2. 9↑ + 5↓

3. 4↑ + 8↓

4. 7↑ + 12↓

5. 10↓ + 6↑

6. 5↓ + 12↑

7. 9↑ + 9↓

8. 8↓ + 2↓

9. 5↓ + 15↑

10. 2↑ + 15↓

11. 2↑ + 6↓ + 9↑

12. 5↓ + 1↑ + 3↓

13. 4↑ + 7↓ + 3↑ + 6↓

14. 9↓ + 5↑ + 10↑ + 2↓

15. 12↑ + 8↓ + 10↓ + 5↑

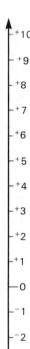

This nomogram can be used for addition.

You need to use a ruler.

Try to see how it works.

Use the nomogram to help you to answer these questions:

1. $5 + 3$
2. $9 + 6$
3. $2 + 8$
4. $8 + 8$
5. $5 + 0$
6. $8 + {}^-2$
7. $9 + {}^-5$
8. $3 + {}^-9$
9. $6 + {}^-6$
10. ${}^-4 + 4$
11. ${}^-8 + 3$
12. ${}^-8 + 9$
13. ${}^-5 + 0$
14. ${}^-6 + {}^-9$
15. ${}^-7 + {}^-2$
16. ${}^-1 + 9$
17. $4 + {}^-1$
18. ${}^-9 + {}^-9$
19. $2 + {}^-8$
20. ${}^-8 + 2$

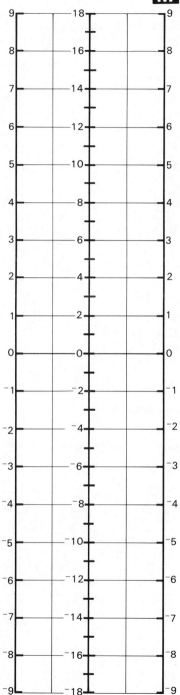

Exercise 7

A Find the value of:

1. $7 + {}^-5$	**9.** ${}^-8 + {}^-3$	**17.** ${}^-1 + 8 + {}^-4$
2. $2 + {}^-3$	**10.** ${}^-2 + {}^-2$	**18.** ${}^-5 + {}^-6 + {}^-2$
3. $10 + {}^-7$	**11.** ${}^-1 + {}^-9$	**19.** $7 + {}^-2 + {}^-3$
4. $8 + {}^-10$	**12.** ${}^-12 + {}^-11$	**20.** $2 + {}^-9 + 10$
5. ${}^-6 + 4$	**13.** $11 + {}^-4$	**21.** $5 + {}^-12 + 3$
6. ${}^-1 + 10$	**14.** ${}^-5 + 6$	**22.** ${}^-3 + {}^-11 + 6$
7. ${}^-7 + 6$	**15.** ${}^-9 + {}^-6$	**23.** ${}^-10 + {}^-9 + 25$
8. ${}^-14 + 7$	**16.** ${}^-9 + 3$	**24.** $6 + {}^-5 + {}^-10$

B Find the value of:

1. $8 + (-4)$	**9.** $(-6) + (-5)$	**17.** $(-3) + 10 + (-4)$
2. $2 + (-4)$	**10.** $(-2) + (-7)$	**18.** $(-7) + (-3) + (-1)$
3. $12 + (-3)$	**11.** $(-4) + (-4)$	**19.** $9 + (-4) + (-4)$
4. $6 + (-8)$	**12.** $(-4) + (-9)$	**20.** $3 + (-10) + 7$
5. $(-5) + 4$	**13.** $10 + (-4)$	**21.** $8 + (-14) + 4$
6. $(-2) + 7$	**14.** $(-2) + 6$	**22.** $(-6) + (-3) + 5$
7. $(-11) + 1$	**15.** $(-7) + (-3)$	**23.** $(-12) + (-4) + 21$
8. $(-12) + 5$	**16.** $(-8) + 5$	**24.** $9 + (-7) + (-9)$

Exercise 8

Find the missing numbers to make each statement correct:

1. $6 + \boxed{?} = 15$	**11.** $5 + \boxed{?} = 0$
2. $8 + \boxed{?} = 3$	**12.** ${}^-2 + \boxed{?} = 0$
3. $\boxed{?} + {}^-3 = 7$	**13.** $\boxed{?} + {}^-10 = 0$
4. $\boxed{?} + {}^-6 = {}^-4$	**14.** ${}^-11 + \boxed{?} = {}^-19$
5. $1 + \boxed{?} = {}^-3$	**15.** $\boxed{?} + {}^-6 = {}^-10$
6. ${}^-2 + \boxed{?} = 3$	**16.** $\boxed{?} + 7 = 1$
7. ${}^-9 + \boxed{?} = {}^-8$	**17.** $\boxed{?} + {}^-2 = 17$
8. $\boxed{?} + 6 = {}^-4$	**18.** ${}^-7 + \boxed{?} = 6$
9. $\boxed{?} + 7 = 2$	**19.** ${}^-8 + \boxed{?} = {}^-20$
10. ${}^-6 + \boxed{?} = {}^-9$	**20.** $\boxed{?} + 3 = {}^-9$

Subtraction of Directed Numbers

Consider the calculation $^+12 - {}^+5$

Since $^+12 = 12$ and $^+5 = 5$ then

$$^+12 - {}^+5$$
$$= 12 - 5$$
$$= \underline{\underline{7}}$$

Here are two more examples of subtraction:

e.g. 1 $\quad {}^+3 - {}^+9$
$$= 3 - 9$$
$$= \underline{\underline{{}^-6}}$$

e.g. 2 $\quad {}^-4 - {}^+7$
$$= {}^-4 - 7$$
$$= \underline{\underline{{}^-11}}$$

The examples above show subtraction of positive numbers. Subtraction of negative numbers is more of a problem and is dealt with in the following exercise.

Exercise 9 ▨ M

This exercise is divided into five sections. Each section deals with subtraction of negative numbers in a different way. It may be necessary to work only through one section.

A 1. Copy these and fill in the missing numbers. (Look for patterns.)

(a) $5 - {}^+3 = 2$
$5 - {}^+2 = \boxed{?}$
$5 - {}^+1 = \boxed{?}$
$5 - 0 = \boxed{?}$
$5 - {}^-1 = \boxed{?}$
$5 - {}^-2 = \boxed{?}$
$5 - {}^-3 = 8$
$5 - {}^-4 = \boxed{?}$
$5 - {}^-5 = \boxed{?}$
$5 - {}^-6 = \boxed{?}$
$5 - {}^-7 = \boxed{?}$
$5 - {}^-8 = \boxed{?}$

(b) $^-5 - {}^+3 = {}^-8$
$^-5 - {}^+2 = \boxed{?}$
$^-5 - {}^+1 = \boxed{?}$
$^-5 - 0 = \boxed{?}$
$^-5 - {}^-1 = \boxed{?}$
$^-5 - {}^-2 = \boxed{?}$
$^-5 - {}^-3 = {}^-2$
$^-5 - {}^-4 = \boxed{?}$
$^-5 - {}^-5 = \boxed{?}$
$^-5 - {}^-6 = \boxed{?}$
$^-5 - {}^-7 = \boxed{?}$
$^-5 - {}^-8 = \boxed{?}$

2. (a) If $5 - {}^-3 = 5$? 3, what is the missing operation?

(b) If ${}^-5 - {}^-3 = {}^-5$? 3, what is the missing operation?

B Six villages, P, Q, R, S, T and U, lie on a hillside.
Their altitudes are shown in the diagram below.
Three of the villages, P, Q and R, are above sea-level while three villages, S, T and U, are below sea-level.
Note that the altitude of Q is ${}^+45$ m while the altitude of T is ${}^-25$ m (25 m below sea-level).

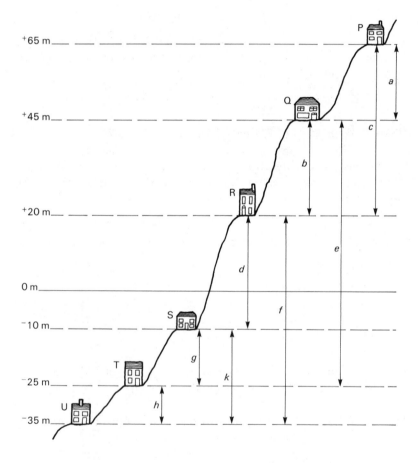

1. (a) What is the vertical distance marked a?

(b) What is the difference in altitude between villages P and Q?

(c) What is the value of $65 - 45$?

2. (*a*) What is the vertical distance marked *b*?

(*b*) What is the difference in altitude between villages Q and R?

(*c*) What is the value of $45 - (+20)$?

3. (*a*) What is the vertical distance marked *c*?

(*b*) What is the difference in altitude between P and R?

(*c*) What is the value of $65 - {}^{+}20$?

4. (*a*) What is the vertical distance marked *d*?

(*b*) What is the difference in altitude between R and S?

(*c*) What is the value of ${}^{+}20 - {}^{-}10$?

5. (*a*) What is the difference in altitude between Q and T?

(*b*) What is the value of $(+45) - (-25)$?

6. (*a*) What is the difference in altitude between R and U?

(*b*) What is the value of $(+20) - (-35)$?

7. (*a*) What is the vertical distance marked *g*?

(*b*) What is the difference in altitude between S and T?

(*c*) What is the value of ${}^{-}10 - {}^{-}25$?

8. (*a*) What is the vertical distance marked *h*?

(*b*) What is the difference in altitude between T and U?

(*c*) What is the value of $(-25) - (-35)$?

9. (*a*) What is the difference in altitude between S and U?

(*b*) What is the value of ${}^{-}10 - {}^{-}35$?

10. (*a*) What is the difference in altitude between P and T?

(*b*) What is the value of $65 - {}^{-}25$?

11. (*a*) What is the difference in altitude between Q and U?

(*b*) What is the value of $(+45) - (-35)$?

12. (*a*) What is the difference in altitude between R and T?

(*b*) What is the value of $(+20) - (-25)$?

13. If $40 - {}^{-}15 = 40\ \boxed{?}\ 15$, what is the missing operation?

14. Work out:

(*a*) $70 - {}^{-}25$ (*b*) ${}^{-}15 - {}^{-}40$

321

C

$$-10\ -9\ -8\ -7\ -6\ -5\ -4\ -3\ -2\ -1\ \ 0\ +1\ +2\ +3\ +4\ +5\ +6\ +7\ +8\ +9\ +10$$

In the diagram above each step taken by the Martian is one position on the number line.

1. Answer the following questions. (Show steps backwards with a negative sign, *e.g.* ⁻7 means 'seven steps backwards'.)

	How many steps does the Martian take in walking from:	Answer these:
(a)	⁺2 to ⁺9 ? ?	9 − 2 = ?
(b)	⁺4 to ⁺10? ?	10 − 4 = ?
(c)	⁺6 to ⁻3 ? ?	⁻3 − 6 = ?
(d)	⁺5 to ⁺1 ? ?	1 − 5 = ?
(e)	⁻8 to ⁻3 ? ?	⁻3 − ⁻8 = ?
(f)	⁻10 to ⁻7 ? ?	⁻7 − ⁻10 = ?
(g)	⁻6 to ⁺9 ? ?	9 − ⁻6 = ?
(h)	⁻3 to ⁺7 ? ?	7 − ⁻3 = ?
(i)	⁻2 to ⁻10? ?	⁻10 − ⁻2 = ?
(j)	⁻1 to ⁻8 ? ?	⁻8 − ⁻1 = ?
(k)	⁻8 to ⁻1 ? ?	⁻1 − ⁻8 = ?
(l)	⁻6 to 6 ? ?	6 − ⁻6 = ?

2. If 9 − ⁻4 = 9 ? 4, what is the missing operation?

D Copy and complete:

	Previous temperature (°C)	New temperature (°C)	Change in temperature (°C)	Calculation
1.	4	12	+ [?]	$12 - 4 =$ [?]
2.	7	[?]	+ 11	[?] $- 7 = 11$
3.	$^-9$	5	+ [?]	$5 - {^-9} =$ [?]
4.	$^-10$	9	+ [?]	$9 - {^-10} =$ [?]
5.	$^-13$	[?]	+ 20	[?] $- {^-13} = 20$
6.	12	2	− [?]	$2 - 12 =$ [?]
7.	$^-2$	[?]	− 9	[?] $- {^-2} = {^-9}$
8.	[?]	14	+ 6	$14 -$ [?] $= 6$
9.	[?]	$^-5$	− 12	$^-5 -$ [?] $= {^-12}$
10.	$^-6$	[?]	− 8	[?] $- {^-6} = {^-8}$
11.	$^-16$	− 7	+ [?]	$^-7 - {^-16} =$ [?]
12.	[?]	$^-15$	− 12	$^-15 -$ [?] $= {^-12}$
13.	$^-12$	[?]	$^-5$	[?] $- {^-12} = {^-5}$
14.	[?]	$^-1$	$^+7$	$^-1 -$ [?] $= 7$

E **1.** Work out the following:

(a) $5-5$	(e) $23-23$	(i) $^-12-^-12$
(b) $3-3$	(f) $^-8-^-8$	(j) $^-37-^-37$
(c) $9-9$	(g) $^-2-^-2$	(k) $^-85-^-85$
(d) $100-100$	(h) $^-4-^-4$	(l) $^-100-^-100$

2. If $6-^-3=6\boxed{?}3$, what is the missing operation?

Exercise 10

A A nomogram can also be used for subtraction of directed numbers. Look again at the nomogram in Exercise 6 on p. 317 and try to work out how it can be used for subtraction.

B Use the nomogram to help you to answer these questions:

1.	$12-8$	**11.**	$^-4\ -\ ^-9$	
2.	$10-3$	**12.**	$^-16-^-7$	
3.	$3-10$	**13.**	$^-15-^-8$	
4.	$7-0$	**14.**	$13-7$	
5.	$0-7$	**15.**	$1\ -\ ^-7$	
6.	$3-^-2$	**16.**	$^-10-^-1$	
7.	$^-7-^-1$	**17.**	$^-2\ -\ ^-6$	
8.	$2-^-4$	**18.**	$0\ -\ ^-3$	
9.	$^-3-^-3$	**19.**	$^-6\ -\ ^-4$	
10.	$^-8-^-2$	**20.**	$^-14-^-8$	

Exercise 11

Work these out:

A

1.	$12-^+3$	**9.**	$^-7-^-12$	**17.**	$4-^-6-^+9$
2.	$3-^+5$	**10.**	$18-^-10$	**18.**	$^-7-^-4-^-8$
3.	$9-^-3$	**11.**	$^-10-^+18$	**19.**	$^-10-^-3-^+2$
4.	$2-^-8$	**12.**	$11-^-11$	**20.**	$3-^-2-14$
5.	$^-3-^+3$	**13.**	$^-11-^-11$	**21.**	$12-3-^-5$
6.	$^-12-^+7$	**14.**	$^-11-^+11$	**22.**	$^-8-^-12-5$
7.	$^-12-^-7$	**15.**	$0-^-9$	**23.**	$^-15-^-4-^-15$
8.	$^-7-^+12$	**16.**	$^-15-^+8$	**24.**	$^-1-9-^-10$

B **1.** $10 - (+7)$ **9.** $(-5) - (-14)$ **17.** $7 - (-3) - (+8)$
    2. $2 - (+6)$ **10.** $19 - (-7)$ **18.** $(-1) - (-6) - (-9)$
    3. $7 - (-4)$ **11.** $(-7) - (+19)$ **19.** $(-8) - (-1) - (+3)$
    4. $3 - (-6)$ **12.** $(+13) - (-13)$ **20.** $(+5) - (-4) - (+11)$
    5. $(-6) - (+4)$ **13.** $(-13) - (-13)$ **21.** $(+16) - (+2) - (-4)$
    6. $(-14) - (+5)$ **14.** $(-13) - (+13)$ **22.** $(-11) - (-15) - (+4)$
    7. $(-14) - (-5)$ **15.** $0 - (-4)$ **23.** $(-7) - (-12) - (-7)$
    8. $(-5) - (+14)$ **16.** $(-9) - (+6)$ **24.** $(-1) - (+13) - (-9)$

Addition and Subtraction of Directed Numbers

Exercise 12

Work these out:

1. (a) $6 + {}^-4$
    (b) $6 - {}^+4$
    (c) $6 - 4$

5. (a) ${}^-13 + {}^-5$
    (b) ${}^-13 - {}^+5$
    (c) ${}^-13 - 5$

9. (a) ${}^-12 - {}^-11$
    (b) ${}^-12 + {}^+11$
    (c) ${}^-12 + 11$

2. (a) $8 + {}^-1$
    (b) $8 - {}^+1$
    (c) $8 - 1$

6. (a) $3 - {}^-7$
    (b) $3 + {}^+7$
    (c) $3 + 7$

10. (a) $0 - {}^-14$
    (b) $0 + {}^+14$
    (c) $0 + 14$

3. (a) $5 + {}^-8$
    (b) $5 - {}^+8$
    (c) $5 - 8$

7. (a) $15 - {}^-13$
    (b) $15 + {}^+13$
    (c) $15 + 13$

11. (a) ${}^-18 - {}^-17$
    (b) ${}^-18 + {}^+17$
    (c) ${}^-18 + 17$

4. (a) ${}^-2 + {}^-6$
    (b) ${}^-2 - {}^+6$
    (c) ${}^-2 - 6$

8. (a) ${}^-4 - {}^-6$
    (b) ${}^-4 + {}^+6$
    (c) ${}^-4 + 6$

12. (a) ${}^-18 + {}^-17$
    (b) ${}^-18 - {}^+17$
    (c) ${}^-18 - 17$

Exercise 13

Find the missing numbers that will make each statement correct:

1. $\boxed{?} - {}^+2 = 8$ **6.** $12 + \boxed{?} = 10$

2. $\boxed{?} - {}^+8 = {}^+3$ **7.** $\boxed{?} - {}^-6 = 16$

3. $\boxed{?} - 5 = {}^+4$ **8.** $4 - \boxed{?} = {}^+13$

4. $7 - \boxed{?} = {}^+2$ **9.** $-4 + \boxed{?} = 8$

5. $\boxed{?} + {}^-6 = {}^-5$ **10.** $\boxed{?} - 10 = {}^-13$

11. $^-11 - \boxed{?} = {}^-8$

12. $\boxed{?} - {}^-11 = {}^+5$

13. $2 - \boxed{?} = {}^-6$

14. $\boxed{?} + {}^-7 = {}^-12$

15. $^-10 + \boxed{?} = {}^-6$

16. $2 + \boxed{?} = {}^-5$

17. $\boxed{?} - 1 = {}^-9$

18. $\boxed{?} + 13 = 9$

19. $^-13 - \boxed{?} = {}^-20$

20. $^-2 + \boxed{?} = {}^-3$

21. $\boxed{?} + {}^+8 = {}^+21$

22. $^-12 + \boxed{?} = {}^-6$

23. $^-9 - \boxed{?} = 2$

24. $\boxed{?} - 12 = {}^-22$

25. $\boxed{?} - {}^-9 = {}^+24$

26. $\boxed{?} + {}^-17 = {}^-3$

27. $7 - \boxed{?} = 23$

28. $^-12 + \boxed{?} = {}^-24$

29. $\boxed{?} + {}^-12 = {}^+9$

30. $\boxed{?} - {}^-9 = {}^-6$

Exercise 14

A Find the value of:

1. (a) $4 + 7 - 9 + 6$
(b) $4 + 6 + 7 - 9$

2. (a) $3 - 12 + 10 + 4$
(b) $3 + 10 + 4 - 12$
(c) $3 + 10 - 12 + 4$

3. (a) $5 - 13 + 12 - 7$
(b) $5 + 12 - 13 - 7$
(c) $5 + 12 - 7 - 13$

4. (a) $8 - 9 - 12 + 4 - 5$
(b) $8 + 4 - 9 - 12 - 5$
(c) $8 + 4 - 12 - 9 - 5$

5. (a) $7 - 10 - 9 + 3 - 2$
(b) $7 + 3 - 10 - 9 - 2$

6. (a) $9 - 11 - 4 + 10 - 1$
(b) $9 + 10 - 11 - 4 - 1$

7. (a) $^-3 + 8 + 5 - 4$
(b) $8 + 5 - 3 - 4$

8. (a) $^-7 + 4 - 9 + 3 + 12$
(b) $4 + 3 + 12 - 7 - 9$
(c) $4 + 3 - 7 + 12 - 9$

9. (a) $^-1 + 9 + 12 - 6 + 8$
(b) $9 + 12 + 8 - 1 - 6$
(c) $9 - 1 - 6 + 12 + 8$

10. (a) $15 - 9 - 8 + 2 + 12$
(b) $15 + 2 + 12 - 9 - 8$
(c) $15 + 2 - 9 - 8 + 12$

11. (a) $^-2 + 8 - 3 + 4 - 5 + 9$
(b) $8 + 4 + 9 - 2 - 3 - 5$

12. (a) $1 - 12 + 2 + 15 - 3 - 7$
(b) $1 + 2 + 15 - 12 - 3 - 7$

B Look carefully at the questions and answers to part A. Note how it is possible to simplify a question by rearranging the terms.

Exercise 15

Find the value of:

1. $4.8 + 6.3 - 7.9$
2. $2.7 - 5.6 + 7.8$
3. $1.9 - 7.1 + 2.8$
4. $2\frac{1}{2} - 3\frac{3}{4} + 4\frac{1}{4}$
5. $3\frac{1}{8} - 5\frac{1}{2} + 7\frac{3}{4}$
6. $8.642 - 9.817$

7. $2.6 + 1.4 - 3.8 - 5.2$
8. $1.7 - 4.1 + 6.3 - 2.5$
9. $5\frac{3}{10} - 2\frac{4}{5} + 1\frac{7}{10}$
10. $4.02 - 7.65 + 1.44$
11. $2.84 + 0.7 - 5.9 - 1.23$
12. $0.6 - 0.9 + 0.62 - 0.54$

Exercise 16   Algebraic Substitution

If $a = 4, b = {}^-2, c = 0, d = {}^-1$ and $e = {}^-3$, find the value of:

1. $a + b$
2. $b + e$
3. $d + b$
4. $d + a$
5. $a + d$
6. $a + e$
7. $c + e$
8. $d + e$
9. $e + d$
10. $b + c$

11. $a + b + e$
12. $d + e + a$
13. $b + c + e$
14. $a + e + b$
15. $a + d + e$
16. $c + a + d$
17. $b + a + d + e$
18. $a + b + c + d + e$
19. $b + d + a$
20. $d + c + e + b$

21. $a - e$
22. $d - b$
23. $b - a$
24. $a + b - e$
25. $c + e - d - b$
26. $a + b - c + d - e$
27. $a - b + c - d + e$
28. $b + d - e - a$
29. $d - a - b + e$
30. $b - c - d - e - a$

Exercise 17   Like Terms

Simplify where possible:

1. $5k - 6k + 3k + 4k$
2. $2b + 5 - b - 3 + 3b - 1$
3. $p - 2p + 4p - p + 7p$
4. $12 + 2v - 1 + 7v - 9 - 3v$
5. $3f - 5n + 2n - 2f + 3n$
6. $4l + 7 - l - 12 - 3l + 6$
7. $5s + 3t - 4s + 2u - t$
8. $6m + 7 + 3n - 4 + n - 2m$
9. $9u - 7z + u + 2z - 3u + 6z$
10. $2p + 6q - 5p - 3q + 7p$
11. $3i + 8h - 7i - 2h - 4i + 8i$

12. $7l + g - 2l - 6g - 2l + 7g$
13. $2e - 6q + 5e + 12q - 4e$
14. $4a + 3g + 2a$
15. $3c + 5d + 4e$
16. $5x + 6 - 2x - 8 + x + 3$
17. $7v - 9 + 2b - 4v + 6 + 3b$
18. $9 + 3y - 2x + 4w$
19. $5j + 7k - 4l + 2j - l - k$
20. $2p - 3q - 2q + p + s$
21. $3t - 5k - 2t + 3k - t + 2k$
22. $s - 5 - t - 2s + t + 4s + 1$

327

23. $5y - 6z - y + 4n - z$

24. $12h - 7w + 2e - a$

25. $k - v - 2c - 4 + 3v + 1 - k$

26. $3p + q - 5q - 4p + 6q$

27. $x - 4y - 6x - y + 9x$

28. $6a - 5b - 3c - 4c - 8b$

29. $4 - 7d - 9 - d - 7 + 8d$

30. $2 - 6z - 10 + 2z + 3 + 7z$

17 **Functions**

Find the numbers that should be written in the circles:

1. (9) —+12→ (?)

2. (?) —+17→ (25)

3. (41) —−14→ (?)

4. (?) —−29→ (16)

5. (8) —×7→ (?)

6. (?) —×8→ (72)

7. (76) —÷4→ (?)

8. (?) —÷6→ (13)

9. (?) —×12→ (96)

10. (?) —−39→ (56)

11. (7) —×2→ (?) —+9→ (?)

12. (?) —×3→ (21) —−15→ (?)

13. (?) —+7→ (?) —×5→ (45)

14. (?) —−11→ (12) —×7→ (?)

15. (?) —÷8→ (?) —+13→ (25)

16. (9) —×4→ (?) —−8→ (?) —÷7→ (?)

17. (?) —×6→ (42) —−13→ (?) —×2→ (?)

18. (?) —+11→ (?) —×9→ (108) —−49→ (?)

19. (?) —×8→ (?) —−17→ (?) —÷3→ (13)

20. (?) —+8→ (?) —×6→ (?) —−37→ (65)

329

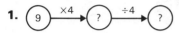
Find the numbers that should be written in the empty circles:

1. (9) $\xrightarrow{\times 4}$ (?) $\xrightarrow{\div 4}$ (?)

6. (?) $\xrightarrow{+9}$ (?) $\xrightarrow{-9}$ (12)

2. (8) $\xrightarrow{+7}$ (?) $\xrightarrow{-7}$ (?)

7. (?) $\xrightarrow{-17}$ (16) $\xrightarrow{+17}$ (?)

3. (?) $\xrightarrow{-12}$ (7) $\xrightarrow{+12}$ (?)

8. (13) $\xrightarrow{+31}$ (?) $\xrightarrow{-31}$ (?)

4. (?) $\xrightarrow{\div 5}$ (9) $\xrightarrow{\times 5}$ (?)

9. (?) $\xrightarrow{\div 7}$ (42) $\xrightarrow{\times 7}$ (?)

5. (?) $\xrightarrow{\times 6}$ (?) $\xrightarrow{\div 6}$ (8)

10. (?) $\xrightarrow{\times 8}$ (?) $\xrightarrow{\div 8}$ (13)

What do you notice about the numbers in the first and last circles in each question?

Consider the function diagram shown here. When 8 is input, the number 9 is output.

(8) $\xrightarrow{\times 2}$ (16) $\xrightarrow{-7}$ (9)

If n is input, multiplying by 2 gives $2n$; then subtracting 7 causes $2n - 7$ to be output.

(n) $\xrightarrow{\times 2}$ ($2n$) $\xrightarrow{-7}$ ($2n - 7$)

(If x had been input the output would have been $2x - 7$.)

We can write $\qquad n \longrightarrow 2n - 7$
which can be read as 'n maps to $2n - 7$'.

Since $\qquad n \longrightarrow 2n - 7$

$\qquad 8 \longrightarrow 2 \times 8 - 7 = 16 - 7 = 9$ (which was obtained before)

Similarly, $6 \longrightarrow 2 \times 6 - 7 = 12 - 7 = 5$
and if 6 had been input in the given function diagram, 5 would have been output.

So $n \longrightarrow 2n - 7$ describes the given function diagram.

Exercise 3

Write mappings to describe the function diagrams in each question in Exercise 1. Use any letters you wish.

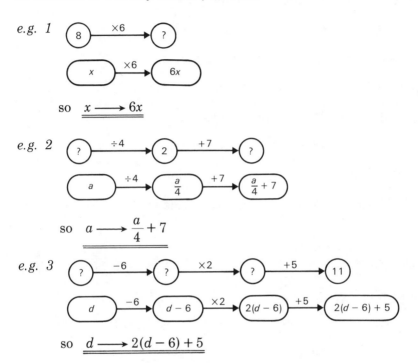

e.g. 1

so $x \longrightarrow 6x$

e.g. 2

so $a \longrightarrow \dfrac{a}{4} + 7$

e.g. 3

so $d \longrightarrow 2(d - 6) + 5$

Exercise 4

Write mappings for each of the following statements:

e.g. Double then substract 10.

$$k \longrightarrow 2k - 10$$

1. Double then add 9.

2. Multiply by 4 then subtract 3.

3. Halve then subtract 6.

4. Find one-third then add 8.

5. Add 6 then multiply by 4.

6. Subtract 12 then divide by 5.

7. Subtract 9 then multiply by 10.

8. Add 7 to three times the number.

9. Subtract 3 from one-quarter of the number.

10. Add 8, multiply by 2, then subtract 12.

11. Subtract 1, multiply by 4, then subtract 6.

12. Add 7, divide by 3, then subtract 2.

13. Subtract 9, divide by 6, then add 14.

14. Multiply by 3, subtract 2, then double.

15. Multiply by 8, subtract 5, then divide by 3.

Exercise 5 ▬▬▬▬▬▬▬▬▬▬▬▬▬▬▬▬▬▬▬▬▬▬▬ **M**

Draw function diagrams for the given mappings:

e.g. 1 $\qquad t \longrightarrow 4t + 8$

e.g. 2 $\qquad a \longrightarrow \dfrac{(5a + 7)}{2}$

1. $x \longrightarrow 2x + 3$

2. $p \longrightarrow 5p - 4$

3. $c \longrightarrow 8c - 7$

4. $w \longrightarrow 7w + 16$

5. $d \longrightarrow \dfrac{d}{4} + 6$

6. $m \longrightarrow \dfrac{m}{7} - 12$

7. $u \longrightarrow 2(u - 5) + 10$

8. $e \longrightarrow 7(e + 4) - 25$

9. $l \longrightarrow \dfrac{(4l + 9)}{5}$

10. $y \longrightarrow 6(3y + 2)$

11. $n \longrightarrow 5(4n - 7)$

12. $z \longrightarrow \dfrac{(6z - 8)}{6}$

Exercise 6

A Write statements for each of the mappings in Exercise 5.

e.g. 1 $t \longrightarrow 4t + 8$

Multiply by 4 then add 8.

e.g. 2 $a \longrightarrow \dfrac{(5a + 7)}{2}$

Multiply by 5, add 7, then divide by 2.

B Write statements for each of these mappings:

1. $b \longrightarrow 9b + 1$

2. $q \longrightarrow 6q - 7$

3. $v \longrightarrow 10v - 10$

4. $r \longrightarrow 5r + 11$

5. $s \longrightarrow \dfrac{s}{5} + 15$

6. $j \longrightarrow \dfrac{j}{2} + 15$

7. $x \longrightarrow 3(x + 9)$

8. $t \longrightarrow \dfrac{(t + 3)}{6}$

9. $w \longrightarrow 4(2w + 3)$

10. $h \longrightarrow 5(h - 4) + 7$

11. $n \longrightarrow \dfrac{(n - 6)}{3} - 5$

12. $m \longrightarrow \dfrac{(7m + 12)}{4}$

Exercise 7   **M**

Copy the following, then complete them as in the examples:

e.g. 1 $\boxed{x}$ $\xrightarrow{+4}$ $\boxed{x + 4}$ $\xrightarrow{\times 6}$ $\boxed{6(x + 4)}$

is the mapping $x \to 6(x + 4)$.
This mapping can also be written as $x \to 6x + 24$.

e.g. 2 $\boxed{k}$ $\xrightarrow{-2}$ $\boxed{k - 2}$ $\xrightarrow{\times 3}$ $\boxed{3(k - 2)}$ $\xrightarrow{-4}$ $\boxed{3(k - 2) - 4}$

is the mapping $k \longrightarrow 3(k - 2) - 4$
which is $k \longrightarrow 3k - 6 - 4$
or $k \longrightarrow 3k - 10$

1.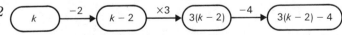

$\boxed{c}$ $\xrightarrow{+3}$ $\boxed{c + 3}$ $\xrightarrow{\times 2}$ $\boxed{2(c + 3)}$

2. m → -5 → $m - 5$ → $\times 9$ → ?

3. u → -10 → ? → $\times 8$ → ?

4. t → $+8$ → ? → $\times 7$ → ?

5. x → $\times 2$ → ? → -5 → ? → $\times 3$ → ?

6. a → $\times 5$ → ? → $+7$ → ? → $\times 7$ → ?

7. p → -3 → ? → $\times 8$ → ? → -9 → ?

8. y → $+9$ → ? → $\times 10$ → ? → -27 → ?

9. l → $+7$ → ? → $\times 4$ → ? → $+14$ → ?

10. v → -13 → ? → $\times 7$ → ? → $+45$ → ?

Exercise 8

Do the two function diagrams shown here give the same output?
Give a reason for your answer.

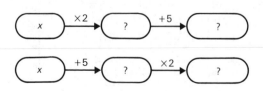

x → $\times 2$ → ? → $+5$ → ?

x → $+5$ → ? → $\times 2$ → ?

Exercise 9

Copy the given diagrams and fill in any missing numbers. Find, also, the functions that could be written in place of the question marks above the arrows.

1. (17) —-4→ $(?)$ —$\boxed{?}$→ (18)

2. (12) —$\boxed{?}$→ (8) —$+7$→ $(?)$

3. (4) —$\times 2$→ $(?)$ —$+3$→ $(?)$

4. $(?)$ —$\times 3$→ (15) —$\boxed{?}$→ (11)

5. $(?)$ —$+7$→ (13) —$\times 2$→ $(?)$

6. (4) —$\times 3$→ $(?)$ —$+6$→ $(?)$

7. (4) —$+6$→ $(?)$ —$\times 3$→ $(?)$

8. $(?)$ —$\div 3$→ $(?)$ —-6→ (4)

9. (5) —$\boxed{?}$→ (7) —$\boxed{?}$→ (21)

10. $(?)$ —$\times 4$→ (12) —$\boxed{?}$→ (19)

11. (6) —$\boxed{?}$→ (12) —-4→ $(?)$

12. (7) —$\boxed{?}$→ (10) —$\boxed{?}$→ (5)

13. $(?)$ —$\times 5$→ (20) —$+3$→ $(?)$

14. $(?)$ —-3→ (20) —$\div 5$→ $(?)$

15. $(?)$ —$+3$→ (20) —$\times 5$→ $(?)$

16. $(?)$ —$\div 4$→ (7) —$\boxed{?}$→ (9)

17. (9) —$\boxed{?}$→ (18) —$+8$→ $(?)$

18. (9) —$+4$→ $(?)$ —$\times 2$→ $(?)$

19. (11) —$\times 2$→ $(?)$ —$\boxed{?}$→ (30)

20. (11) —$\boxed{?}$→ (15) —$\boxed{?}$→ (30)

Exercise 10

Copy and complete these mapping diagrams:

1. x —$\times 4$→ y

3	$\boxed{?}$
9	$\boxed{?}$
$\boxed{?}$	20
$\boxed{?}$	28

2.

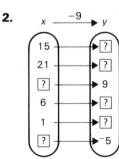

x —-9→ y

15	$\boxed{?}$
21	$\boxed{?}$
$\boxed{?}$	9
6	$\boxed{?}$
1	$\boxed{?}$
$\boxed{?}$	-5

3. $x \xrightarrow{\div 7} y$

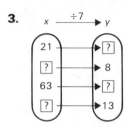

21 → ?
? → 8
63 → ?
? → 13

7. $x \xrightarrow{\div 6} y \xrightarrow{-4} z$

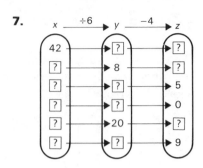

42 → ? → ?
? → 8 → ?
? → ? → 5
? → ? → 0
? → 20 → ?
? → ? → 9

4. $x \xrightarrow{\times 2} y \xrightarrow{-6} z$

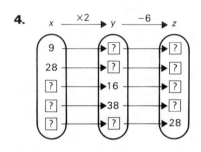

9 → ? → ?
28 → ? → ?
? → 16 → ?
? → 38 → ?
? → ? → 28

8. $x \xrightarrow{+9} y \xrightarrow{\div 4} z$

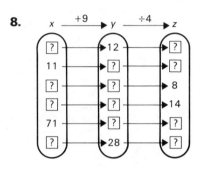

? → 12 → ?
11 → ? → ?
? → ? → 8
? → ? → 14
71 → ? → ?
? → 28 → ?

5. $x \xrightarrow{\times 8} y \xrightarrow{+9} z$

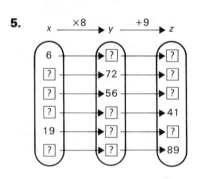

6 → ? → ?
? → 72 → ?
? → 56 → ?
? → ? → 41
19 → ? → ?
? → ? → 89

9. $x \xrightarrow{\times 4} y \xrightarrow{\times 5} z$

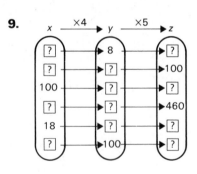

? → 8 → ?
? → ? → 100
100 → ? → ?
? → ? → 460
18 → ? → ?
? → 100 → ?

6. $x \xrightarrow{+5} y \xrightarrow{\times 7} z$

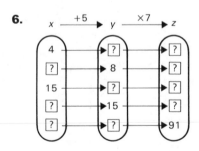

4 → ? → ?
? → 8 → ?
15 → ? → ?
? → 15 → ?
? → ? → 91

10. $x \xrightarrow{-12} y \xrightarrow{\times 9} z$

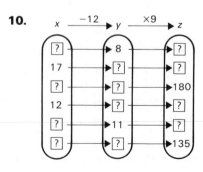

? → 8 → ?
17 → ? → ?
? → ? → 180
12 → ? → ?
? → 11 → ?
? → ? → 135

Copy and complete:

1.

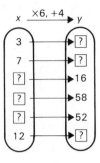

3.

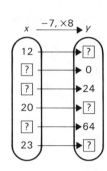

2.

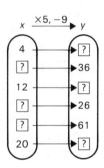

4.

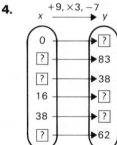

If $f(x) = 8x$

$f(3) = 8 \times 3 = 24$

and $f(9) = 8 \times 9 = 72$

If $h(x) = 5x - 7$

$h(3) = 5 \times 3 - 7 = 15 - 7 = 8$

$h(8) = 5 \times 8 - 7 = 40 - 7 = 33$

$h(1) = 5 \times 1 - 7 = 5 - 7 = {}^-2$

and $h(0) = 5 \times 0 - 7 = 0 - 7 = {}^-7$

1. If $f(x) = 6x$, find:
  (a) $f(7)$ (c) $f(12)$ (e) x, when $f(x) = 18$
  (b) $f(9)$ (d) $f(x)$, when $x = 8$ (f) x, when $f(x) = 60$

2. If $g(x) = x + 15$, find:
  (a) $g(8)$ (c) $g(37)$ (e) x, when $g(x) = 24$
  (b) $g(14)$ (d) $g(x)$, if $x = 49$ (f) x, when $g(x) = 68$

3. Given that $h(t) = 4t + 9$, find:
  (a) $h(3)$ (c) $h(15)$ (e) t, if $h(t) = 17$
  (b) $h(0)$ (d) $h(t)$, if $t = 12$ (f) t, if $h(t) = 49$

4. Given that $k(t) = 7t - 12$, find:
  (a) $k(5)$ (c) $k(1)$ (e) t, if $k(t) = 30$
  (b) $k(0)$ (d) $k(t)$, if $t = 8$ (f) t, if $k(t) = 51$

5. Given that $u(x) = 25 - x$, find:
  (a) $u(12)$ (c) $u(30)$ (e) x, if $u(x) = 17$
  (b) $u(25)$ (d) $u(x)$, when $x = 19$ (f) x, if $u(x) = {}^-5$

6. If $f(t) = 50 - 2t$, find:
  (a) $f(8)$ (c) $f(30)$ (e) t, if $f(t) = 26$
  (b) $f(16)$ (d) $f(t)$, if $t = 35$ (f) t, if $f(t) = 0$

7. If $g(a) = 9a + 23$, find:
  (a) $g(0)$ (c) $g(10)$ (e) a, if $g(a) = 41$
  (b) $g(4)$ (d) $g(a)$, if $a = 1$ (f) a, if $g(a) = 95$

8. Given that $h(x) = 10x + 18$, find:
  (a) $h(5)$ (c) $h(14)$ (e) x, if $h(x) = 48$
  (b) $h(0)$ (d) $h(x)$, if $x = 19$ (f) x, if $h(x) = 178$

9. If $p(t) = 2(3t + 5)$, find:
  (a) $p(2)$ (c) $p(0)$ (e) t, if $p(t) = 34$
  (b) $p(5)$ (d) $p(t)$, if $t = 8$ (f) t, if $p(t) = 70$

10. Given that $f(n) = 8(4n - 9)$, find:
  (a) $f(3)$ (c) $f(10)$ (e) n, if $f(n) = 56$
  (b) $f(6)$ (d) $f(n)$, if $n = 8$ (f) n, if $f(n) = 216$

A Think of a number. Double it. Add 4.

1. Copy and complete the mapping diagram to satisfy the above.

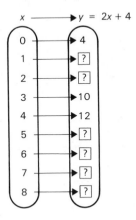

2. Copy and complete the table using the mapping diagram in question 1 to help you:

x	$y = 2x + 4$
0	4
1	?
2	?
3	10
4	12
5	?
6	?
7	?
8	?

3. Draw a pair of axes as shown. (Use a scale of 2 cm to 1 unit on the x-axis and 1 cm to 1 unit on the y-axis.) Plot a graph of y against x.

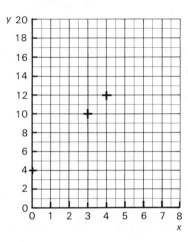

B Think of a number. Multiply it by 3. Subtract 4.

1. Draw and complete either a mapping diagram or a table. Let the set of x values used be $\{0, 1, 2, 3, 4, 5, 6\}$.

2. Draw a pair of axes as shown. Use a scale of 2 cm to 1 unit on the x-axis and 1 cm to 1 unit on the y-axis.

3. Plot a graph of y against x.

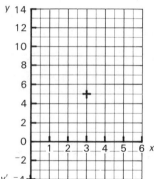

Exercise 14

e.g.

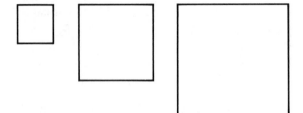

A square of side 1 cm has a perimeter of 4 cm.
A square of side 2 cm has a perimeter of 8 cm.
A square of side 3 cm has a perimeter of 12 cm.
etc.

If l cm = the length of the side of the square and P cm = the perimeter, then

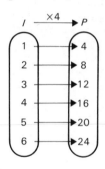

the perimeter = 4 × the length
i.e. $P = 4 \times l$
or $P = 4l$
(we can miss out the × sign)

340

1. If l cm = the length of the side of an equilateral triangle, and if P cm = the perimeter of the triangle, then write a formula for P in terms of l.

2. Referring to the squares in the figure, if the length of the sides is l cm and n is the number of dots on the perimeter, find a formula for n in terms of l. (Note that when $l = 3$, $n = 12$.)

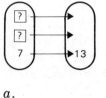

3. Ann and Marie share 20 jelly babies. If Marie has m jelly babies when Ann has a jelly babies:
   (a) Make a mapping diagram for a and m. Choose your own values for a.
   (b) Write a formula giving m in terms of a.

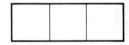

Exercise 15   **M**

1.

The rectangles above are made up of squares (1 cm squares). n stands for the number of squares and P cm for the perimeter of each rectangle.
   (a) copy and complete the following mapping diagram and table.

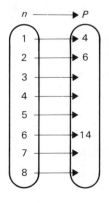

No. of squares, n	1	2	3	4	5	6	7	8
Perimeter, P (cm)	4	6	?	?	?	14	?	?

(b) Now plot a graph.

(c) Try to write a formula for P in terms of n.

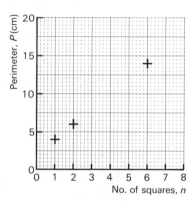

2. If each of the given rectangles measures 3 cm by 2 cm, and if n stands for the number of rectangles in each figure, and P cm stands for the perimeter, then:

(a) Make out a mapping diagram for rectangles up to $n = 8$.

(b) Make out a table showing n and P.

(c) Plot a graph of P against n. Let n be along the horizontal axis (2 cm to 1 unit) and P along the vertical axis (1 cm to 2 units).

(d) Try to find a formula for P in terms of n.

Exercise 16 ██ **M**

Copy and complete the following mapping diagrams:

1. To change miles into kilometres, multiply by 1.6:

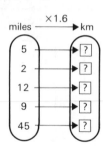

2. To change kilometres to miles, multiply by 0.625:

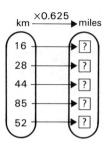

3. To change kilograms into pounds, multiply by 2.2:

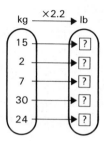

4. To change inches into centimetres, multiply by 2.54:

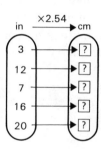

18 Symmetry

We can see symmetry in many things.

Symmetry occurs in nature (in leaves, berries, wheat, fruit, butterflies, birds, snowflakes, crystals, the human face, etc.), although it may not be perfect. It occurs in architecture (in buildings throughout the world—both ancient and modern), in painting, sculpture, and design (carvings, furniture, wallpaper and fabric designs), in music, and even in the letters of our alphabet.

After you have tried some of the following work, look back at the above list and make a scrapbook using some of the ideas. Collect photographs, newspaper articles, drawings, etc., that show some sort of symmetry.

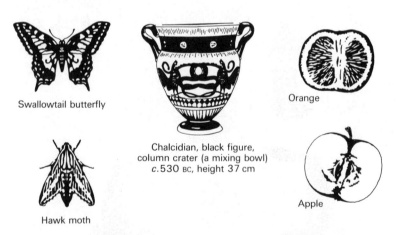

Swallowtail butterfly

Chalcidian, black figure,
column crater (a mixing bowl)
c.530 BC, height 37 cm

Orange

Hawk moth

Apple

Snow crystals are often arranged in six rays or segments, and no two crystals are alike.

The pattern (or picture) below was made as follows:

1. Fold a piece of paper once.

2. Open it out.

3. Make a few small ink blots on the paper. (Paint could be used.)

4. Fold the paper along the first fold and gently rub the back. (The ink will spread, so this step must be carried out very carefully indeed.)

5. Open the paper again and let the ink dry.

Now make your own pattern. Be very careful at step 4.

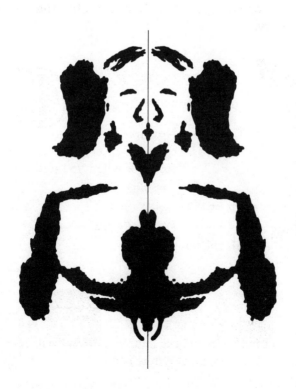

Exercise 2

1. Use a piece of paper. Fold it *once*. Cut out any shape, as shown, using scissors. Put the other piece down out of the way.

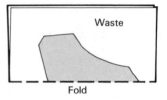

Unfold the shape you have cut out.

What do you notice about the shape of the piece of paper that you have unfolded?
How many *lines of symmetry** has it got?

2. Fold another piece of paper as before. This time, cut out a shape which, when unfolded, will give a man, or a woman.

3. Fold another piece of paper.

Now fold it *again* in the other direction. Keep the folded edges together when you fold the paper this second time.

Cut out any shape. Unfold the piece of paper with the shape you have cut out.

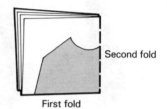

What do you notice about the shape you have cut out?
How many lines of symmetry has it got?

*See the glossary, p. 434.

Exercise 3

1. Make *one fold* in a piece of paper.
   With one straight cut, make a shape which, when unfolded, will be an *isosceles triangle*.

2. Make *one fold* in another piece of paper.
   With one straight cut, make a shape which, when unfolded, will be a *right-angled isosceles triangle*. (You are allowed to use a ruler for measuring to help you with this triangle.)

3. Make *one fold* in another piece of paper.
   Using two straight cuts, make a shape which, when unfolded, will give you a *kite*.

4. The outline pattern in Fig. 1 was obtained by folding a piece of paper in half, then folding it a second time (Fig. 2). Pieces were then cut from the folded piece of paper to give the final shape in Fig. 1.

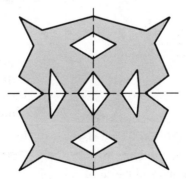

Fig. 1

Make your own symmetrical pattern in this way. (Note that the pattern has *two* lines of symmetry.)

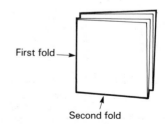

First fold ⟶

Second fold

Fig. 2

Exercise 4

For each of these problems, fold a piece of paper *twice*.

By cutting, then unfolding, try to make:
1. a rectangle,
2. a square (use two straight cuts),
3. a square (use one straight cut),
4. a parallelogram,
5. a rhombus.

Exercise 5

A For these, make *three folds* as shown:

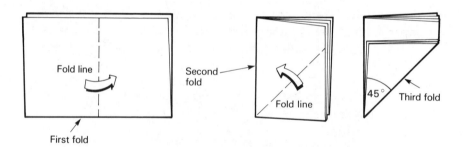

1. Make some single straight cuts.
   There are five different ways you can do this:

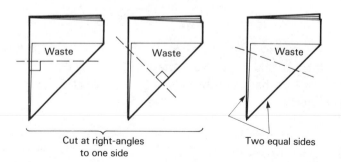

348

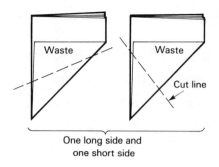

One long side and
one short side

Try these cuts after three folds.
How many lines of symmetry does each pattern leave?

2. Make *three folds*.
Now try two straight cuts as shown. (The cuts may be at any angle.) Note the number of lines of symmetry each time.

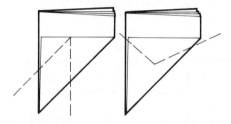

3. Make *three folds* in another piece of paper as shown.
Cut out pieces of paper then unfold to show a symmetrical pattern.

How many lines of symmetry does it have?

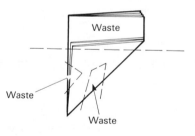

B Now make *four folds* as shown. (You need to use thin paper.)
The 45° angle should be folded to give a $22\frac{1}{2}$° angle.
Experiment as for the three folds (part A).

Write down the number of lines of symmetry each time.

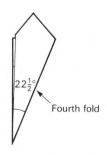

349

Exercise 6

Draw a straight line 73 mm in length.

Bisect the line using a pair of compasses.

Note that the perpendicular bisector is a line of symmetry.

Exercise 7 **M**

A A printer wanted to print some tickets. This is how he saw the printing just before he started to make the tickets.

> ADMISSION £1·50
> AVAILABLE
> REFRESHMENTS
> 30th May
> in Memorial Hall
> YOUTH CLUB DISCO

Some letters have not been turned around. Why not?
Write what is on the tickets.

B List the letters of the alphabet and mark on them any lines of symmetry.

e.g.

 A **B** **H**

1. List the set of letters that have a horizontal axis of symmetry.

2. List the set of letters that have a vertical axis of symmetry.

3. List the set of letters have have both a horizontal and a vertical axis of symmetry.

4. List the set of letters have have more than two axes of symmetry.

C Print these words as a printer might see them:

1. WRITE
2. RIGHT
3. WRONG
4. MUM
5. DOCTOR

6. ALPHABET
7. NIL
8. NOTHING
9. NOUGHT
10. ZERO

11. NUMERICAL
12. FAST
13. JINX
14. VISIBILITY
15. QUIZ

Exercise 8   M

Copy the following. Complete each letter so that the broken lines are lines of symmetry.

WONDERFUL

FANTASTIC

MARVELLOUS

TERRIFIC

STUPENDOUS

THE BEST, SUPERB

UNPARALLELED

SECOND TO NONE

ALL THE ABOVE

WORDS DESCRIBE

MATHEMATICS

Exercise 9

Some letters of the alphabet can be made by folding a piece of paper, cutting out, then unfolding again.

Which letters of the alphabet can be made in this way?

e.g.

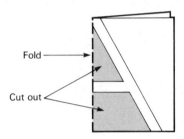

Exercise 10 M

Copy these shapes. Where possible, draw in the lines of symmetry for each shape. Some shapes have one line of symmetry, some have more than one, some may have none.

1.

2.

3.

4.

5.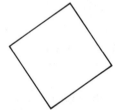

6.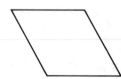

7.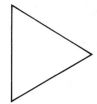

10.

8.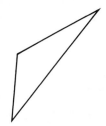

11.

9.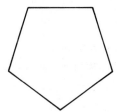

12.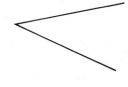

Exercise 11 M

In each sketch, the line or lines of symmetry have been shown together with part of the shape.
Copy and complete each shape.

1.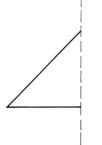

2.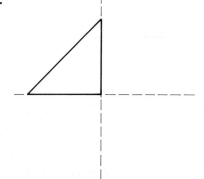

3.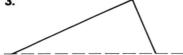

6.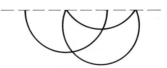

4.

7.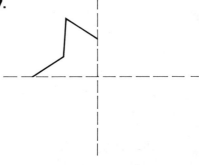

5.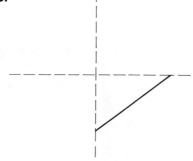

8.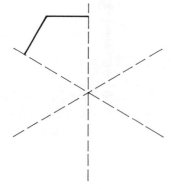

Exercise 12

Design and make a symmetrical mask.

Copy these shapes on to squared paper.
Complete each one so that the broken lines are lines of symmetry.

1.

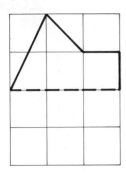

4.

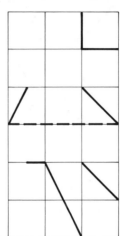

2.

5.

3.

355

6.

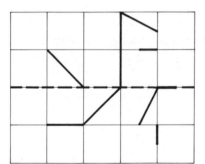

8.

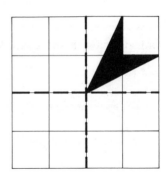

7.

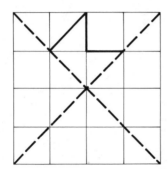

9.

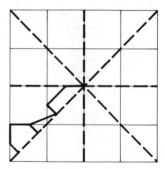

Exercise 14

What can you see?

Two faces?

A vase?

Try to draw your own *optical illusion.*

Copy the semi-detached house below and its ground-floor plan. That is, draw in the right-hand house.

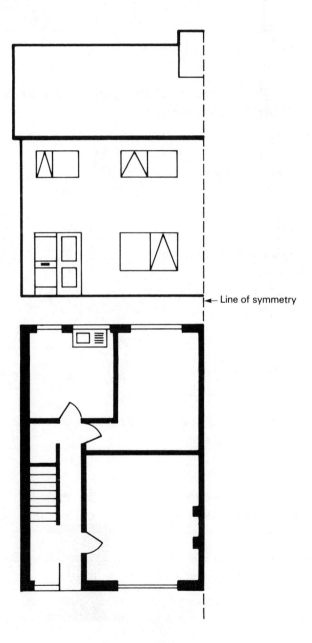

← Line of symmetry

Exercise 16

Music can sometimes be written symmetrically. This tune is symmetrical.

Write your own symmetrical tune.

Exercise 17   Properties of Polygons Directly Related to their Symmetries

A *Triangles*

1. This triangle has no axes of bilateral symmetry.
   What sort of triangle is it?

2. This triangle has exactly three axes of bilateral symmetry.
   What sort of triangle is it?

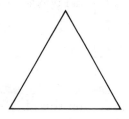

3. Try to find a triangle with exactly one axis of bilateral symmetry. If you find one, write its name.

4. Try to find a triangle with exactly one axis of bilateral symmetry. If you find one write its name.

B *Quadrilaterals*

Try to find quadrilaterals with the given number of axes of bilateral symmetry. There may be no possible answer, or there may be more than one.

Draw each answer you find and name each quadrilateral. Mark on each drawing the equal angles and the equal sides.

1. no axes,	**3.** two axes,	**5.** four axes.
2. one axis,	**4.** three axes,	

C *Pentagons*

Try to find pentagons with the given number of axes of symmetry. Draw each answer you find and mark on each drawing the equal angles and equal sides.

1. no axes, **3.** two axes, **5.** four axes,
2. one axis, **4.** three axes, **6.** five axes.

D *Hexagons*

Try to find hexagons with the given number of axes of symmetry. Draw each answer you find and mark on each drawing the equal angles and equal sides.

1. no axes, **5.** four axes,
2. one axis, **6.** five axes,
3. two axes, **7.** six axes.
4. three axes,

E Investigate other polygons in the same way as in point D. Write what you notice.

Exercise 18 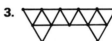 **M**

Use a mirror on this shape to make all the following shapes. The part of the original drawing behind the mirror should be ignored.

e.g. 1

e.g. 2

1.   **2.**   **3.**

359

4.

5.

6.

7.

8.

9.

10.

11.

12.

13.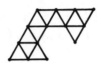

14.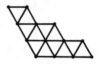

15.

16.

17.

18.

19.

20.

21.

22.

23.

24.

25.

26.

19 Using a Calculator

Exercise 1   The Idea of an Inverse

For each question, key the given answer into your calculator; then carry out any necessary calculations to obtain the missing number:

A
1. $\boxed{?} + 37 = 106$
2. $\boxed{?} \times 71 = 18\,034$
3. $\boxed{?} - 198 = 640$
4. $\boxed{?} + 563 = 2938$
5. $\boxed{?} + 8.47 = 40.16$
6. $\boxed{?} \times 6.8 = 30.804$
7. $\boxed{?} \div 0.19 = 6.47$
8. $\boxed{?} \times 0.99 = 2.772$
9. $\boxed{?} - 258 = 324$
10. $\boxed{?} \div 49 = 24\,941$

11. $\boxed{?} \times 38 = 4066$
12. $\boxed{?} \div 217 = 156$
13. $\boxed{?} - 15.6 = 108.9$
14. $\boxed{?} \div 4.2 = 1.88$
15. $\boxed{?} \times 0.086 = 0.061\,404$
16. $\boxed{?} \div 5.03 = 0.0279$
17. $\boxed{?} - 209.7 = 841.9$
18. $\boxed{?} + 28.85 = 372.3$
19. $\boxed{?} \div 0.068 = 146$
20. $\boxed{?} \times 0.8 = 0.3$

B
1. $\boxed{?} \times 12 + 7 = 187$
2. $\boxed{?} \div 6 + 38 = 45$
3. $\boxed{?} \times 18 - 84 = 87$
4. $\boxed{?} \div 9 - 1.8 = 5.5$
5. $\boxed{?} \times 7.4 + 1.5 = 1.6702$
6. $\boxed{?} \div 0.03 + 3.68 = 10$
7. $\boxed{?} \times 0.205 + 0.501 = 888\,45$
8. $\boxed{?} \times 0.35 - 0.059 = 0.5871$
9. $\boxed{?} \times 9 \times 7 = 384.3$
10. $\boxed{?} \div 2.3 \times 6 = 44.4$

11. $\boxed{?} \times 7 \div 21 = 13$
12. $\boxed{?} \div 0.8 \div 1.9 = 1.2$
13. $\boxed{?} \times 0.75 \times 0.14 = 0.882$
14. $\boxed{?} \times 3.2 \div 1.6 = 3.8$
15. $\boxed{?} \div 1.5 \div 4.2 = 0.056$
16. $\boxed{?} \div 3.3 \div 0.25 = 5.61$
17. $\boxed{?} + 86 - 45 = 119$
18. $\boxed{?} - 1.7 - 4.8 = 4.4$
19. $\boxed{?} - 0.74 + 0.56 = 0.73$
20. $\boxed{?} + 9.3 + 4.9 = 32.5$

C **1.** ($\boxed{?} - 14) \times 8 = 72$

2. ($\boxed{?} + 84) \div 17 = 9$

3. ($\boxed{?} - 582) \div 39 = 62$

4. ($\boxed{?} + 9.6) \times 5.2 = 93.6$

5. ($\boxed{?} - 23.6) \div 0.02 = 2570$

6. ($\boxed{?} - 0.55) \times 3.5 = 1.26$

7. ($\boxed{?} + 1.7) \times 8.2 = 57.4$

8. ($\boxed{?} + 5.8) \div 4.3 = 4.16$

D **1.** ($\boxed{?} \times 6.2 - 18.98) \div 0.4 = 81.2$

2. ($\boxed{?} + 6.9) \div 0.8 \times 1.2 = 28.44$

3. ($\boxed{?} \div 0.7 + 6.8) \times 3.5 = 39.9$

4. ($\boxed{?} \times 58 + 2.6) \times 1.7 = 9.9416$

5. ($\boxed{?} \div 9.5 - 4.7) \times 0.32 + 17.6 = 33.44$

6. ($\boxed{?} \times 1.5 - 1.5) \div 1.5 + 1.5 = 4.2$

7. (($\boxed{?} - 61.2) \times 14 + 3.84) \div 2.56 = 178.6875$

8. (($\boxed{?} - 0.291) \div 0.27 + 5.12 - 1.63) \div 7.7 \times 46.2 = 3234$

9. (($\boxed{?} \div 0.8 \times 12 + 115) \times 0.086 - 41.2) \div 0.028 = 1600$

10. (($\boxed{?} + 3.1) \times 2.4 - 13.7 + 8.5) \div 3.5 = 4$

Calculator Practice

Exercise 2

In each question, two numbers are given.
Key the first number into a calculator. Try to obtain the second
number on the display by depressing *no more than three keys.*

e.g. 96, 12

   96 $\boxed{\div}$ $\boxed{8}$ $\boxed{=}$ 12

1. 42, 7

2. 9, 17

3. 91, 82

4. 56, 8

5. 16, 80

6. 77, 85

7. 112, 28

8. 114, 19

9. 14, 84

10. 91, 13

11. 1201, 1192

12. 237, 79

13. 76, 684

14. 199, 205

15. 291, 97

16. 216, 208

17. 435, 87

18. 53, 212

19. 38, 304

20. 189, 27

Exercise 3

Using a calculator, carry out the calculations so that the display on the calculator shows the correct answer. Write down the actual calculation that you carry out. Do not add or subtract more than two numbers.

A You are not allowed to use the 9 key:

1. $543 + 289$	**11.** $4839 - 2560$	**21.** $5930 - 2089$
2. $346 - 159$	**12.** $780 - 549$	**22.** $7523 - 3499$
3. $6592 + 2025$	**13.** $4076 - 2932$	**23.** $8931 + 3952$
4. $2729 - 1473$	**14.** $365 - 189$	**24.** $9489 - 1362$
5. $1976 - 745$	**15.** $4916 + 3479$	**25.** $5893 + 3898$
6. $3482 - 1927$	**16.** $7293 - 2984$	**26.** $9289 - 780$
7. $7924 - 3958$	**17.** $3947 + 2934$	**27.** $999 - 324$
8. $6893 - 3192$	**18.** $5929 + 7643$	**28.** $999 + 476$
9. $369 + 420$	**19.** $9349 - 420$	**29.** $999 + 783$
10. $5497 + 3605$	**20.** $8394 - 4907$	**30.** $999 + 888$

B You are not allowed to use the 8 or the 9 keys:

1. $738 + 492$	**6.** $587 - 498$	**11.** $4983 - 1108$
2. $5392 - 2827$	**7.** $499 - 201$	**12.** $695 - 218$
3. $7983 - 3649$	**8.** $3999 - 1994$	**13.** $978 + 798$
4. $9348 + 4895$	**9.** $5938 + 2747$	**14.** $5987 - 2109$
5. $439 + 357$	**10.** $729 + 377$	**15.** $9998 + 7899$

C You are not allowed to use the 7, 8 or 9 keys:

1. $692 - 457$	**6.** $728 - 389$	**11.** $1469 + 3828$
2. $2714 + 4935$	**7.** $6749 - 3878$	**12.** $5809 + 7902$
3. $6937 - 1488$	**8.** $7000 - 4987$	**13.** $989 - 798$
4. $483 + 569$	**9.** $4086 + 3907$	**14.** $989 + 798$
5. $537 + 347$	**10.** $8903 - 4687$	**15.** $9889 + 7887$

Exercise 4

The diagram shows the number keys on a calculator:

1. List the numbers from 1 to 20. Next to each one, where possible, show how the number can be obtained on the calculator's display by pressing only four keys (two number keys, one operation key ($\boxed{+}$, $\boxed{-}$, $\boxed{\times}$ or $\boxed{\div}$) and the 'equals' key, which is the fourth key). Note that the two number keys used *must be neighbouring keys*. (For example, $\boxed{3}$ has the neighbours $\boxed{2}$, $\boxed{5}$ and $\boxed{6}$; while $\boxed{8}$ has the neighbours $\boxed{4}$, $\boxed{5}$, $\boxed{6}$, $\boxed{7}$ and $\boxed{9}$.)

2. For which numbers in question 1 is it necessary to use diagonal neighbours?

3. List all the possible ways of obtaining 4 in the display by pressing only four keys, as for question 1.

Exercise 5   'Zero it'

1. Key in any starting number into your calculator.

2. Choose any number key on the calculator.

3. By using the selected number key and any operation key and/or the $\boxed{=}$ key as often as you need, try to obtain 0 in the display in as few steps as possible.

   For example, using the starting number 49 and the number key $\boxed{6}$, one way of obtaining zero in the display is:

   49 $\boxed{+}$ $\boxed{6}$ $\boxed{+}$ $\boxed{6}$ $\boxed{+}$ $\boxed{6}$ $\boxed{-}$ $\boxed{6}$ $\boxed{6}$ $\boxed{=}$ $\boxed{\times}$ $\boxed{6}$ $\boxed{-}$ $\boxed{6}$ $\boxed{=}$

Exercise 6   'Reversal'

This is a game for one person.

Object of the game: To reverse the digits of a number.

A 1. Key in any three-digit number into your calculator, where all three digits are different.
   (Write down this three-digit number.)

2. (a) Press either $\boxed{+}$, $\boxed{-}$, $\boxed{\times}$, or $\boxed{\div}$.

(b) Press a number key.

(c) Press $\boxed{=}$.

3. Repeat question 2 as many times as you need until the three digits are reversed. Count the number of steps you take.

Try to take as few steps as possible.
Record your steps. See the following example.

e.g. Key in: 489   (984 is required.)

$\boxed{\times}$ $\boxed{2}$ $\boxed{=}$ gives 978.

$\boxed{+}$ $\boxed{6}$ $\boxed{=}$ gives 984   (the required number).

B Try to reverse:

1. a four-digit number,

2. a five-digit number,

3. a six-digit number,

4. a seven-digit number,

5. an eight-digit number.

Exercise 7   Find a Factor

A (A game for two players and two calculators)

Object of the game: To keep a whole number in the display.

1. Both players key in the first number given overleaf (i.e. part (a), 35).

2. Both should work out *in their heads* a factor of that number. Factors used should be less than or equal to 10. The factor 1 should not be used.

3. Both should then use their calculators to divide the numbers on the display by the factors they thought of.

4. When both players have pressed $\boxed{=}$ on their calculators, they should show the numbers on the displays to each other.

5. If the display is a whole number, a point is scored. If it is a decimal, no points are scored.

6. The steps given should be repeated for each given number.

The person with the most points wins.

Note The teacher can *time* the game by allowing a certain number of seconds to find a factor of each number.

(*a*) 35	(*e*) 39	(*i*) 84	(*m*) 378	(*q*) 748
(*b*) 60	(*f*) 130	(*j*) 111	(*n*) 822	(*r*) 595
(*c*) 24	(*g*) 63	(*k*) 119	(*o*) 582	(*s*) 243
(*d*) 26	(*h*) 156	(*l*) 258	(*p*) 672	(*t*) 728

B Play the game again, but this time, the player who has the smaller whole number on the display after dividing by the factor gets a point. The other player gets no points. If the same number is on each display, both players get a point.

Note that the factors used should still be less than or equal to 10. Again, the factor 1 is not allowed.

C (For two players and one calculator)

1. The first player thinks of a number.

2. The second player keys that number into the calculator.

3. The second player works out *in his or her head* a factor of that number. Factors used should be less than or equal to 10. The factor 1 should not be used.

4. The second player then uses the calculator to divide the displayed number by the factor thought of.

5. On pressing $\boxed{=}$, if the display is a whole number, the second player gets a point. If the display is a decimal, the first player suggests a factor. The original displayed number is now divided by this new factor. If the result is a whole number, the first player gets a point, but if the display is a decimal, neither gets a point.

6. The game is repeated with the players changing places.

7. Play several games.

The winner is the player who gets most points.

20 **Simple Equations**

Exercise 1

In the following, some numbers have been smudged. Work out what the numbers must be.

1. ⬛ + 8 = 15
2. ⬛ − 9 = 12
3. ⬛ + 5 = 31
4. ⬛ + 12 = 26
5. ⬛ − 4 = 17

6. ⬛ + 15 = 38
7. ⬛ − 13 = 15
8. ⬛ − 11 = 21
9. 11 + ⬛ = 21
10. 19 + ⬛ = 46

11. 3 × ⬛ = 21
12. ⬛ × 7 = 42
13. ⬛ ÷ 4 = 8
14. 8 × ⬛ = 56
15. ⬛ ÷ 3 = 12

Exercise 2

Find the unknown numbers if:

1. I think of a number, add 7 and get 15.
2. I think of a number, subtract 7 and get 15.
3. I think of a number, add 9 and get 13.
4. A number is added to 6 to give 18.
5. A number is multiplied by 6 to give 54.
6. I think of a number, multiply it by 4 and get 44.
7. Eight is subtracted from a number to give 12.
8. I think of a number, divide it by 6 and get 5.

The sentences in Exercise 2 could have been written as equations using a letter to stand for each unknown number. Note that any letter whatsoever may be used.

The following sentences have been changed into equations:

e.g. 1 I think of a number, add 4 and get 15.

$$n \quad + 4 \quad = \quad 15$$

367

e.g. 2 Five times a certain number gives 40.

$$5 \times x = 40$$

This may be written as: $5x = 40$

e.g. 3 A number, when multiplied by 9 gives 27.

$$t \times 9 = 27$$

This may be written as: $9t = 27$

(The order of multiplying can be changed, e.g. $5 \times 4 = 4 \times 5$, and this is true for multiplication of any two numbers, so $t \times 9 = 9 \times t = 9t$)

Exercise 3

A For each of the following sentences, form an equation and find the unknown number:

e.g. 1 I think of a number, add 4 and get 15.
Let the number be n,
then $n + 4 = 15$
so $n = 11$
and the number is $\underline{\underline{11}}$

e.g. 2 When a number is multiplied by 5, the answer is 40.
Let the number be x,
then $5x = 40$
and $x = 8$
so the number is $\underline{\underline{8}}$

1. I think of a number, add 3 and get 17.

2. I think of a number, subtract 6 and the answer is 11.

3. A number, when multiplied by 2, gives 18.

4. When 13 is added to a number, the answer is 29.

5. When a number is multiplied by 9, the answer is 63.

6. By subtracting 12 from a number, we get 13.

7. By taking 17 from a number, we get 23.

8. When a number is divided by 5, the answer is 6.

Exercise 4

The symbol '=' is sometimes read as 'is equal to', 'is the same as' or just 'is'. (There are other ways of reading '=' as well as those given here.)

Write as many words or phrases as you can for each of the following symbols.

1. =   **2.** +   **3.** −   **4.** ×   **5.** ÷

Exercise 5

Write a sentence for each of the following equations

e.g. 1 $n + 2 = 11$
        I think of a number, add 2 and get 11.

1. $n + 10 = 15$ **4.** $3t = 24$ **7.** $\dfrac{m}{7} = 4$
2. $x - 5 = 9$ **5.** $u - 20 = 3$
3. $p + 17 = 22$ **6.** $8h = 32$ **8.** $k + 22 = 50$

Exercise 6

A Find the value of:

1. $8 - 8$ **5.** $13 + 8 - 8$ **9.** $16 - 9 + 9$
2. $15 - 15$ **6.** $21 + 17 - 17$ **10.** $34 - 28 + 28$
3. $49 - 49$ **7.** $59 + 39 - 39$ **11.** $68 - 29 + 29$
4. $102 - 102$ **8.** $76 + 82 - 82$ **12.** $87 - 100 + 100$

B Simplify:

1. $g + 8 - 8$ **5.** $2d + 11 - 11$ **9.** $8y - 40 + 40$
2. $a + 12 - 12$ **6.** $4k - 13 + 13$ **10.** $3c + 18 - 18$
3. $l - 19 + 19$ **7.** $20 + 3z - 20$ **11.** $9f - 25 + 25$
4. $14 + v - 14$ **8.** $19 + 7t - 19$ **12.** $50 + 5r - 50$

C Copy and complete:

1. $b + 8 - \boxed{?} = b$

2. $e + 15 - \boxed{?} = e$

3. $w - 18 + \boxed{?} = w$

4. $2g + 7 - \boxed{?} = 2g$

5. $7j - 21 + \boxed{?} = 7j$

6. $36 + p - \boxed{?} = p$

7. $29 + 2m - \boxed{?} = 2m$

8. $4u - 1 + \boxed{?} = 4u$

9. $6h + 35 - \boxed{?} = 6h$

10. $41 + 3s - \boxed{?} = 3s$

Exercise 7

You have probably been able to find the answers to the equations given so far without using any particular method. For some equations you need to be better organised.

A Here is a balance. A packet of jelly babies and 4 jelly babies on one pan are balanced by 7 jelly babies on the other pan.

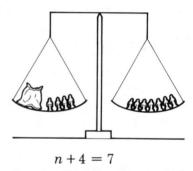

If there are n jelly babies in the bag, we can write:

$n + 4 = 7$

1. If we take 4 jelly babies off the left-hand pan, the balance tips as shown. What should we do to balance the scales again? (Do not put the 4 jelly babies back on the pan!)

2. How many jelly babies are left on the right-hand pan?

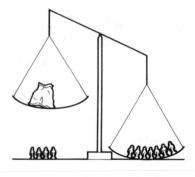

We can write:

so

$n + 4 - 4 = 7 - 4$

$\underline{n = 3}$

3. How many jelly babies are there in the packet?

Summing up:

$n + 4 \quad = 7$ (was the original equation)

$n + 4 - 4 = 7 - 4$ (taking 4 from each side)

$\underline{\underline{n = 3}}$ (by simplifying)

B On the balance shown, 2 bags of jelly babies on the left-hand pan are balanced by 8 jelly babies on the right-hand pan.

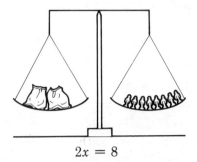

If there are x jelly babies in each bag, we can write the equation:

$$2x = 8$$

1. If you halve the number of packets on the left-hand pan, what must you do to the jelly babies on the right-hand pan?

We can now write:

$$\frac{2x}{2} = \frac{8}{2}$$

so

$$\underline{\underline{x = 4}}$$

2. How many jelly babies are there in each packet?

Exercise 8

Solve the following equations:

e.g. 1 $\quad x - 13 \quad = 19$

$\qquad x - 13 + 13 = 19 + 13$

$\qquad \underline{\underline{x = 32}}$

e.g. 2 $\quad \dfrac{x}{3} = 12$

$\qquad 3 \times \dfrac{x}{3} = 3 \times 12$

$\qquad \underline{\underline{x = 36}}$

1. $x + 10 = 17$

2. $a - 3 = 6$

3. $d + 2 = 7$

4. $e + 9 = 24$

5. $y - 7 = 19$

6. $2t = 24$

7. $5f = 45$

8. $3h = 27$

9. $22 = z + 14$

10. $48 = 4k$

11. $\dfrac{u}{2} = 8$

12. $\dfrac{c}{3} = 6$

13. $2x = 96$

14. $10 = \dfrac{m}{5}$

15. $7l = 91$

16. $43 = g + 18$ **20.** $\dfrac{v}{4} = 18$ **23.** $48 = 6w$

17. $9n = 126$ **24.** $45 = 16 + y$

18. $q - 37 = 63$ **21.** $b - 15 = 12$ **25.** $s - 14 = 14$

19. $21 + q = 30$ **22.** $\dfrac{r}{8} = 8$

Exercise 9

Solve these equations. Note that a number of answers will be decimal or vulgar fractions.

1. $x + 8 = 13$ **6.** $a - 2 = 9$ **11.** $3d = 7.5$

2. $x - 5 = 14$ **7.** $w + 1\frac{1}{2} = 3\frac{1}{2}$ **12.** $5f = 13$

3. $5x = 35$ **8.** $c - 3 = 2.25$ **13.** $2q = 8\frac{6}{7}$

4. $3x = 18$ **9.** $2s = 15$ **14.** $4g = 13$

5. $\dfrac{x}{4} = 12$ **10.** $\dfrac{t}{3} = 1\frac{1}{2}$ **15.** $\dfrac{z}{6} = \frac{1}{9}$

Exercise 10

Solve these equations. Note that most of the answers will be negative.

1. $a + 5 = 9$ **5.** $t + 12 = 2$ **9.** $10 = c + 30$

2. $b + 9 = 5$ **6.** $d + 7 = 24$ **10.** $11 = 23 + y$

3. $8 + f = 1$ **7.** $15 + x = 6$ **11.** $19 + h = 12$

4. $6 + n = 5$ **8.** $5 = p + 20$ **12.** $3 = 27 + m$

Exercise 11

For each problem, form an equation then solve it:

1. Andrew has p pencils and Nina has 13. If they have 31 pencils altogether, how many has Andrew?

2. Colin had m marbles. He lost 16 and then had 8 left. How many marbles did he start with?

3. Gina has f felt-tipped pens. If she had 6 times as many, she would have 42 altogether. How many does she have?

4. Derek is 11 years old. His sister Lisa is *l* years old. Together their ages total 27 years. How old is Lisa?

5. There were *g* girls and 17 boys in a class. If there were 26 pupils in the class altogether, how many were girls?

6. Emlyn is one-third of the age of his dad who is *d* years old. Emlyn is 13 years old. How old is his dad?

7. Caroline had *s* sweets and ate 8 of them. If she then had 13 left, how many did she start with?

8. My house number is *h*. My friend's house number is 4 times as big as my number, and her number is 152. What is my house number?

9. When 23 is added to a number, the result is 82. Find the number.

10. I think of a number, subtract 17 and the result is 17. Find the number.

Equations Involving Two Operations

Exercise 12 **M**

Copy and complete:

A *e.g. 1* 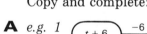   *e.g. 2*

1.

5.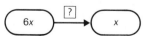

2.

6.

3.

7.

4.

8.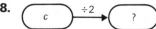

9. (?) →$+3$→ (y)

11. (v) →-21→ (?)

10. (?) →$\div 8$→ (m)

12. (?) →$\times 9$→ (w)

B *e.g. 1* (b) →$\times 4$→ ($4b$) →-7→ ($4b - 7$)

e.g. 2 ($3e + 4$) →-4→ ($3e$) →$\div 3$→ (e)

1. (h) →$\times 2$→ (?) →-1→ (?)

2. (q) →$\boxed{?}$→ ($7q$) →$+6$→ (?)

3. (u) →$\div 3$→ (?) →$\boxed{?}$→ ($\dfrac{u}{3} - 9$)

4. ($2a - 4$) →$+4$→ (?) →$\boxed{?}$→ (a)

5. ($5s + 3$) →$\boxed{?}$→ ($5s$) →$\boxed{?}$→ (s)

6. ($\dfrac{x}{2} + 7$) →-7→ (?) →$\boxed{?}$→ (x)

7. ($8 + 6l$) →$\boxed{?}$→ ($6l$) →$\boxed{?}$→ (l)

8. ($9d + 8$) →$\boxed{?}$→ (?) →$\div 9$→ (d)

9. ($5 + \dfrac{r}{5}$) →$\boxed{?}$→ ($\dfrac{r}{5}$) →$\boxed{?}$→ (r)

10. ($8y - 3$) →$\boxed{?}$→ ($8y$) →$\boxed{?}$→ (y)

374

11. $2 + 7n$ → [?] → $7n$ → [?] → n

12. $4c + 9$ → [?] → $4c$ → [?] → c

C 1. $2l - 6$ → [?] → ? → [?] → l

2. $4e + 1$ → [?] → ? → [?] → e

3. $6p - 9$ → [?] → ? → [?] → p

4. $8k + 6$ → [?] → ? → [?] → k

5. $8 + 2y$ → [?] → ? → [?] → y

6. $3x - 7$ → [?] → ? → [?] → x

7. $2 + 5d$ → [?] → ? → [?] → d

8. $8g - 4$ → [?] → ? → [?] → g

9. $7m + 3$ → [?] → ? → [?] → m

10. $5b - 7$ → [?] → ? → [?] → b

11. $9 + 3t$ → [?] → ? → [?] → t

12. $4h - 5$ → [?] → ? → [?] → h

375

13.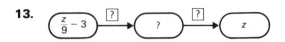

$\left(\dfrac{z}{9} - 3\right)$ →[?] (?) →[?] (z)

14.

$\left(2 + \dfrac{a}{7}\right)$ →[?] (?) →[?] (a)

15.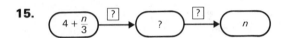

$\left(4 + \dfrac{n}{3}\right)$ →[?] (?) →[?] (n)

16.

$\left(\dfrac{c}{6} + 5\right)$ →[?] (?) →[?] (c)

On the balance shown, 2 bags of jelly babies and 3 jelly babies, on the left-hand pan, are balanced by 11 jelly babies on the right-hand pan.

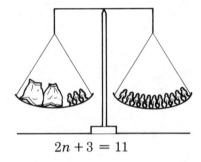

If there are n jelly babies in each bag, we can write:

$$2n + 3 = 11$$

If the 3 loose jelly babies are taken off the left-hand pan, the scales will tip as shown.

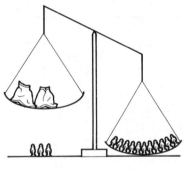

To balance the scales again, 3 jelly babies must now be removed from the right-hand pan as shown.

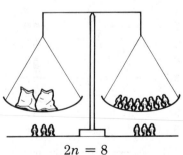

The equation for this is now:

$$2n = 8$$

The scales remain balanced if we halve the number of bags on the left-hand pan and halve the number of jelly babies on right-hand pan.

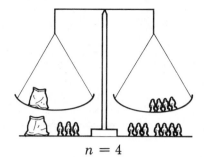

This leaves the equation: $n = 4$

Summing up:

$2n + 3$	$= 11$	(was the original equation)
$2n + 3 - 3$	$= 11 - 3$	(taking 3 from each side)
$2n$	$= 8$	(by simplifying)
$\underline{n =\ \ 4}$		(by dividing both sides by 2)

To check the answer, LHS* $= 2n + 3$

When $n = 4$,   LHS $= 2 \times 4 + 3$
$= 8 + 3$
$= 11$
$=$ RHS*

Note that $\left(2n + 3\right) \xrightarrow{-3} \left(2n\right) \xrightarrow{\div 2} \left(n\right)$ shows that it is necessary to subtract the 3 before dividing by 2. Dividing by 2 first may create problems. Try it. $\left(2n + 3\right) \xrightarrow{\div 2} \left(?\right) \xrightarrow{\boxed{?}} \left(n\right)$

Exercise 13

Solve these equations:

1. $2m - 3 = 11$
2. $4a + 7 = 15$
3. $3v + 5 = 26$
4. $5x - 9 = 31$
5. $3k - 11 = 28$
6. $6f + 4 = 46$
7. $7y - 5 = 58$
8. $6 + 2h = 22$

9. $14 + 3p = 20$
10. $4l - 13 = 19$
11. $6e + 14 = 32$
12. $2w + 15 = 33$
13. $21 = 4g + 9$
14. $10 = 5n - 20$
15. $47 = 5w - 8$
16. $2c + 3 = 11$

17. $4d - 5 = 19$
18. $7 = 1 + 2e$
19. $4 + 2h = 16$
20. $53 = 3n + 11$
21. $5 = 2m - 5$
22. $32 = 2 + 3n$
23. $18 + 3j = 66$
24. $6 + 4r = 38$

*LHS means left-hand side, and RHS means right-hand side.

25. $\dfrac{x}{2} + 6 = 10$ **27.** $\dfrac{t}{7} + 8 = 11$ **29.** $12 = \dfrac{c}{6} + 5$

26. $\dfrac{d}{3} - 2 = 6$ **28.** $7 + \dfrac{z}{4} = 11$ **30.** $2 = \dfrac{q}{4} - 1$

Exercise 14

Solve these equations. Most of the answers are decimal or vulgar fractions.

1. $2x + 3 = 8$ **9.** $8x + 19 = 20$ **17.** $10x + 9 = 47$
2. $2x - 5 = 4$ **10.** $2x - 6 = 21$ **18.** $24 = 13 + 4x$
3. $4x - 9 = 13$ **11.** $6x - 13 = 53$ **19.** $12.5 = 7x - 5$
4. $4x + 8 = 15$ **12.** $19 + 3x = 32$ **20.** $12 = 10x - 49$
5. $3x + 10 = 21$ **13.** $5x - 20 = 60$ **21.** $6x + 4 = 30$
6. $5x - 1 = 17$ **14.** $18 + 2x = 39$ **22.** $11 + 8x = 48$
7. $3x + 4 = 25$ **15.** $2x + 3 = 9\frac{1}{2}$ **23.** $31 = 19 + 5x$
8. $8x - 3 = 31$ **16.** $4x - 6 = 20$ **24.** $11 = 9x - 2\frac{1}{2}$

Exercise 15

Form an equation from each of these diagrams.
Solve each equation for x.

e.g. 1 Both sides must balance each other. The forces (given in newtons) and their distances (in metres) from the *fulcrum* (the point of balance) cause both sides to have the same turning effect (called its 'moment').

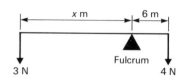

The moment of the left-hand side $= 3 \times x$
The moment of the right-hand side $= 4 \times 6$

Hence, $3 \times x = 4 \times 6$

that is, $3x = 24$

$$\underline{x = 8}$$

378

e.g. 2

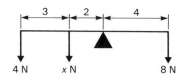

The moment of the left-hand side $= x \times 2 + 4 \times 5$

$\qquad\qquad\qquad\qquad\qquad\qquad = 2x + 20$

The moment of the right-hand side $= 8 \times 4$

$\qquad\qquad\qquad\qquad\qquad\qquad\quad = 32$

Hence, $\qquad\qquad\qquad\qquad 2x + 20 = 32$

$$2x + 20 - 20 = 32 - 20$$

$$2x = 12$$

$$\underline{\underline{x = \;\; 6}}$$

1.
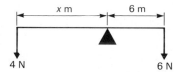

2.
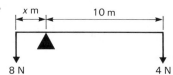

3.
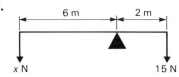

4.
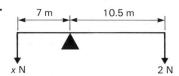

5.
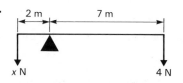

6.
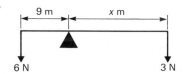

7.
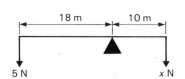

8.
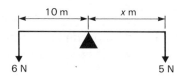

9.
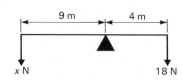

10.
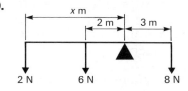

379

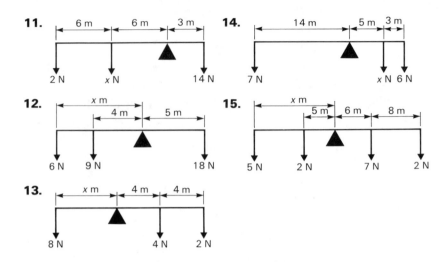

11. 6 m | 6 m | 3 m — 2 N, x N, 14 N

14. 14 m | 5 m | 3 m — 7 N, x N, 6 N

12. x m, 4 m, 5 m — 6 N, 9 N, 18 N

15. x m, 5 m, 6 m, 8 m — 5 N, 2 N, 7 N, 2 N

13. x m, 4 m, 4 m — 8 N, 4 N, 2 N

The following problem has been written as an equation:

I think of a number, multiply it by 4 then add 5. The result is 29.

| t | $\times$ | 4 | $+$ 5 | $= 29$ |

that is, $4t$ $+ 5$ $= 29$

This can be solved to find the number.

Exercise 16

For each problem, form an equation then solve it:

1. I think of a number, multiply it by 2 then add 7.
   The result is 19. Find the number.

2. I think of a number, multiply it by 3 then subtract 8.
   The answer is 7. Find the number.

3. Fives times a number, minus 3, gives 17. Find the number.

4. I think of a number, double it then subtract 9, and get the answer 15. Find the number.

5. When 11 is added to 4 times a number, the result is 39. Find the number.

6. 29 pupils are in a class. $6x$ are present and 5 are absent. Find x.

7. Jeff has $8t$ marbles. If he was given 26 more he would have 98 marbles altogether. Find t.

8. A piece of rope is l m long. Four of these pieces together with a piece that is 12 m long would give a total length of 44 m. Find the length of the piece of rope.

9. Anita is $9a$ years old and Niall is 13 years old. Their ages total 31 years.
   (a) Find the value of a.   (b) Find Anita's age.

10. Carl weighed $7w$ kg. If he was 15 kg lighter, he would weigh 27 kg.
   (a) Find w.   (b) Find how heavy Carl is.

Equations that Use Like Terms

Exercise 17

Simplify each equation then solve it:
1. $3x - x + 7x - 4x = 30$
2. $4n + 3 + n - 3n + 6 = 15$
3. $8t - 3t + 1 - t - 8 = 13$
4. $3m + 10 - 2m - 9 + 5m = 25$
5. $7 + 2h + 6h - 13 - 5h = 24$
6. $5y - 4 + y - 6 + 2y = 46$
7. $13c - 2 + 4c + 18 - 7c = 36$
8. $k - 9 + 12k - 4k + 5 = 68$
9. $6 - 10 + 2z + 7 + 5z = 66$
10. $9a - 3 - 6a - 2 + 17 = 51$
11. $2u + 8 - 3u - 2 + 6u = 41$
12. $1 - f + 6 + 3f - 20 = 19$
13. $2p - 41 - 3p + 6 + 7p = 37$
14. $6 - e + 7 + 9e - 4e = 37$
15. $2w - 7 - 8 + 3w + 3w = 49$
16. $15 - g - 3 + 4g + 4g = 40$
17. $5q + 20 - 3q - 16 + 10 = 21$
18. $2 - 5r + 2r - 9 + 7r = 19$
19. $6b + 1 - 10 - 2b + 6b = 15$
20. $13 - v + 3 + 8v - 2v = 25$

Exercise 18

Find the value of x in each of the following:

1.

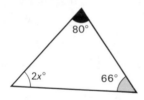

2.

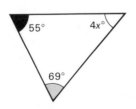

3.

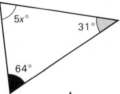

4.

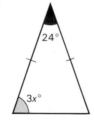

5.

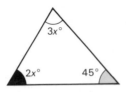

6.

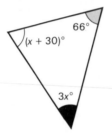

7.

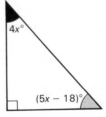

8.

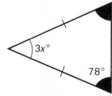

9.

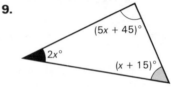

10.

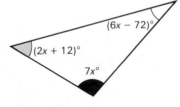

11.

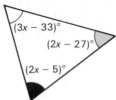

12.

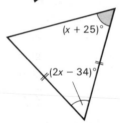

Exercise 19

Copy and complete the crossnumber puzzle:

Across

1. $3x - 11 = 28$
3. $5x - 90 = 15$
6. $2x - 18 = 60$
7. $x - 12 = 42$
8. $6x = 210$
9. $8x - 5 = 27$
10. $2x - 9 = 39$
12. $2x - x + 10 = 72$
14. As 14 down
15. $3x + 93 = 360$
17. $4x + 27 - 2x = 133$
19. As 19 down
20. $\dfrac{x}{4} + 26 = 40$
21. $3x - 1 + 2x + 30 = 214$
22. $\dfrac{x}{5} - 3 = 4$
24. $3x - 12 + 2x + 30 + 4x = 90$
26. $2x - x + 16 + 3x - 51 = 69$
28. $71 = 3x + 17$
29. $8x - 120 = 360$
30. As 30 down
31. $7x + 137 = 235$
33. $9x - 14 - x + 21 - 63 = 128$
35. $5x + 76 - x + 63 + 5x = 193$
36. As 36 down
37. $4x + x - 49 + 2x - 37 = 229$
38. $\dfrac{x}{3} - 19 = 9$

Down

1. $2x + 12 = 50$
2. $x + 38 = 180$
3. $x + 14 = 37$
4. $x - 66 = 90$
5. $4x = 68$
6. $3x - 8 = 100$
9. As 9 across
11. $2x + 4 = 100$
13. $5x - 5 = 120$
14. $6x - 15 = 27$
16. $3x - 20 - 2x - 13 = 60$
18. $7x - 150 - 2x + 22 = 32$
19. $2x + 24 + 9x - 70 + x = 62$
20. $x - 12 - 10 + 3x + 78 = 276$
22. $x - 4x - 15 + 11x + 37 = 270$
23. $\dfrac{x}{8} - 2 = 0$
24. As 24 across
25. $x - 4x + 18 + 10x - 53 = 42$
26. $39 + \dfrac{x}{7} = 43$
27. $12 - 3x - 99 + 5x = 117$
30. $46 = 8x + 18 + 6x$
32. $53 = \dfrac{x}{2} + 16$
34. $90 - x - 11 + 5x = 231$
35. As 35 across
36. $\dfrac{x}{2} + 3\frac{1}{2} = 6$

21 Co-ordinates

Exercise 1

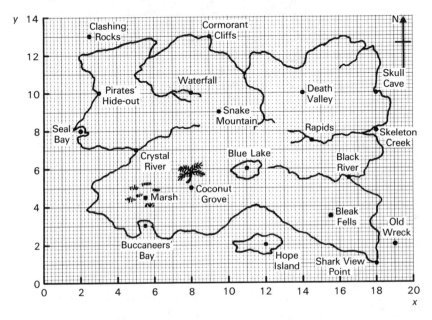

A Which places on the map above are given by the following pairs of co-ordinates?

1. $(5, 7)$
2. $(8, 10)$
3. $(18, 1)$
4. $(19, 2)$

5. $(11, 6)$
6. $(9, 13)$
7. $(18, 8)$

8. $(2.5, 13)$
9. $(5.5, 4.5)$
10. $(14\frac{1}{2}, 7\frac{1}{2})$

B Give the pair of co-ordinates for each of the following places:

1. Coconut Grove
2. Pirates' Hide-out
3. Death Valley
4. Seal Bay
5. Hope Island

6. Skull Cave
7. Buccaneers' Bay
8. Snake Mountain
9. Black River
10. Bleak Fells

384

This is a game for two players but it can easily be adapted for four players.

One playing surface of squared paper is needed per game. All players use the same playing surface.

Axes should be marked and numbered as shown. (Do not use less than 8 squares. You may use more than 8 or even more than 10.)

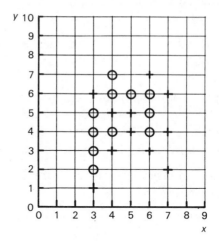

1. The first player calls out a pair of co-ordinates, e.g. (4, 5), and the second player marks the first player's position with a cross.

2. The second player now calls out a pair of co-ordinates, e.g. (5, 6), and the first player marks the second player's position with a circle.

3. Play continues until one of the players gets 5 marks in a straight line (vertically, horizontally or diagonally).

In the game above, the first player (the crosses) won, using a diagonal line. (3, 6) (4, 5) (5, 4) (6, 3) (7, 2) gave the winning line.

Notes   Any player who calls out a point that has already been marked, loses that turn. (It is counted as a turn, but no point is marked.)

If a player marks the wrong point then he or she must, when told, mark the correct point, i.e. the other player has got a free point: e.g. if player 2 calls (4, 6) and player 1 marks (6, 4), then player 2 is allowed both positions and is given (4, 6) and (6, 4).

385

Exercise 3

A Which places on the map opposite are given by the following pairs of co-ordinates?

1. (24, 22)　　　**3.** (25, 19)　　　**5.** (26.7, 20)

2. (30, 20)　　　**4.** (25.5, 22.5)　　**6.** (28.6, 19.3)

B Instead of using pairs of co-ordinates, a place can be identified by a *grid reference*. For example, Henders Farm is at 270 220 and Horton Wood is at 231 185. (*Note* Since Horton Wood covers a large area, a reference is given for a point in the middle of the wood.)

Which places on the map are identified by the following grid references?

1. 260 220　　　**3.** 300 215　　　**5.** 269 192

2. 260 200　　　**4.** 249 213　　　**6.** 247 225

C Give the grid reference and the pair of co-ordinates for each of these:

1. White Farm,

2. the church with the spire ( ),

3. the four public houses (PH),

4. the golf course ( ),

5. the railway station (●),

6. the level crossing (LC),

7. the point where the A-road becomes a dual carriageway,

8. Colcott Farm,

9. the car park (**P**),

10. the bus station (●),

11. the windmill ( ),

12. the public telephone ( ),

13. the post offices (P),

14. the bridges over the railway,

15. the bridges over the river,

16. the point where the railway tunnel goes under the road,

17. the church with a tower ( ),

18. the embankment ( ).

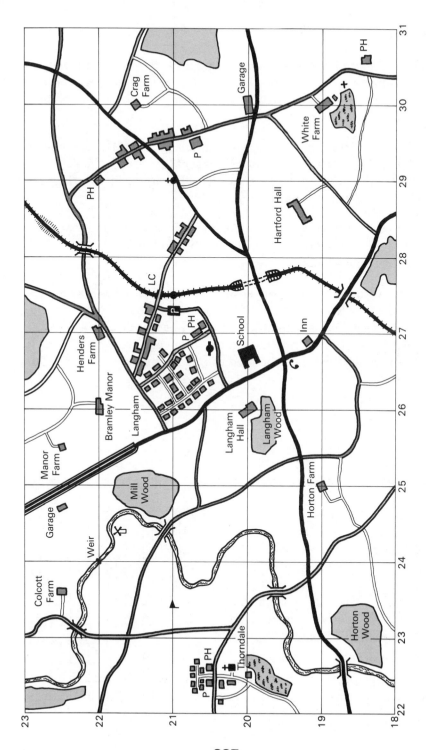

History of Co-ordinates

The method of plotting points using x- and y-axes and pairs of co-ordinates is due to René Descartes (1596–1650) who was born in France. His method was called *co-ordinate geometry* (or 'analytical geometry' or 'Cartesian geometry')

A few days after René was born, his mother died. He was a pale, sickly child. At the age of eight he was sent to a Jesuit school. Due to his ill-health he was allowed to spend each morning in bed. He spent most of that time thinking.

After leaving school, he became a soldier. He travelled and continued to study. At the age of 32 he went to live in Holland. In 1637, his work was first published.

Queen Christina, the 19-year-old queen of Sweden, persuaded Descartes, in 1649, to go to Sweden to teach her. Unfortunately, for Descartes, he was unable to stay in bed each morning — the queen insisted on having her lessons in a cold library at 5 a.m. It was too much for him — he died of pneumonia in February 1650.

Exercise 4

Draw a pair of axes as shown. Use a scale of 2 cm to 1 unit on both axes. Label the x-axis from 0 to 7, and the y-axis from 0 to 10. Answer all the questions on the same piece of graph paper using the same pair of axes.

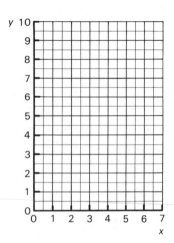

For each question, plot the points and join them in the given order using straight lines.
Inside each shape, write its full name.

1. $(4,1)$ $(7,1)$ $(7,2)$ $(4,2)$ $(4,1)$

2. $(5,8)$ $(6,8)$ $(6\frac{1}{2},9)$ $(6,10)$ $(5,10)$ $(4\frac{1}{2},9)$ $(5,8)$

3. $(0.5,3)$ $(2.5,3)$ $(2.5,5)$ $(0.5,5)$ $(0.5,3)$

4. $(2,0)$ $(0,0)$ $(1,2\frac{1}{2})$ $(2,0)$

5. $(3\frac{1}{2},3\frac{1}{2})$ $(4\frac{1}{2},4\frac{1}{2})$ $(7,4\frac{1}{2})$ $(6,3\frac{1}{2})$ $(3\frac{1}{2},3\frac{1}{2})$

6. $(0,8.5)$ $(0,9.5)$ $(1,10)$ $(2,8.5)$ $(0,8.5)$

7. $(3.5,5.5)$ $(6,5.5)$ $(6,7)$ $(3.5,5.5)$

8. $(1.5,5.7)$ $(2.3,7.5)$ $(1.5,8)$ $(0.7,7.5)$ $(1.5,5.7)$

9. $(3,8)$ $(4,9)$ $(3,10)$ $(2,9)$ $(3,8)$

10. $(3.5,7.5)$ $(5,7.5)$ $(3,5.5)$ $(2.5,6.5)$ $(3.5,7.5)$

Exercise 5

Draw a pair of axes as shown.
Use a scale of 1 cm to 1 unit on both axes.
Label the x-axis from $^-8$ to 8 and the y-axis from $^-10$ to 10.
Answer all the questions on the same piece of graph paper using the same pair of axes.

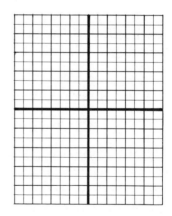

For each question, plot the points and join them in the given order using straight lines.
Inside each shape, write its full name.

1. $(0,2)$ $(1,4)$ $(5,4)$ $(4,2)$ $(0,2)$

2. $(7,5)$ $(7,9)$ $(1,7)$ $(7,5)$

3. $(2,1)$ $(2,^-2)$ $(^-1,^-2)$ $(^-1,1)$ $(2,1)$

4. $(3,^-3)$ $(5,^-3)$ $(7,^-5)$ $(7,^-7)$ $(5,^-9)$ $(3,^-9)$ $(1,^-7)$ $(1,^-5)$ $(3,^-3)$

5. $(4,10)$ $(4,9)$ $(^-4,9)$ $(^-4,10)$ $(4,10)$

6. $(^-3,7)$ $(^-1.5,5.5)$ $(^-3,^-2)$ $(^-4.5,5.5)$ $(^-3,7)$

7. $(^-6,^-3)$ $(^-4,^-4)$ $(^-5,^-6)$ $(^-7,^-6)$ $(^-8,^-4)$ $(^-6,^-3)$

8. $(3, ^-1) (4, 1) (6, 1) (8, ^-1) (3, ^-1)$

9. $(0, ^-8) (^-3, ^-10) (^-6, ^-8) (^-3, ^-6) (0, ^-8)$

10. $(^-5, 3) (^-8, 4) (^-7, 0) (^-8, ^-2) (^-5, ^-2) (^-4, ^-1) (^-5, 3)$

Exercise 6 ▬▬▬▬▬▬▬▬▬▬▬▬▬▬▬▬▬▬▬▬▬ **M**

Draw a pair of axes as shown. Plot the following points on one graph and join them in the given order with a *smooth curve.* At the end of each question, lift your pencil and start again at the next question.

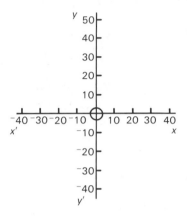

1. $(12, 8) (10, 8) (8, 7.5) (5, 7) (3, 6) (1, 5) (^-1.5, 3.5) (^-3, 2) (^-4, 0)$
$(^-5, ^-2) (^-6, ^-6) (^-5, ^-10) (^-2, ^-15) (0, ^-18) (2, ^-20) (6, ^-23)$
$(8, ^-25) (10, ^-27)$

2. $(10, ^-27) (8, ^-27) (5, ^-26.5) (2, ^-26)$

3. $(2, ^-26) (1, ^-27) (0, ^-27.5) (^-2, ^-30) (^-5, ^-31)$

4. $(^-13, 31) (^-10, 30.5) (^-5, 30) (^-2, 29.5) (0, 29) (3, 28.5) (5, 28)$
$(10, 26.5) (13, 25) (15, 24) (18, 22) (20, 20) (23, 17) (24, 14)$
$(25, 11) (26, 8) (27, 5) (27, 0) (28, ^-5) (28, ^-10) (27.5, ^-14)$
$(27, ^-16) (26, ^-20) (24, ^-23)$

5. $(^-32.5, 1) (^-30, 2.5) (^-27, 2) (^-25, 1) (^-23, 0) (^-20, ^-1) (^-16, ^-2)$
$(^-11, ^-3) (^-9, ^-3) (^-7, ^-2) (^-5, ^-2)$

6. $(^-5, ^-31) (^-2, ^-31) (^-0.5, ^-30.5)$

7. $(^-2, ^-31) (^-2, ^-32)$

8. $(^-2, ^-32) (0, ^-32) (5, ^-31.5) (10, ^-31) (14, ^-31) (15, ^-30) (14.5, ^-29)$
$(15, ^-28) (17, ^-27.5) (20, ^-27) (25, ^-26) (28, ^-25) (29, ^-24) (31, ^-22)$
$(32.5, ^-20) (33.5, ^-17.5) (35, ^-15) (36, ^-12) (36.5, ^-10) (37, ^-7)$
$(37, ^-4) (36.5, ^-1)$

9. $(34, 28)$ $(34, 24)$ $(35, 20)$ $(36, 16)$ $(37.5, 11)$ $(38, 8)$ $(38, 5)$ $(38, 3)$ $(38, 0)$ $(38, ^-2)$ $(38, ^-5)$ $(37, ^-7)$

10. $(34, 28)$ $(33, 27)$ $(32.5, 25.5)$

11. $(38, 50)$ $(35, 45)$ $(32.5, 40)$ $(31, 35)$ $(31, 30)$ $(31.5, 29)$ $(32.5, 25.5)$

12. $(32, 49)$ $(35, 50)$ $(38, 50)$

13. $(32.5, 50)$ $(32, 49)$

14. $(32.5, 50)$ $(28, 48)$

15. $(29, 49.5)$ $(28, 48)$

16. $(29, 49.5)$ $(27, 48.5)$

17. $(28, 50)$ $(27, 48.5)$

18. $(28, 50)$ $(25, 48)$

19. $(26, 49.5)$ $(25, 48)$

20. $(26, 49.5)$ $(24, 48)$ $(22.5, 47)$

21. $(23, 48.5)$ $(22.5, 47)$

22. $(23, 48.5)$ $(21, 47)$ $(18, 45)$ $(17, 43)$ $(15.5, 40)$ $(15, 38)$ $(15, 35)$ $(15, 33)$ $(16, 30)$ $(17, 28)$ $(18.5, 25)$ $(20, 22)$ $(21, 20)$ $(22, 18.5)$

23. $(^-33.5, 3.5)$ $(^-31, 4)$ $(^-30, 4)$ $(^-31.5, 2.5)$ $(^-32.5, 1)$

24. $(^-33, 5)$ $(^-31, 5.5)$ $(^-31, 5)$ $(^-32, 4.5)$ $(^-33.5, 3.5)$

25. $(^-24, 31)$ $(^-25, 30)$ $(^-27, 28)$ $(^-28, 26)$ $(^-29, 24)$ $(^-30, 20)$ $(^-30, 18)$ $(^-29.5, 15)$ $(^-30, 14)$ $(^-31, 12)$ $(^-30, 11)$ $(^-28, 10.5)$ $(^-26, 11)$ $(^-24, 11.5)$ $(^-22, 13)$ $(^-20, 14)$ $(^-18, 13)$ $(^-17, 12)$ $(^-15.5, 10)$ $(^-16, 8)$ $(^-18, 7)$ $(^-20, 6)$ $(^-22, 5.5)$ $(^-25, 6)$ $(^-27, 6.5)$ $(^-30, 6.5)$ $(^-32, 6)$ $(^-33, 5)$

26. $(^-24, 31)$ $(^-25, 35)$ $(^-24.5, 38)$ $(^-24, 40)$ $(^-23, 41)$ $(^-21, 42)$ $(^-21, 41)$ $(^-21, 39)$ $(^-22, 37)$ $(^-22, 35)$ $(^-22, 33)$

27. $(^-22, 33)$ $(^-19.5, 33)$

28. $(^-19.5, 33)$ $(^-19.5, 37)$ $(^-19, 39)$ $(^-18, 41)$ $(^-17, 42)$ $(^-16, 43)$ $(^-15.5, 42)$ $(^-16, 40)$ $(^-16.5, 37)$ $(^-16, 35)$ $(^-15, 33)$ $(^-13, 31)$

29. $(^-17, 31)\ (^-19, 27)$

30. $(^-19, 27)\ (^-17, 28)$

31. $(^-17, 28)\ (^-17, 25)$

32. $(^-17, 25)\ (^-15, 28)\ (^-15, 31)\ (^-16.5, 33.5)$

33. $(^-16.5, 33.5)\ (^-17, 33)$

34. $(^-25, 21)\ \ (^-24, 22)\ \ (^-23, 22)\ \ (^-22.5, 21)\ \ (^-23, 20)\ \ (^-25, 19)$
$(^-25.5, 20)\ (^-25, 21)$

35. $(^-31.5, 15.5)\ (^-29.5, 15)$

36. $(^-37, 13.5)\ (^-33, 14)\ (^-30, 14)$

37. $(^-30, 14)\ (^-34, 12)$

38. $(^-30, 11)\ (^-31.5, 9.5)$

39. $(^-27, 13.5)\ (^-22, 13)\ (^-18, 11)$

40. $(^-27, 13)\ (^-24, 12)\ (^-21, 11)\ (^-18, 8)$

41. $(^-27, 12)\ (^-26, 11)\ (^-24, 10)$

42. $(^-28, 12)\ (^-26, 9)$

Exercise 7

On the same pair of axes, plot the given pairs of points and join them with straight lines. For each question, write the co-ordinates of the point of intersection of each pair of lines. (Use a scale of 1 cm to 1 unit on both axes. The x-axis should range from $^-9$ to 6, while y-values should range from $^-6$ to 13.)

1. (*a*) $(6, 7)$ and $(4, 13)$
   (*b*) $(6, 11)$ and $(4, 9)$

2. (*a*) $(2, 13)$ and $(^-1, 10)$
   (*b*) $(4, 11)$ and $(^-2, 13)$

3. (*a*) $(6, 3)$ and $(4, ^-3)$
   (*b*) $(6, ^-2)$ and $(4, 2)$

4. (*a*) $(1, 8)$ and $(^-4, 8)$
   (*b*) $(^-1, 6)$ and $(^-3, 10)$

5. (*a*) $(1, 5)$ and $(5, 3)$
   (*b*) $(4, 3)$ and $(2, 5)$

6. (*a*) $(^-7, 0)$ and $(^-3, 2)$
   (*b*) $(^-3, ^-2)$ and $(^-7, 4)$

7. (a) $(^-5, ^-6)$ and $(^-9, ^-2)$ **10.** (a) $(^-9, 9)$ and $(^-6, 6)$
   (b) $(^-6, ^-3)$ and $(^-8, ^-5)$ (b) $(^-9, 7\frac{1}{2})$ and $(^-5, 7\frac{1}{2})$

8. (a) $(^-7, 10)$ and $(^-5, 13)$ **11.** (a) $(3, 7)$ and $(^-3, 4)$
   (b) $(^-4, 11)$ and $(^-8, 12)$ (b) $(1, 4)$ and $(^-1, 7)$

9. (a) $(3, ^-6)$ and $(^-1, ^-4)$ **12.** (a) $(2, ^-1)$ and $(^-4, ^-4)$
   (b) $(2, ^-4)$ and $(0, ^-6)$ (b) $(^-2, ^-2)$ and $(1, ^-3\frac{1}{2})$

Exercise 8

Find the co-ordinates of the mid-point of the straight line that joins
each pair of points:

1. $(1, 3)$ $(1, 11)$ **11.** $(8, ^-3)$ $(0, 0)$
2. $(3, 2)$ $(9, 2)$ **12.** $(^-8, 4)$ $(^-2, ^-4)$
3. $(5, 1)$ $(5, 7)$ **13.** $(^-2, 8)$ $(14, ^-4)$
4. $(4, 6)$ $(4, 9)$ **14.** $(9, ^-9)$ $(^-3, 3)$
5. $(^-6, 2)$ $(^-6, 10)$ **15.** $(4, ^-4)$ $(^-2, ^-2)$
6. $(9, ^-1)$ $(2, ^-1)$ **16.** $(^-1, 0)$ $(0, 10)$
7. $(2, 3)$ $(8, 11)$ **17.** $(8, ^-7)$ $(^-2, ^-1)$
8. $(12, 1)$ $(4, 9)$ **18.** $(14, 6)$ $(^-12, ^-6)$
9. $(15, 10)$ $(11, 5)$ **19.** $(^-1, ^-8)$ $(^-9, ^-2)$
10. $(^-7, 4)$ $(3, 10)$ **20.** $(16, 6)$ $(^-6, 16)$

Exercise 9

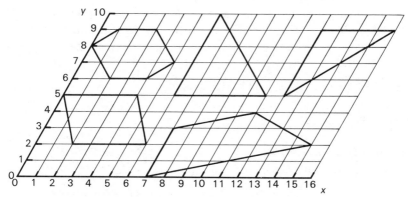

Write the co-ordinates of the vertices of:

1. the parallelogram,   **4.** the equilateral triangle,
2. the trapezium,   **5.** the isosceles triangle.
3. the hexagon,

Exercise 10

A Plot the following points on a square grid (ordinary graph paper) and also on a grid of rhombuses (as used in Exercise 9). Join the points in the given order, using straight lines, to form a closed shape. Write the name of each shape drawn. All the shapes can be drawn on the same square grid and on the same grid of rhombuses.

For both grids, the x-values range from 0 to 20 and the y-values from 0 to 16.

1. $(1, 11)$ $(1, 15)$ $(5, 15)$ $(5, 11)$ $(1, 11)$
2. $(1, 7)$ $(2, 10)$ $(5, 9)$ $(4, 6)$ $(1, 7)$
3. $(1, 3)$ $(3, 1)$ $(5, 3)$ $(3, 5)$ $(1, 3)$
4. $(7, 10)$ $(9, 15)$ $(11, 10)$ $(7, 10)$
5. $(8, 9)$ $(11, 6)$ $(6, 4)$ $(8, 9)$
6. $(12, 1)$ $(6, 1)$ $(12, 5)$ $(12, 1)$
7. $(12, 12)$ $(12, 16)$ $(18, 16)$ $(18, 12)$ $(12, 12)$
8. $(17, 10)$ $(17, 6)$ $(13, 6)$ $(17, 10)$
9. $(14, 0)$ $(20, 1)$ $(19, 6)$ $(14, 0)$

B Draw and label on both the square grid and the grid of rhombuses the following shapes, if they can be drawn. If a shape cannot be drawn, write 'IMPOSSIBLE'. You need to draw a pair of axes on both grids. For each question the shapes drawn use the same co-ordinates. Try to find shapes that can still be given the same name when drawn on either grid.

e.g.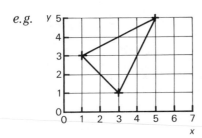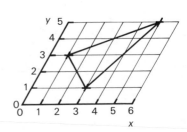

The triangles are isosceles on both grids.

394

Try these shapes in the same way:

1. a parallelogram,
2. a rhombus
3. an obtuse-angled triangle,

4. a rectangle,
5. a square,
6. a right-angled triangle.

Exercise 11

Draw a pair of axes using values
of x from $^-8$ to $^+8$ ($^-8 \leqslant x \leqslant 8$),
and values of y from $^-8$ to $^+12$
($^-8 \leqslant y \leqslant 12$).

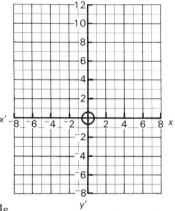

It is possible for all these
questions to be answered using
the same pair of axes.

1. $(0, 0)$, $(^-1, ^-2)$, and $(3, ^-4)$
   are vertices of a rectangle. Find:

   (a) the fourth vertex,
   (b) the co-ordinates of the point
   of intersection of the diagonals.

2. Join the points $(0, ^-6)$, $(^-4, ^-4)$, $(^-8, ^-6)$, $(^-4, ^-8)$, $(0, ^-6)$ in
   the given order using straight lines:
   (a) What shape is obtained?
   (b) What are the co-ordinates of the point of intersection of
   the diagonals?

3. $(2, 1)$, $(6, 3)$ and $(7, 1)$ are three vertices of a kite:
   (a) Find the co-ordinates of the fourth vertex.
   (b) Write the co-ordinates of the two points at which sides of
   the kite cross the x-axis.

4. $(6, ^-4)$, $(5, ^-8)$, and $(1, ^-6)$ are the vertices of a triangle. Find
   the co-ordinates of the point of intersection of the medians*.

5. $(5, 6)$, $(\boxed{?}, \boxed{?})$, $(6, 11)$, $(\boxed{?}, \boxed{?})$, taken in that order, are
   the vertices of a square.
   (a) Find the missing co-ordinates.
   (b) Find the co-ordinates of the point of intersection of the
   diagonals.

*See the glossary, p. 435.

395

6. The diagonals of a square intersect at ($^-$6, 10). If ($^-$7, 12) is one vertex of the square, what are the co-ordinates of the other vertices?

7. (1, 11) is the mid-point of diagonal AC of parallelogram ABCD. A is the point (4, 12) and D is ($^-$1, 12). Find the co-ordinates of the other two vertices.

8. XYZ is an isosceles triangle in which XY = XZ. X is (1, 3), Y is ($^-$7, 5) and ZY is parallel to the y-axis. Find the co-ordinates of point Z.

9. In triangle LMN, L is ($^-$2, 1) M is ($^-$8, $^-$2) and N is ($^-$5, $^-$3). A lies on LM such that AN is an altitude* of the triangle. Find the co-ordinates of A.

10. PQRS is an isosceles trapezium where PQ = RS. If P is the point ($^-$4, 6), S the point (5, 3) and if Q lies on the y-axis such that the y-coordinate is 8, find the co-ordinates of point R.

Exercise 12

Four people tried to find some hidden treasure.
They were given four pairs of co-ordinates each.

Ann was given   (7, 6), (4, 4), (2, 6), (3, 9).
Brian was given   (4, 7), (3, 9), (2, 10), (6, 9).
Charles was given   (6, 5), (8, 3), (2, 1), (4, 4).
Deborah was given (1, 3), (5, 3), (4, 7), (1, 9).

The co-ordinates of all four people had to be plotted, and then joined to give the path to the treasure. *Straight lines* had to be used. Each person's part of the journey had to be followed, one after the other. The point at which one person's part of the journey ended was where the next person's part of the journey began.

After the whole journey had been drawn, no lines should have crossed each other.

Neither the given order of the names, nor the order of the pairs of co-ordinates are in the correct order for the journey.

*See the glossary, p. 433.

Draw a pair of axes and label them as shown.
Plot the points and sort out the correct order.
Show the whole journey and find *two* possible places for the treasure.

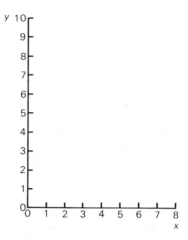

Exercise 13   Graphs from Tables

1. On a certain journey, I travel at a steady 80 km per hour. The given table shows how far I travel every hour.

Time taken, t (h)	0	1	2	3	4	5
Distance travelled, s (km)	0	80	160	240	320	400

Use the table to plot a graph of distance against time. Draw your axes as shown.

Use a scale of 4 cm to 1 h on the horizontal axis and 1 cm to 25 km on the vertical axis.

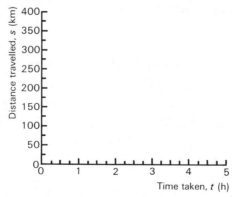

Now use your graph to help you to answer these questions:
(a) How far have I travelled in $1\frac{1}{2}$ h?
(b) How long does it take me to travel 300 km?

2.

Height of drop (cm)	100	150	200	250	300	350
Height of bounce (cm)	60	90	120	150	180	210

In a science experiment, a ball was dropped from various heights and the height of its bounce was measured. The table above shows the results.

Plot a graph. (The diagram suggests a suitable scale.)

Use your graph to help you to answer these questions:
(a) How high would the ball bounce if I dropped it from 400 cm?
(b) If the ball bounces to a height of 30 cm, from what height was it dropped?
(c) If the ball was dropped from 175 cm how high would it bounce?
(d) From what height should the ball be dropped in order to bounce to a height of 195 cm?

3. Normally, in an experiment the points, when plotted, do not lie in a line, but they do *suggest* a line.

In this science experiment, a spring was fixed at one end and a force was applied to the other. The spring obviously increased its length. This new length was noted. This was repeated for other forces and the following table produced.

Force (N)	1	2	3	4	5	6	7	8	9
Length (cm)	31	32	33	33	35	35	37	37	38

(*a*) Plot these points. Use a scale of 2 cm to 5 cm on the vertical axis and 2 cm to 1 N on the horizontal axis.

Draw a 'line of best fit'*.

(i) What force is needed to stretch the spring to 34 cm?

(ii) How long was the unstretched spring?

(*b*) This table shows the extension of the spring and the force used:

Force (N)	1	2	3	4	5	6	7	8	9
Extension (cm)	1	2	3	3	5	5	7	7	8

Plot the points. Use a scale of 2 cm to 1 cm on the vertical axis and 2 cm to 1 N on the horizontal axis.

Draw the line of best fit.

4. In a science experiment, soup was heated until it boiled. It was then left to cool and its temperature was noted every minute. While it was cooling, the windows and doors were opened for a while. Here is a table of results:

Time, t (min)	0	1	2	3	4	5	6	7	8	9	10	11	12	13	14	15
Temperature, T (°C)	100	98	94	91	87	83	80	78	75	73	70	68	67	65	63	62

Time, t (min)	16	17	18	19	20	21	22	23	24	25	26	27	28	29	30
Temperature, T (°C)	61	60	59	58	56	54	50	46	42	40	38	37	36	35	34

Plot a graph of these results. Use a scale of 2 cm to 5 min on the time axis and 1 cm to 10 °C on the temperature axis.

Use your graph to find:

(*a*) the temperature of the soup after $9\frac{1}{2}$ min.

(*b*) the temperature of the soup after $27\frac{1}{2}$ min.

(*c*) the time taken for the soup to cool to 89 °C.

(*d*) the time taken for the soup to cool to 77 °C.

(*e*) the time taken before the doors and windows were opened.

*See the glossary, p. 434.

22 Indices and Square Roots

The square has an area of $9\,\text{cm}^2$ and the dot pattern shows the square number 9.

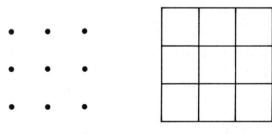

There are 3 rows of 3 dots $(3 \times 3 = 9)$.

There are 3 rows of 3 squares $(3 \times 3 = 9)$.

We can write this as $3^2 = 9$.

3^2 means 3×3 and is read as 'three squared'.

This cube is made up of eight
1 cm cubes. Each layer has
2 rows of 2 cubes and there
are 2 layers.
So there are $2 \times 2 \times 2$ cubes.
We can write this as $2^3 = 8$.

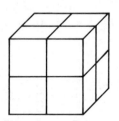

2^3 means $2 \times 2 \times 2$ and is
read as 'two cubed'.

$2^4 = 2 \times 2 \times 2 \times 2$ and is read as 'two to the power four'.
The 4 is called the *power* or the *index* (plural: *indices*).
The index 4 indicates there are 4 factors of 2.
The notation 2^4 is called *index form*.

$16 = 2 \times 2 \times 2 \times 2 = 2^4$ in index form.

$9 = 3 \times 3 \qquad = 3^2$ in index form.

$125 = 5 \times 5 \times 5 \quad = 5^3$ in index form.

Also, $p \times p \times p \times p = p^4$ in index form.

400

Exercise 1

A Write in index form:

1. $c \times c \times c \times c \times c$
2. $x \times x \times x \times x$
3. $7 \times 7 \times 7 \times 7 \times 7 \times 7$
4. $n \times n \times n \times n \times n \times n \times n$

5. $t \times t \times t \times t \times t \times t \times t \times t \times t$
6. $4 \times 4 \times 4 \times 4 \times 4$
7. $g \times g \times g \times g \times g \times g \times g \times g$
8. $y \times y \times y \times y \times y \times y \times y \times y \times y \times y$

B Find the value of:

1. 6^2
2. 10^2
3. 9^2
4. 12^2
5. 15^2

6. 2^5
7. 3^4
8. 1^7
9. 0^{10}
10. 5^4

11. 4^3
12. 2^7
13. 9^3
14. 10^8
15. 3^5

16. 7^3
17. 20^3
18. 8^3
19. 4^6
20. 2^{12}

21. 100^2
22. 100^3
23. 100^4
24. 30^3
25. 12^3

C Find the missing indices:

1. $49 = 7^{?}$
2. $25 = 5^{?}$
3. $27 = 3^{?}$
4. $121 = 11^{?}$

5. $10\,000 = 10^{?}$
6. $729 = 3^{?}$
7. $64 = 8^{?} = 2^{?}$
8. $256 = 4^{?} = 2^{?} = 16^{?}$

Indices on a Calculator

If your calculator has the key $\boxed{x^2}$ on it then you can quickly square numbers. Try this to find 4^2:

Key in: $\boxed{\text{AC}}$ $\boxed{4}$ $\boxed{x^2}$ You should get the answer 16.

Note i $\boxed{\text{AC}}$ is used to clear the display. (It may be a different key on your calculator.)

ii You may need to use a function key for $\boxed{x^2}$ to work:

e.g. $\boxed{\text{AC}}$ $\boxed{4}$ $\boxed{\text{F}}$ $\boxed{x^2}$ or an inverse key,

e.g. $\boxed{\text{AC}}$ $\boxed{4}$ $\boxed{\text{INV}}$ $\boxed{x^2}$

On many calculators this method of squaring works:

Key in: $\boxed{\text{AC}}$ $\boxed{4}$ $\boxed{\times}$ $\boxed{=}$

Try it.

401

Some calculators have a special key to find powers of numbers. Check your calculator. The key probably looks like this $\boxed{x^y}$, or this $\boxed{y^x}$.

To find 6^5, key in: $\boxed{AC}$ $\boxed{6}$ $\boxed{x^y}$ $\boxed{5}$ $\boxed{=}$. Try it. You should obtain the answer 7776.

(*Note* A function key or an inverse key may need to be pressed before using $\boxed{x^y}$.)

Exercise 2

Use a calculator to find the value of:

1. 7^6	**5.** 6^9	**9.** 12^4	**13.** 1.2^5	**17.** 1.27^3
2. 9^5	**6.** 4^{10}	**10.** 14^4	**14.** 0.5^5	**18.** 3.81^2
3. 3^{11}	**7.** 8^5	**11.** 19^5	**15.** 1.3^7	**19.** 8.5^4
4. 2^{15}	**8.** 11^3	**12.** 21^5	**16.** 2.4^4	**20.** 1.01^3

Exercise 3

1. Investigate the units digits of square numbers and write what you notice.

For example, can you find a number, which, when squared, ends in a 9, a 2, and so on?

2. What numbers, when squared, have a units digit of 4

Exercise 4   Palindromes

A *palindrome* reads the same backwards as forwards. For example, 3 146 413 is a palindrome.

1. $11^2 = 121$ and is a palindrome.
Is 121^2 a palindrome?

2. Is 22^2 a palindrome?

3. $101^2 = 10\,201$ and is a palindrome.
Try to find some more square numbers that are palindromes.

Exercise 5

Write in index form:

e.g. $a \times a \times a \times b \times b \times a \times b = \underline{a^4 b^3}$

1. $k \times k \times l \times k \times k \times l$
2. $d \times d \times d \times e \times d \times e \times e \times e \times e$
3. $v \times w \times v \times w \times v \times w \times v \times w$
4. $f \times h \times h \times f \times f \times h \times h \times h$
5. $z \times z \times z \times u \times z \times z \times z \times u$
6. $r \times q \times q \times q \times r \times r \times r \times r \times r \times q \times r$
7. $j \times s \times s \times j \times m \times j \times m \times s \times s \times s$
8. $3 \times 3 \times 5 \times 3 \times 5 \times 5 \times 3 \times 3$
9. $d \times e \times d \times e \times f \times e \times d \times e \times e \times d \times d$
10. $n \times c \times c \times p \times c \times p \times n \times c \times p \times p \times p \times c \times p$

Exercise 6

Find the value of the following:

e.g. $2^3 \times 5^2 = 8 \times 25 = \underline{200}$

1. $2^2 \times 3^3$
2. $2^3 \times 3^2$
3. $5^3 \times 2$
4. $6^2 \times 2^2$
5. $7^2 \times 2^3$
6. $3^2 \times 8^2$
7. $3^2 \times 4^3$
8. $2^3 \times 5^3$
9. $10^4 \times 5^3$
10. $5^2 \times 4^3$
11. $6^3 \times 2^3$
12. $3^4 \times 9^2$

Exercise 7

Find the value of:

1. (a) $2^3 \times 2^2$ (b) 2^5
2. (a) $3^2 \times 3^3$ (b) 3^5
3. (a) $3^2 \times 3^4$ (b) 3^6
4. (a) $10^4 \times 10^3$ (b) 10^7
5. (a) $4^2 \times 4^3$ (b) 4^5
6. (a) $3^4 \times 3^3$ (b) 3^7
7. (a) $5^2 \times 5^3$ (b) 5^5
8. (a) $2^5 \times 2^6$ (b) 2^{11}

Note $x^4 \times \qquad x^3$

$$= x \times x \times x \times x \ \times \ x \times x \times x$$

$$= \underline{\underline{x^7}}$$

and $a^2 \times \qquad b^3 \times a \times \qquad b^4$

$$= a \times a \ \times \ b \times b \times b \ \times \ a \ \times \ b \times b \times b \times b$$

$$= \underline{\underline{a^3 b^7}}$$

403

Exercise 8

Where possible, simplify the following, leaving your answers in index form:

e.g. 1 $a^4 \times a^2 \times a^3 = \underline{\underline{a^9}}$

e.g. 2 $b^3 \times c^4 \times c^2 \times b^4 \times b = \underline{\underline{b^8 c^6}}$

1. $d^3 \times d^5$

2. $n^7 \times n^6$

3. $e^8 \times e^6$

4. $4^3 \times 4^6$

5. $t^3 \times t^{14}$

6. $g^7 \times g^2 \times g^4$

7. $z^3 \times z^9 \times z^7$

8. $w^4 \times w \times w^3 \times w^6$

9. $p^{10} \times p^3 \times p^4 \times p^8$

10. $7^4 \times 7^5 \times 7 \times 7^3$

11. $5^4 \times 3^6$

12. $k^7 \times k^4 \times k^9 \times k$

13. $f^3 \times y^4 \times f^2 \times y^3$

14. $h^6 \times m \times m^3 \times h^3 \times m^8$

15. $j \times v^4 \times j^2 \times v^4 \times j^3$

16. $q^6 \times u^4$

17. $l^4 \times l^3 \times r^3 \times r^4$

18. $s^5 \times d^5 \times d \times d^4 \times d^9$

19. $w \times f \times f \times w^2 \times w^9 \times w^3$

20. $l^6 \times m^3 \times l^4 \times m^7$

21. $g^{14} \times h^2 \times g^{13} \times h^{12} \times g^2$

22. $p^3 \times q^3 \times p^6 \times p^{10} \times p^9 \times q^7$

23. $t \times u^{10} \times t^{10} \times w^{12} \times t^9 \times u^3 \times w^2$

24. $x^4 \times y^3 \times z^5 \times x^3 \times y^2 \times z^4$

Exercise 9

Find the value of:

1. (a) $\dfrac{2^6}{2^2}$ (b) 2^4

2. (a) $\dfrac{3^5}{3^3}$ (b) 3^2

3. (a) $\dfrac{10^7}{10^4}$ (b) 10^3

4. (a) $\dfrac{2^9}{2^3}$ (b) 2^6

5. (a) $\dfrac{3^7}{3^2}$ (b) 3^5

6. (a) $\dfrac{5^5}{5}$ (b) 5^4

Exercise 10

Simplify the following, leaving your answers in index form:

1. $\dfrac{x^6}{x^2}$

2. $\dfrac{8^5}{8^3}$

3. $9^7 \div 9^2$

4. $\dfrac{n^{10}}{n^6}$

5. $\dfrac{3^9}{3^6}$

6. $p^{12} = p^4$

7. $g^{13} \div g^4$

8. $\dfrac{u^{15}}{u}$

9. $7^{10} \div 7$　　**11.** $t^{20} \div t^7$　　**13.** $\dfrac{s^8}{s^5}$　　　**15.** $12^{21} \div 12^{17}$

10. $\dfrac{m^{18}}{m^{11}}$　　　**12.** $k^{12} \div k^{11}$　　**14.** $h^{16} \div h^7$　　**16.** $\dfrac{w^{17}}{w^8}$

Note　　$4x^3 \times 3x^2$

$$= 4 \times x^3 \times 3 \times x^2$$
$$= 4 \times 3 \times x^3 \times x^2$$
$$= 12 \times x^5$$
$$= \underline{\underline{12x^5}}$$

Exercise 11

Simplify, leaving your answers in index form:

e.g. 1　$3h^5 \times 4h^3 = \underline{\underline{12h^8}}$

e.g. 2　$5p^2qr^5 \times 3p^3q^4r^3 = \underline{\underline{15p^5q^5r^8}}$

1. $2m^4 \times 3m^2$

2. $3e^3 \times 5e^5$

3. $4c^5 \times c^4$

4. $8v^4 \times 9v^9$

5. $7a^6 \times 3a$

6. $9t \times 4t^8$

7. $4n^5 \times 7n^3$

8. $6z^4 \times 9z^{10}$

9. $3w \times 8w^9$

10. $4u^6 \times 5u^{10}$

11. $8s^2 \times 7s^9$

12. $7p^{10} \times 5p^{12}$

13. $4k^2l^3 \times 2k^4l^2$

14. $6b^6d^3 \times 4b^5d^3$

15. $5fg^3h^2 \times 5f^3g^4h$

16. $2a^2b^3 \times 6b^2a^4$

17. $3c^3e^3f^2 \times 3f^3c^3e^4$

18. $8mn \times nm$

19. $9stu \times 5us$

20. $8x^2yz^2 \times 9x^2yz^2$

21. $4q^4v^2e^6 \times 8q^3$

22. $6j^3k^5 \times 6k^3j^5l^4$

23. $2w^9r^6j^4 \times 7jwr$

24. $5c^3d^4 \times 6d^3h^7$

Exercise 12

1. (a) $3 + 3 + 3 + 3 = \boxed{?}$　　(c) $3 \times 3 \times 3 \times 3 = \boxed{?}$

　　(b) 　　　　$4 \times 3 = \boxed{?}$　　(d) 　　　　　$3^4 = \boxed{?}$

2. Simplify:

　(a) $x + x + x + x + x$　　　　(b) $x \times x \times x \times x \times x$

3. If $n = 4$, find the value of:

　(a) $n + n + n$　　　　　　(c) $n \times n \times n$

　(b) $3n$　　　　　　　　　(d) n^3

4. If $p = 3$, find the value of:
(a) $2p + 2p + 2p$ (c) $2p \times 2p \times 2p$
(b) $6p$ (d) $8p^3$

5. Simplify:
(a) $3g + 2g$ (b) $3g \times 2g$

6. If $g = 7$, find the value of:
(a) $3g + 2g$ (c) $3g \times 2g$
(b) $5g$ (d) $6g^2$

7. Find the value of:
(a) 2 lots of 4,   (b) 2 to the power 4.

8. Which is the greater, 5 lots of 3 or 5 to the power 3?

Square Roots

$$9 = 3^2 \quad \text{(9 is the } square \text{ of 3)}$$

We can write: $\sqrt{9} = 3$ (the *square root* of 9 is 3)

Also, since $4^2 = 16$, the square root of 16 is 4.

That is: $\sqrt{16} = 4$

Note that the square root symbol, $\sqrt{}$ may be given as $\sqrt{}$ on some calculators.

Exercise 13

Find these square roots without using a calculator:

1. $\sqrt{25}$ 6. $\sqrt{64}$ 11. $\sqrt{900}$ 16. $\sqrt{3600}$

2. $\sqrt{4}$ 7. $\sqrt{100}$ 12. $\sqrt{169}$ 17. $\sqrt{8100}$

3. $\sqrt{49}$ 8. $\sqrt{400}$ 13. $\sqrt{2500}$ 18. $\sqrt{225}$

4. $\sqrt{81}$ 9. $\sqrt{144}$ 14. $\sqrt{1600}$ 19. $\sqrt{361}$

5. $\sqrt{36}$ 10. $\sqrt{121}$ 15. $\sqrt{4900}$ 20. $\sqrt{289}$

Exercise 14

Use a calculator to find these square roots:

1. $\sqrt{529}$
2. $\sqrt{961}$
3. $\sqrt{1089}$
4. $\sqrt{5329}$
5. $\sqrt{9801}$

6. $\sqrt{6561}$
7. $\sqrt{3844}$
8. $\sqrt{2116}$
9. $\sqrt{17.64}$
10. $\sqrt{29.16}$

11. $\sqrt{1.5129}$
12. $\sqrt{2352.25}$
13. $\sqrt{316.84}$
14. $\sqrt{277\,729}$
15. $\sqrt{538\,756}$

Exercise 15

Try to discover a method of finding square roots of numbers on a calculator without using the square-root key. Write an explanation of your method.

Exercise 16   Using Formulae

1. The area, A cm^2, of a square is given by $A = l^2$. Find the value of A, if the length l of each side of the square is:
   (a) 7 cm   (b) 13 cm

2. The formula $A = 6l^2$ gives the total surface area of a cube with edge l units. Find the total surface area of a cube if each edge measures 8 cm.

3. $V = l^3$ gives the volume of a cube with edge l units. Find the volume of a cube if its edge measures 9 cm.

4. (a) $A = 12r^2$ gives an approximate value for the surface area of a sphere. Use it to estimate the surface area of a sphere when the radius r, is 5 cm.

   (b) $A = \dfrac{25r^2}{2}$ gives a better estimate for the surface area of a sphere than the formula in part (a). Use this formula to estimate the surface area of a sphere when the radius, r, is 5 cm.

   (c) Find the difference between your answers to parts (a) and (b).

5. $A = 3r^2$ estimates the area of a circle. Use the formula to estimate the area of a circle with radius 6 cm.

6. Use the formula $V = 4r^3$ to find V when $r = 6$.

7. Use the formula $s = 5t^2$ to find s when:
(a) $t = 4$ (b) $t = 2.5$

8. Use the formula $T = 3m^4$ to find T when $m = 8$.

9. Use the formula $A = l^2$ to find the length, l, of a side of a square, when:
(a) the area, $A = 64 \, \text{cm}^2$ (b) the area, $A = 196 \, \text{m}^2$

10. Use $s = 5t^2$ to find the time taken, t seconds, for a body to fall a distance, s, of 45 m.

11. The surface area of a cube, A, is $150 \, \text{cm}^2$. Find the length of each edge of the cube, l, if $A = 6l^2$.

12. The area of a circle, A, is estimated to be $147 \, \text{cm}^2$. Find its radius, r, if $A = 3r^2$.

23 Statistics

Permutations

Exercise 1

1. Make several copies of this flag.

   Colour the two parts of each flag as follows. (Each flag should be different.)

   (a) Use exactly two colours to colour the two parts. How many different flags can be made with the same two colours?

   (b) Select three different colours. Now using two of these three colours at a time, make as many different flags as you can. How many different flags can be made?

   (c) Now select four different colours. Using two of these four colours at a time, make as many different flags as you can. How many different flags can be made?

   (d) Select five different colours. Using two of these five colours at a time, make as many different flags as you can. How many different flags can be made?

2. Make several copies of this flag.

   Colour the three parts of each flag as follows. (Each flag should be different.)

   (a) Select three different colours. How many different flags can be made with your three colours?

   (b) Select four different colours. Using three of these colours at a time, make as many different flags as you can. How many different flags can be made?

3. Make several copies of this flag.

   Use four different colours to make as many different flags as you can. How many different flags can be made?

Here is a domino: . This is the same domino: .

(Changing the numbers around does not make a different domino.)
If a full set of dominoes only uses the numbers 0 and 1, there can only be three dominoes in the set, namely:

| 1 | 4 | | 4 | 1 | | 0 | 0 | | 0 | 1 | | 1 | 1 |

If the full set of dominoes uses only the numbers 0, 1, 2 and 3, here is a full set:

| 0 | 0 | | 0 | 1 | | 0 | 2 | | 0 | 3 |

| 1 | 1 | | 1 | 2 | | 1 | 3 |

| 2 | 2 | | 2 | 3 |

| 3 | 3 | There are ten dominoes in this full set.

1. Copy and complete the following table. Draw each full set of dominoes.

	Numbers used	Total number of dominoes in a full set
(a)	0, 1	3
(b)	0, 1, 2	?
(c)	0, 1, 2, 3	10
(d)	0, 1, 2, 3, 4	?
(e)	0, 1, 2, 3, 4, 5	?
(f)	0, 1, 2, 3, 4, 5, 6	?
(g)	0, 1, 2, 3, 4, 5, 6, 7	?

2. What do you notice about the numbers in the final column of the table?

Pictograms

(*Pictograms* are sometimes called *pictographs* or *ideographs*.)

Exercise 3

1. The pictogram shows the shoe sizes of a number of pupils:

(*a*) How many pupils wore size 4?

(*b*) How many pupils wore size 6?

(*c*) Which size did most pupils wear?

(*d*) How many more wore size 5 than size 3?

(*e*) If the pictogram shows the shoe sizes of all the pupils in a class, how many pupils must there be in that class?

(*f*) Write a sentence about the information shown in the pictogram.

Shoe Sizes

Key: stands for 2 pupils

411

2. The following table gives the number of houses built by a builder between April and September:

(*a*) Draw a pictogram to represent this information.

Do not forget to give your pictogram a title and a key.

(*b*) Write a sentence about the pictogram.

Month	Number built
April	12
May	16
June	11
July	14
August	11
September	9

Let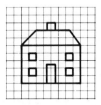

stand for 2 houses.

Exercise 4

Give as many reasons as you can why this pictogram is misleading:

Size	Number of faulty televisions
36 cm	
41 cm	
51 cm	
59 cm	

Tally Charts

1. *Data* was collected to show the numbers of children in families.
A *tally chart* was used to collect the data.

Number of children in each family	Tally	Frequency
1	﷼﷼ ﷼﷼ IIII	14
2	﷼﷼ ﷼﷼ ﷼﷼ ﷼﷼ ﷼﷼ III	
3	﷼﷼ ﷼﷼ ﷼﷼ I	
4	﷼﷼ ﷼﷼	10
5	﷼﷼ ﷼﷼ III	13
6	IIII	4
7	﷼﷼	5
8		0
9	I	1
10	I	1

(*a*) How many families had 3 children in them?
(*b*) How many families had 2 children in them?
(*c*) What was the total number of families questioned in this
survey?

2. Make out a tally chart to find the number of children in each
family for the pupils in your class.

3. The numbers of tickets sold by 75 pupils were:

3	2	1	2	0	2	3	1	2	5	2	2	0	2	3
1	2	2	0	4	2	4	2	2	3	1	0	0	5	2
4	5	2	2	1	1	0	2	2	2	5	2	1	4	6
5	1	2	0	0	2	2	2	1	3	2	4	5	2	5
4	0	2	2	2	1	1	3	5	2	5	1	4	3	2

Draw up a tally chart for this data.

Exercise 6   Tally Charts and Pictograms

A **1.** 48 pupils were asked how far they lived from school. Here are the results of the survey, the distances being given to the nearest kilometre.

4	9	12	3	1	1	2	3	3	1	2	7
5	4	6	4	3	2	4	5	3	2	5	4
4	3	1	2	2	10	6	4	2	4	6	4
12	10	6	10	4	1	2	2	4	3	4	3

(*a*) Make a tally chart for this data.

(*b*) Draw a pictogram to show the information. (Choose your own shape.)

(*c*) Use the results shown in your pictogram to help you to write a sentence about distances pupils live from school.

2. The table shows the number of fish caught by five people:

Name	Belinda	Kieran	Bob	Herol	Mr Fishwick
Number caught	6	8	3	5	14

(*a*) Draw a pictogram for this data.

(*b*) Write a sentence about your pictogram.

B Carry out the following *surveys*. For some of them you will need to make a tally chart. Draw a pictogram for each one.
Write a sentence about the results of each survey.

1. Use a travel brochure to find the average number of hours of sunshine per day for each month of the year (or for part of the year) at any place you choose.

2. Find the favourite TV channel for all the pupils in your class.

3. Carry out a survey of the musical instruments played by pupils in your class.

4. Find the favourite pop group of pupils in your class (or in your year at school). You may need to list six or seven pop groups and let people choose a group from your list.

Bar Charts

Bar charts are sometimes called *block graphs* or *column graphs*.

Exercise 7

Both of the following bar charts show the same information. The only difference between them is that the first bar chart has a space between each column.

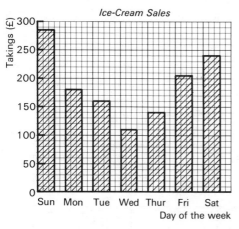

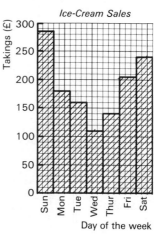

Answer these questions using the given graphs:

1. How much was taken on Monday?

2. How much more were Friday's takings than Wednesday's?

3. On which day were the takings £80 more than Tuesday's takings?

4. What were the total takings for the week?

5. Give a possible reason for the:
  (*a*) poor takings on Wednesday.   (*b*) good takings on Sunday.

Exercise 8

This table shows the force of the wind at sea. It is measured on the Beaufort scale.

A bar chart can be drawn using the results in the table.

Scale no.	Wind force	Wind velocity (km/h)
0	calm	0
3	gentle breeze	15
5	fresh breeze	35
6	strong breeze	45
7	near gale	55
8	gale	70
10	storm	95
11	violent storm	110

This type of graph is called a *horizontal bar chart:*

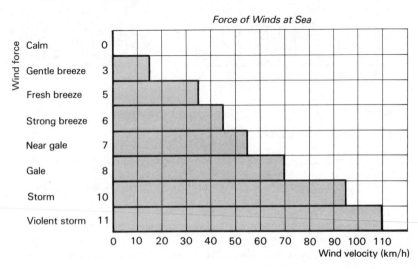

Force of Winds at Sea

1. What is the velocity of a gale?

2. What wind velocity is twice that of a fresh breeze?

3. What is the difference in velocity between a storm and a gentle breeze?

4. What is the difference in velocity between a storm and a near gale?

Exercise 9

Draw bar charts from these tables.

Write a sentence about each bar chart.

1. The number of patients admitted each day to casualty in a hospital was:

Day	Mon	Tue	Wed	Thur	Fri	Sat	Sun
Number admitted	108	98	95	92	125	140	90

2. *Number of Calories per 100 g of Food*

Food	Number of calories	Food	Number of calories
Poached egg	140	Lettuce	10
Fried egg	240	Pork chop	350
Boiled potatoes	75	Gammon	915
Chips	240	Roast Turkey	175
Potato crisps	560	Apple	45
Fresh tomatoes	20	Baked beans	90

Exercise 10

1. Copy this tally chart:

Day of Birthday this Year

Day	Tally	Frequency
Mon		
Tue		
Wed		
Thur		
Fri		
Sat		
Sun		

2. Complete your tally chart for the pupils in your class (or for the pupils in your year group).

3. Draw a neat table of your results.

4. Draw a bar chart of your results (see below for an idea of how to do this). You must decide how big your bar chart will be.

Do not forget to give your bar chart a title.

Both axes on your bar chart must be labelled.

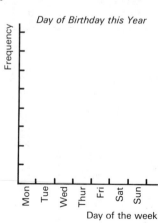

Day of Birthday this Year

Exercise 11

Carry out at least two of the following surveys.

Draw a tally chart, a table and a bar chart for each survey.

1. The month in which pupils in your class (or year group) were born. The tally chart should have the headings:

Month	Tally	Frequency

2. The number of pupils absent each day in your class.
(Use a register to collect the information.)
Headings:
Day   Tally   Frequency

3. The number of pupils absent during a certain week for several classes.
Headings:
Class   Tally   Frequency

4. The most popular sport to watch.
Headings:
Sport   Tally   Frequency
(A prepared list of sports can be used and people should then choose one from that list.)

5. The most popular sport to play.
Headings:
Sport   Tally   Frequency

6. How pupils travel to school.
Headings:
Method of travel   Tally   Frequency
(Methods of travel can include: walk, cycle, bus, car, other.)

Exercise 12

1. (a) Draw a horizontal bar chart from this table:

Lengths of Tunnels (rounded to nearest 0.1 km)

Tunnel	Place	Length (km)
Simplon	Switzerland–Italy	19.8
Hokurika	Japan	13.9
Lötschberg	Switzerland	14.5
Apennine	Italy	18.5
Flathead	USA	11.0
St Gotthard	Switzerland	14.9
Cascade	USA	12.5
Fréjus	France–Italy	12.8

(b) Write a sentence about your bar chart.

2. Here are the heights of some tall structures:

Structure	Place	Height (m)
Empire State Building	New York	449
Eiffel Tower	Paris	321
British Telecom Tower	London	189
Sears Tower	Chicago	443
Blackpool Tower	Blackpool	158
St Paul's Cathedral Spire	London	149
Woolworth Building	New York	241
Great Pyramid of Cheops	Giza, Egypt	146

3. Draw a bar chart to show the heights of some of the highest mountains in the world. (Find the heights correct to the nearest 100 m.)

Component Bar Charts

Exercise 13

This bar chart shows the number of people travelling on a certain bus route:

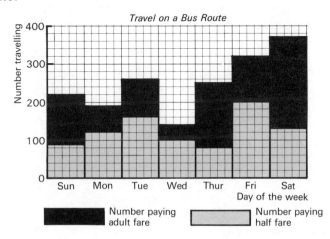

1. How many paying half fare travelled on Tuesday?

2. How many paying adult fare travelled on Friday?

3. How many more people paid full fare than half fare on Saturday?

4. If the adult fare was £3, while half fare was £1.80, what were Thursday's takings?

5. How many paying half fare travelled throughout the whole week?

6. What was the total number of travellers on the bus route for the week?

7. Calculate the total weekly takings if half fare cost £1.80, while the full adult fare was £3.50.

8. Write a sentence about bus travel using the results in this bar chart.

421

Exercise 14

The table below shows the stopping distances for cars, under perfect conditions. (The calculation was based on values in imperial units quoted in the UK Highway Code; braking distances have been rounded up to the nearest whole metre.) At each given velocity, the stopping distance is split into 'thinking distance' and 'braking distance'.

Draw a horizontal bar chart to show this information.

By shading, let each block show both the thinking and braking distances.

Stopping Distances of Cars

Velocity	Thinking distance	Braking distance	Total stopping distance
32 km/h	6 m	6 m	12 m
48 km/h	9 m	14 m	23 m
64 km/h	12 m	24 m	36 m
80 km/h	15 m	38 m	53 m
96 km/h	18 m	54 m	72 m
112 km/h	21 m	74 m	95 m

Graphs from Experiments

Exercise 15 $\boxed{M}$

A An ordinary die is used throughout these questions.

1. For some dice games you need to throw a six to start.
   Alan and Ken play a game. Ken said that he would throw a three to start and not a six.
   Alan tried to throw a six to start.
   Who is likely to start playing first?

2. (*a*) Is it easier to throw a three than a six?

(*b*) Is it easier to throw a one than a three?

3. Try this experiment:

(*a*) Copy the tally chart given below.

(*b*) Throw a die about 100 times.
Show your results on the tally chart.

(*c*) Draw a bar chart of your results.

(*d*) Which number turned up the most?

Number on the die	Tally	Frequency
1	?	?
2	?	?
3	?	?
4	?	?
5	?	?
6	?	?

(*e*) Copy the given frequency table:

(*f*) Collect data from the class to find the frequency for each number. Complete the table.

(*g*) Draw a bar chart of the class's results.

(*h*) Which number turned up the most for the whole class?

Throwing a Die

Number on the die	Frequency
1	?
2	?
3	?
4	?
5	?
6	?

4. Does it matter which number you need to start a game?

B Annette and Karen played a game using a die with the numbers
1, 2, 2, 2, 3 and another 3 on it. They needed to throw the die to start.

1. If Annette tries to throw a 3 to start and Karen tries to throw
   a 2, who is likely to start playing first?

2. (*a*) Is it easier to throw a 3 than a 2?
   (*b*) Is it easier to throw a 2 than a 1?
   (*c*) Is it easier to throw a 3 than a 1?

3. Make a die (or spinner) having the numbers 1, 2, 2, 2, 3 and 3
   on it. Repeat part A, question 3 using this new die (or spinner).

Exercise 16

1. I tossed a coin four times.
   The *outcome* was heads, heads, heads, $\boxed{?}$.
   What do you think the fourth outcome was, heads or tails?

2. Are you certain that your answer to question 1 is correct?

3. Try an experiment.
   Toss a coin 100 times. Collect your results in a tally chart:

Outcome	Tally	Frequency
Head	$\boxed{?}$	$\boxed{?}$
Tail	$\boxed{?}$	$\boxed{?}$

4. Draw a bar chart to show your results.

5. Write a sentence about your results.

6. Total the number of heads obtained by the whole class.
   Total the number of tails.

7. Draw a bar chart of the class's results.

8. Write a sentence about the class's results.

Pie Charts

1. (*a*) Here is a *pie chart:*

Sharing Sweets

It shows how 48 sweets are shared amongst five people.
There are 360° in a full turn. The circle represents 48 sweets.

So   360° stands for 48 sweets,
              180° stands for 24 sweets,
and   90° stands for 12 sweets.

Since the angle for Tina is 90°, Tina gets 12 sweets.
List the names of all five people who shared the sweets.
Next to each name, write the number of sweets that person received.

(*b*) If the angles in the sweets pie chart had measured: Angus 45°, Tina 15°, Brendan 135°, Kate 105°, Rhian 22.5° and Giles 37.5°, the sweets being shared amongst six people, list these names and, next to each name, write the number of sweets received. The total number of sweets shared was still 48.

2. The pie chart shows what was bought by 48 customers at a record shop (each person bought one item):

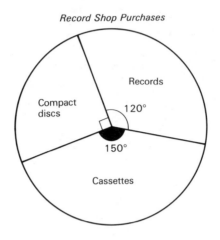

Record Shop Purchases

(a) What fraction of the 48 customers bought records?
(b) What fraction of the 48 customers bought cassettes?
(c) How many customers bought records?
(d) How many customers bought cassettes?
(e) How many customers bought compact discs?
(f) Copy and complete the table to show how the number of purchases and the number of degrees can be worked out.

Number of purchases	Number of degrees
48	360°
24	180°
?	90°
?	30°
?	120°
?	150°

3. A survey was carried out in which 90 people were asked which radio station they preferred to listen to. Here are the results:

Radio 1   36
Radio 2   10
Radio 3   9
Radio 4   5
Local radio   30

Copy and complete the table.

Draw a pie chart to show the number of people who listen to each of the listed radio stations. Use the table to help you.

Number of people	Number of degrees
90	360°
?	120°
?	40°
5	?
9	?
36	?

Exercise 18

1. The pie chart below shows the types of fruit juice preferred by 40 people:

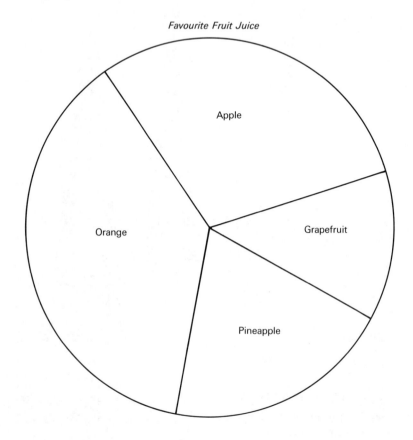

Favourite Fruit Juice

Find the number who preferred:
(*a*) orange juice,
(*b*) apple juice,
(*c*) grapefruit juice,
(*d*) pineapple juice.

2. The pie chart on the next page shows the favourite sport of several people (each person chose one sport).
12 people chose basketball.

Favourite Sport

(*a*) How many people were there altogether in the survey?

(*b*) List each sport and next to each one, write the angle used in the pie chart and the number of people who chose that sport.

3. List five sports. Ask 20 (or 30) people which sport, on your list, they prefer to watch on TV. Show the results of your survey on a pie chart.

4. Draw a pie chart to show how you spent yesterday. List what you did throughout the day. Include sleeping (Your day should show 24 h.)

Write, in your list, the number of degrees you used for each item in your pie chart.

429

5. During 2 h in a restaurant, the following number of meals were served:

gammon 10, steak 7, scampi 5, lamb chops 6, beef 8, steak and kidney pie 15, chicken 21

Draw a pie chart to show these meals.

6. In a certain school, the number of periods per subject were:

maths 6, English 6, music 2, science 4, French 5, geography 3, history 3, RE 2, art 2, technical 4, games 2, PE 1

Draw a subject pie chart.

7. Draw a pie chart to show the subjects you take in one week at your school.

Jagged-Line Graphs

Exercise 19

In hospitals, jagged-line graphs are drawn for each patient. The graph on the next page shows temperature, pulse rate, and respiration. Normally, a graph showing blood pressure is also plotted.

The readings for the graphs shown were taken every 4 h.

1. On which day (0, 1, 2, 3, 4, 5, 6 or 7) and at what time was the temperature at its highest?

2. What was the highest temperature (in °C)?

3. What was the highest pulse rate?

4. What was the pulse rate on day 1 at 6 p.m.?

5. What was the temperature on day 2 at 2 a.m.?

6. What was the difference between the highest and the lowest temperatures?

7. What is 'normal' temperature?

8. What is the 'normal' rate of respiration?

9. The graphs are for a patient who has just had an operation (a 'post-op' patient). Drugs were used to help to lower the temperature. Give the time and day when the drugs began to have an effect.

10. What was the difference between the highest and the lowest pulse rates?

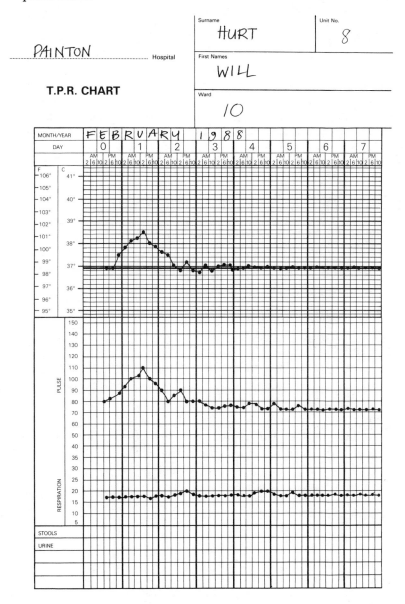

Exercise 20

Draw jagged-line graphs for each of these tables of data or surveys (the vertical axis is normally numbered from zero).

1. *Number Staying at a Small Hotel*

Month	Jan	Feb	Mar	Apr	May	June
Number	142	180	185	240	270	250

Month	July	Aug	Sept	Oct	Nov	Dec
Number	340	372	290	150	135	192

2. Find the monthly temperatures at any place in the world (use an atlas).

3. *Mass of a Baby during the First 16 Weeks of its Life*

Age (weeks)	0	1	2	3	4	5	6	7	8
Mass (kg)	3.2	3	3.2	3.5	3.6	3.8	4	4.2	4.3

Age (weeks)	9	10	11	12	13	14	15	16	
Mass (kg)	4.5	4.7	4.9	5.2	5.3	5.5	5.8	6	

4. Find the total school attendance each week (or each month or each day).

5. Find the temperature in your classroom (or in your home) at the same time each day throughout the week.

Glossary

altitude   (p. 396)

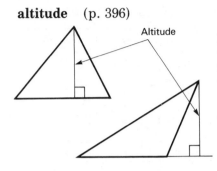

An *altitude* (or 'perpendicular height') of a triangle is a line segment drawn at right-angles to a side of a triangle, or to that side produced, to meet the opposite vertex. Every triangle has three altitudes.

digital root   (pp. 97, 101)

All *digital roots* are single-digit numbers. When the digits of a number are added, a new number is obtained. If this new number is a single-digit number, then it is the digital root of the original number. If the new number is not a single-digit number, then its digits must now be added to give another new number. This process needs to be repeated until a single-digit number is obtained. The single number that is finally obtained in this way is the digital root of the original number.

e.g.   The sum of the digits of 41 868 is 27
(since $4 + 1 + 8 + 6 + 8 = 27$).
Since $2 + 7 = 9$, which is a single-digit number, the digital root of 41 868 is 9.

exterior angle   (p. 187)

When a side of a polygon is produced, an angle is formed between the extended line and its *adjacent* side (that is, the side next to it). The angle formed is an *exterior* angle. Each polygon has several exterior angles.

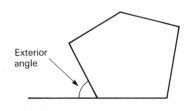

433

line of best fit (p. 398)

Sometimes when points are plotted, they do not follow an exact line. However, the way they lie may suggest a straight line. The 'suggested' line which best fits the plotted points is called the *line of best fit*. It should have about the same number of points on each side of it. The following diagram shows a line of best fit for the given points.

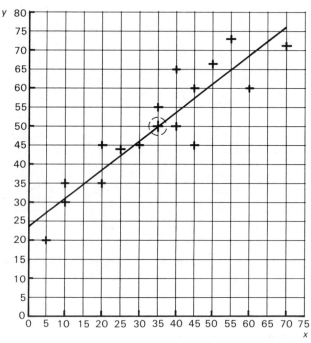

lines of symmetry (p. 346)

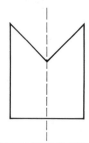

A *line of symmetry* of a shape divides the shape into two identical parts so that if the shape is folded along that line, one half of the shape covers the other half exactly. It is sometimes referred to as an *axis of symmetry*.

This type of symmetry is called *bilateral symmetry* (or *axial symmetry* or *reflective symmetry*).

median (p. 395)

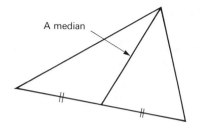

A median

A *median* of a triangle is a line segment that joins a vertex to the mid-point of the opposite side. Every triangle has three medians.

operation (p. 315)

Addition, subtraction, multiplication and division are all arithmetical *operations*. They are, in fact, *binary* operations. That is, they are used to combine two numbers to obtain a single number.

prisms and pyramids (p. 238)

The full names of prisms and pyramids are frequently not used. For example, a triangular-based prism is often referred to as a triangular prism.

quotient (pp. 44, 102)

The *quotient* is the answer you get when you carry out a division question. For example, 5 is the quotient when 15 is divided by 3.

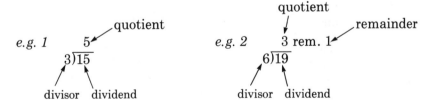

quotient

e.g. 1   5 ← quotient
    3)15
    divisor dividend

quotient

e.g. 2   3 rem. 1 ← remainder
    6)19
    divisor dividend

435